McGRAW-HILL PUBLICATIONS IN INDUSTRIAL ARTS

Chris H. Groneman, *Consulting Editor*

GENERAL WOODWORKING

General woodworking offers many opportunities for making useful articles of good design. (*Courtesy, Public Schools, Fort Worth, Texas.*)

General Woodworking

BY CHRIS H. GRONEMAN

Professor and Head, Industrial Education Department, School of Engineering, The Agricultural and Mechanical College of Texas College Station, Texas

McGRAW-HILL BOOK COMPANY, INC.

New York Toronto London

GENERAL WOODWORKING

Library of Congress Catalog Card Number: 55-7913

III

Foreword

Working with wood can provide many hours of pleasurable and educational activity. Wood possesses a fascinating warmth and adaptability and may be fashioned into many interesting and worth-while projects for the home, lawn, office, and for all the activities of modern life.

Since woodworking is one of the oldest and most widely accepted areas of industrial and practical arts in the educational program, it is natural that *General Woodworking* is one of the first textbooks published of a carefully planned, functional, and practical series of McGraw-Hill Publications in Industrial Arts. When completed, this group of publications will include textbooks in all the major divisions of the industrial-arts field. Together, these textbooks will meet the educational objectives of the industrial-arts program.

Today in the United States, more students are enrolled in woodworking than in any other materials area. Although industrial-arts woodworking is a form of nonvocational education, it may lead the student into a number of different occupational interests and opportunities; and since woodworking is the most popular homecraft activity, it may provide the student with important avocational benefits during his adult life.

General Woodworking will help the teacher to achieve many of the objectives of a well-planned industrial-arts program. It has been planned and written as a guide for one or more years of industrial-arts woodworking and for the home craftsman. The units are so presented that the teacher may select those that are most appropriate to the student's rate of learning and that best fit into the course presented. Where it has been practicable to do so, illustrations have been selected to show the procedure as the student would view it over the instructor's shoulder.

In *General Woodworking* teachers and students will find several interesting topics not often covered in similar books, namely, machine tools, upholstery, plywood construction, and period designs in furniture. A thought-provoking section on settng up a home workshop has been included. The student is also given reference material on trees, forest products, and occupations in the woodworking field.

Dr. Chris H. Groneman, author of *General Woodworking,* is recognized by educators throughout the country for his leadership in the industrial-arts field. His experience has qualified him well to be the author of this book and the Consulting Editor for the McGraw-Hill Publications in Industrial Arts. He has been a teacher and supervisor of industrial arts in high schools, junior colleges, and a state teachers' college. Dr. Groneman joined the staff of the Agricultural and Mechanical College of Texas in 1940, and was appointed Head of the Industrial Education Department in 1948. He did his undergraduate work at and received his Master's Degree from the Pittsburg, Kansas State Teachers College. He received his doctorate from Pennsylvania State College. In addition to his teaching and administrative activities and early practical experience in the building trades, he has written extensively, has served on numerous educational committees, and held offices in various associations of a professional nature, both state and national in scope.

THE PUBLISHERS

Contents

Preface

General Woodworking has been written primarily for the student in woodworking and the home craftsman. It includes basic information on carpentry, furniture and cabinet making, finishing, and upholstering. It is intended to help the reader to develop an understanding and appreciation of the tools and processes involved in woodworking. It is hoped that it will open the way to a constructive hobby and that it will assist the reader to make intelligent selections and repairs of wood products.

Special classroom helps have been provided to assist both the student and the teacher. These include the discussion topics that are given at the end of each unit, numerous suggestions for problems or projects, and a series of dimensioned working drawings.

Section I is devoted to basic general information on reading a working drawing, factors to be considered in purchasing and using lumber, the figuring of board feet, problem solving through the planning of procedures, and necessary and vital safety observances. These are some of the fundamentals which the beginner should understand before endeavoring to work with tool processes.

Section II describes many of the practical and useful hand-tool processes which develop craftsmanship in hand-tool skills with yard and shop lumber. In addition to these processes, this section covers the building of plywood into flat and formed shapes and several techniques for applying finishes and for simple upholstery.

Section III presents the more widely used power machine for the school and home workshop and its many essential operations.

Section IV contains related information regarding forest products, woods industries, occupations, period designs in furniture, and the considerations involved in selecting a location for tools and equipment for a home workshop.

Section V provides suggestions for numerous projects ranging from the very simplest, requiring only a few basic hand-tool skills, to the more complex, which call for a high degree of skill in wood-lathe turning and other machine-tool applications. A pictorial sketch or photograph and the necessary working drawings, complete with dimensions, are provided for each project.

Acknowledgment is sincerely given to the following agencies, companies, and individuals who provided most helpful suggestions, data, photographs, illustrations, and other assistance: American

Forest Products Industries, Washington, D.C.; American Forestry Association, Washington, D.C.; Borden Company, Chemical Division, New York City; Caterpillar Tractor Company, Peoria, Illinois; Delta Power Tool Division, Rockwell Manufacturing Company, Milwaukee, Wisconsin; S. C. Johnson and Son, Inc., Racine, Wisconsin; Mahogany Association, Inc., Chicago, Illinois; National Safety Council, Chicago, Illinois; *The Timberman,* Portland, Oregon; United States Forest Service, Washington, D.C.; West Coast Lumberman's Association, Portland, Oregon; Weyerhaeuser Sales Company, St. Paul, Minnesota; Yates American Machine Company, Beloit, Wisconsin; Fred J. Gross, Manager, Educational Department, Stanley Tools Company, New Britain, Connecticut; Mott B. Heath, Director, Ford Motor Company Industrial Arts Awards Program; Howard Berry, Director, Photographic and Visual Aids Laboratory, Texas A. & M. College, College Station, Texas; L. Bryce Hardeman, Industrial Education Department, Texas A. & M. College; D. W. Fleming, Mechanical Engineering Department, Texas A. & M. College; Rogers L. Barton, Industrial Arts Consultant, Texas Education Agency, Austin; Eleanor Hanover Nance, Illustrator, Bryan, Texas; and my wife, Virginia, for her inspiration and untiring assistance in the preparation of the manuscript.

Chris H. Groneman

GENERAL WOODWORKING

Section I. GENERAL INFORMATION

Unit 1. Introduction to Woodworking

Woodworking is one of the most fascinating, educational, and rewarding of the skilled activities in the school or home workshop. Wood is among the most abundant of all materials, and it may be fashioned with relative ease into very beautiful and useful articles for the home and office. One who is handy in the manipulation of tools and equipment in woodworking is limited only by his own imagination and ingenuity.

Those who take woodworking as a part of their industrial-education program have the opportunity to participate in one of the most practical arts known to mankind. Skill in woodworking lends itself readily to the performance of a multitude of necessary and worth-while jobs for the home and for all the activities of modern life. One feels a great satisfaction and pride in doing one's own work and in having custom-built cabinets and furniture suited to specific tastes and dimensions.

Any purposeful activity must have organized and clear-cut aims or objectives. To assist you in your many hours of educational achievement and recreational endeavor, the following objectives that you may develop and follow are suggested:

1. An active interest in industry and in the problems of production
2. An appreciation of a high standard of workmanship and a recognition of superior workmanship in commodities made of wood
3. A sense of pride in your ability to do useful things in a creditable manner, which may lead to an increased vocational interest
4. An understanding of drawings and the ability to interpret them in order to make something useful or ornamental
5. The recognition of and the application of safe working practices
6. The habit of analyzing and planning orderly performance in wood construction
7. Avocational or hobby interests in woodworking
8. Manipulative dexterity in the handling of tools and machines in woodworking as it applies to wood construction and repair
9. An appreciation of our dependence upon wood and wood products and of the importance of conserving our timberlands

Unit 2. Understanding a Working Drawing

All craftsmen must understand the simple elements involved in reading a working drawing. In industries, special classes are often held for workmen in reading and interpreting working drawings, that is, in blueprint reading. There is only one difference in the drawings they work with and in the drawings you will study. The difference is that they often read white lines on blue background, which are the result of a chemical process in duplicating work from tracings or originals, while you will read black lines on white background in most of your work.

You will need to understand the meanings of the various types of lines and to know how to interpret the views. The working drawing or sketch provides a language which explains to you the dimensions of the various parts of the project and shows you how it is assembled. In studying a drawing, you will follow exactly the same technique that a mechanic or craftsman employs before he attempts to build any part of a project.

Line Symbols

The line symbols in Fig. 2-1 and the subsequent description of each will aid you in reading drawings. Try to apply what you learn from Fig. 2-1 in your study of the drawing in Fig. 2-2. The photograph in (Fig. 2-3) shows the finished appearance of this very interesting modern radio end table and will guide you in understanding the front, top, and right-end views.

Border lines, if they are supplied, are the heaviest of all lines. They are used only for making a neat border around a drawing.

Object lines are fairly heavy and very distinct. They are the lines which represent the visible portion of an object and are very important to the craftsman.

Hidden or invisible lines are represented by short dashes which make up a broken line. They show that portion of an object which needs to be shown but is not visible in the view drawn.

Extension lines are thin, long dashes which extend the edges of a view so that dimension lines may be used effectively between them. These lines should never connect with solid or object lines.

Center lines are light dot-and-dash lines which indicate or mark the center of radius of any curve or circle. Every major arc or circle should have intersecting center lines.

Dimension lines are light lines which include measurements. All dimensions are indicated by this type of line. When you read a drawing, you should assume that the dimension is from the point of the arrow on one end of the dimension line to the point of the arrow on the other end.

Generally a drawing must be reduced in size to get it on a sheet of paper of

Fig. 2-1. Line symbols.

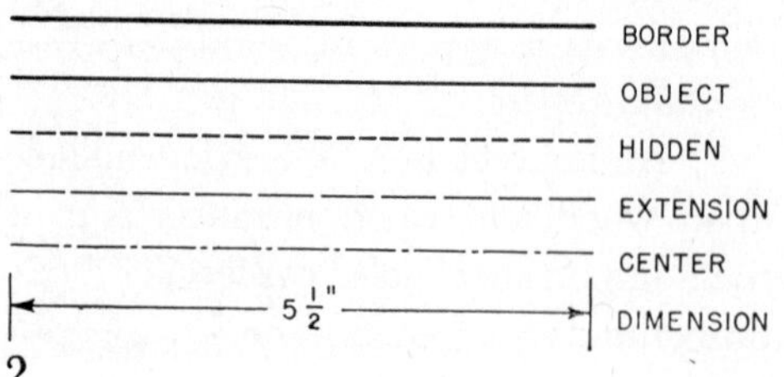

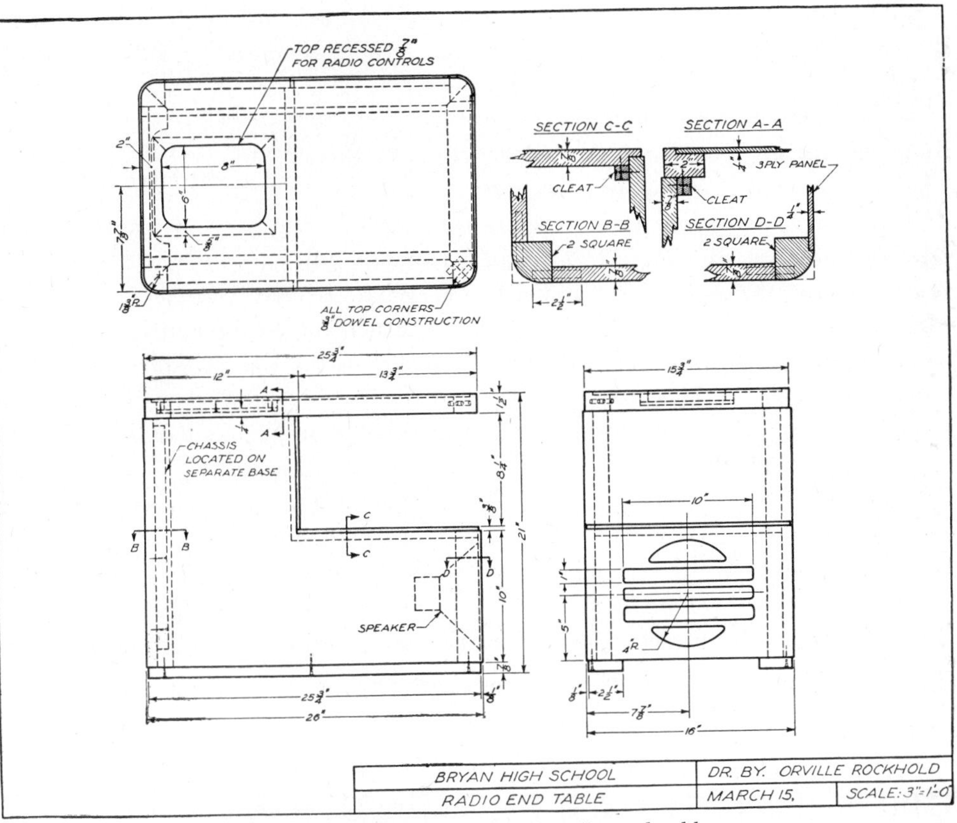

Fig. 2-2. Working drawing of radio end table.

convenient size; hence the draftsman will use a scale to make the reduced drawing. It should be pointed out, however, that all dimensions given on a drawing will be the actual size that the object should be when it is completed.

Views of a Drawing

The working drawing in Fig. 2-2 is a projected three-view drawing. In order to include all measurements and details of construction, it was necessary to show three views: front, top, and right end. Often two views, front and top or front and one end, will be adequate to include all measurements and construction

Fig. 2-3. Radio end table.

details. This is particularly true in drawings of projects to be turned on a lathe.

It is seldom necessary to show more than the three views, as indicated in Fig. 2-2, except for detailed section drawings of construction. It is possible, however, to show six views: front, top, rear, underneath, right end, and left end.

When working drawings are prepared, as shown in Fig. 2-2, they are referred to as *projected orthographic views.*

Sometimes drawings are shown in a *pictorial sketch* with dimensions on it. Such a drawing appears very much like a photograph with dimensions on it. This technique is satisfactory only for projects with little detail and would soon become complicated and confusing on a more advanced or difficult one.

Discussion Topics

In Fig. 2-2 (radio end table):

1. What is the over-all length, height, and width?
2. What is the construction of the corners for the top panel?
3. How is the top assembly fastened to the body or sides?
4. What is the general diameter of the speaker opening?
5. How is the radio chassis supported in the cabinet?
6. What is the thickness of the material used for making the feet?
7. How are the feet fastened to the cabinet?

Unit 3. Purchasing and Measuring Lumber

Before you prepare the Student's Plan Sheet (Fig. 4-1, page 8) for your project, it is essential that you know your materials, how to figure the amount used, and the costs. You will save both time and material if you will make an accurate stock and material listing before you begin to make your project.

Purchasing Terminology

The terms and expressions which you must understand in order to figure a material bill successfully are defined as follows:

Board foot is the measurement by which most yard and cabinet lumber is sold. This means a piece of wood 1 inch thick, 12 inches wide, and 12 inches long. A board less than 1 inch in thickness is usually calculated as though it were 1 inch thick unless it is a piece of plywood. This means that in a board foot you can expect it to measure $\frac{3}{4}$ to $\frac{13}{16}$ inch thick, $11\frac{1}{2}$ to $11\frac{5}{8}$ inches wide, and 12 inches long. In figuring a board 2 inches thick, we will probably get actual stock only $1\frac{5}{8}$ inches thick. The difference between what we figure and what we get is consumed in cutting and sometimes in planing the board to yard and shop dimensions.

The thickness and width in a material bill are always figured in inches ("), and lengths on long boards are figured in feet ('), and the lengths of short pieces are figured in inches. Each will require a different formula.

Standard sizes in softwood lumber are generally available in even widths, such as 2, 4, 6, 8, etc., inches, and in even lengths, such as 8, 10, 12, 14 feet up to 20-foot lengths.

Hardwood lumber comes in the standard thickness, but because of its scarcity, it is cut in any length which can be obtained from the log.

Grades of softwood are *select* and *common*. The categories of select grade run alphabetically from A to D, with grade A as the highest quality. After the lumber has been graded, the prices are made proportionate. Common grade is a general-utility type of lumber which is not as high a quality as select. Its categories run from 1 to 5 with 1 as the best.

Hardwood is graded as *FAS, No. 1 common, and No. 2 common.* FAS means "first and second" and is the highest grade for furniture making. Numbers 1 and 2 admit some defects and are not of as high a quality as FAS.

Surfaces are designated as *rough, S2S,* and *S4S* to indicate the treatment which lumber has had or which you want it to have. Rough means that the lumber is in the rough as it came from the mill and has not been planed. S2S means that it has been surfaced or planed on the two surfaces. S4S means that it has been surfaced or planed on all four sides, both surfaces and edges. S2S and S4S indicate common practices in the treatment of yard lumber.

Methods of drying are indicated by *AD* or *KD*. AD means that the lumber has been dried through natural evaporation in the air. KD refers to lumber which has been kiln-dried, that is, artificially dried.

Methods of cutting are: *plainsawed* or *quartersawed*. The latter is the more expensive because of the way the cutting has to be done. Refer to Unit 35, "Trees and Forests," page 143 to 147.

Sizes in plywood are priced by the square foot, the price depending upon thickness, the kind of veneer used on the surfaces, and the gluing or bonding agent. Standard-sized plywoods vary in thickness from $\frac{1}{8}$ to $\frac{3}{4}$ inch. Generally up to $\frac{3}{8}$ inch in thickness there are three plys; beyond this there are five and sometimes seven.

Exterior-construction, marine, or aircraft plywoods employ a water-resistant phenolic glue or bonding agent, which makes them more expensive.

Grades of plywood are referred to as *G1S* or *G2S* to indicate that either one or both of the surfaces are good. G1S usually means that the opposite side or surface is of unmatched veneer, which is not suitable for showing. G2S indicates that either surface is satisfactory for exposure, and both of them are generally of the same veneer material.

Board Foot Measure

After you have selected the lumber and drawn up a preliminary bill of materials, which shows the lumber in rough or stock size, you will want to figure the number of board feet (bd ft) in each piece, in groups of identical pieces, and in the total board footage. Then you can estimate the cost of the project by *multiplying the number* of board feet by the *cost* per board foot.*

Estimating Finishes

The different kinds of materials and types of finishes make estimating the cost of finishes a difficult problem. However, for all practical purposes many woodworkers estimate that the cost of the finishes average 20 per cent of the cost of the lumber.

Other Costs

There will be additional items to figure in the total cost of a project, such as sandpaper, steel wool, nails, screws, other fastenings, and special hardware. The cost of these items will depend upon the purchasing price and the quantity used.

Discussion Topics

1. What is the difference between a square foot and a board foot?
2. Explain the meaning of the following lumber terms: (*a*) rough, (*b*) S2S, (*c*) S4S, (*d*) FAS, (*e*) AD, (*f*) KD, (*g*) No. 1 common.
3. Prepare a lumber bill for a project which will list the following information: (*a*) kind of wood, (*b*) number of pieces, (*c*) sizes of pieces, (*d*) grade of lumber, (*e*) surface treatment, (*f*) condition of lumber.
   Example: Walnut—6 pcs.—1″ × 6″ × 8′—FAS—S2S—KD
4. Explain the differences between air-dried and kiln-dried lumber.

Practical Problems

Work out these problems in your notebook. Do not write in this book.

* When the length is given in linear or running *feet,* use the following formula:

$$\frac{\text{Number of pieces} \times \text{thickness in inches} \times \text{width in inches} \times \text{length in feet}}{12} = \text{bd ft}$$

Example: To find the board feet in three pieces, 1″ × 8″ × 4′:

$$\frac{\cancel{3} \times 1 \times 8 \times \cancel{4}}{\underset{\cancel{3}}{\cancel{12}}} = 8 \text{ bd ft}$$

When the length is given in linear or running *inches,* use this formula:

$$\frac{\text{Number of pieces} \times \text{thickness in inches} \times \text{width in inches} \times \text{length in inches}}{12 \times 12} = \text{bd ft}$$

Example: To find the board feet in four pieces, 1″ × 10″ × 18″:

$$\frac{\cancel{4} \times 1 \times \overset{5}{\cancel{10}} \times \overset{\cancel{6}}{\cancel{18}}}{\underset{\cancel{3}}{\cancel{12}} \times \underset{\cancel{2}}{\cancel{12}}} = 5 \text{ bd ft}$$

No of pieces	*Thickness*	*Width*	*Length*	*Board feet*	*Kind of wood*	*Cost per foot, cents*	*Total cost*
1	1″	12″	3′	?	Poplar	20	?
1	1″	6″	12′	?	Walnut	40	?
6	2″	10″	7′ 4″	?	Honduras mahogany	52	?
3	$\frac{1}{4}$″	18″	5′	?	Fir plywood	14	?
4	2″	2″	30″	?	Red gum	28	?
6	$\frac{1}{2}$″	10″	40″	?	Yellow pine	18	?
3	$\frac{3}{4}$″	48″	96″	?	White oak Plywood panel	60	?
14	2″	4″	14′	?	Yellow pine	16	?

Unit 4. Planning Your Procedure

Any enterprise or undertaking requires a carefully thought-out plan. The building contractor will approach his problem or project of constructing a dwelling or business building very carefully in order that the proper materials, the correct tools and equipment, and the subcontractors will be available at the designated time. He knows that, if he does this, his structure will be completed in the specified number of days with a minimum of waste in materials and time. Similarly, the dentist or physician approaches his problem or job with a very meticulous, methodical analysis of the procedure necessary to secure the desired results with a minimum of time and effort.

These specialists do not always write out their plan of procedure in detail. You may rest assured, however, that during their training it was necessary for them to plan each step on paper so that the supervisor or teacher could check it and suggest additions, deletions, or a more efficient approach to the solution of the problem.

The project which you intend to build is a problem, and every problem requires a solution. Filling out your *plan sheet* is your approach to solving the problem of building something from wood.

Many plan sheets include the following data: (1) the working drawing (or reference to where it may be

Industrial Arts Woodworking

STUDENT'S PLAN SHEET

Student's name________________________Class__________________

Name of project_______Date started_______Date completed_______

Estimated time__________________Actual time__________________

Personal efficiency: actual time ÷ estimated time = ______%

Source of the drawing_______________________________________

Materials Required

No. of pieces	Description of piece	Sizes	Kind of wood or other materials	Board feet	Unit cost	Extended cost

Total cost__________

Tools:

1.	5.	9.
2.	6.	10.
3.	7.	11.
4.	8.	12.

Order of Procedure:
1.
2.
3.
4.
5.
6.
7.
8.
9.
10.
11.
12.
13.
14.

Approved__________________________________

Fig. 4-1. Student's plan sheet.

found); (2) a listing of the operations or procedure which enumerates the steps that will be followed in building the project; (3) a bill of materials (procedure for figuring materials may be secured from the preceding unit); (4) tools required; (5) references or sources for the project ideas; and (6) the estimated and the actual time required to build the project and the efficiency rating of the one doing the project.

The suggestions given in the form shown in Fig. 4-1, or in one preferred by your teacher, will save much time and money.

Discussion Topics

1. Make a list of 10 professions in which planning or analyzing the procedure in advance is imperative.
2. How might you have made eight mistakes in your project if you had not planned it before you made it?
3. What are the factors which must be considered in planning? (You should think of at least six.)

Unit 5. Safety

The adage "An ounce of prevention is worth a pound of cure" is applicable to safety in the school industrial-arts laboratory, in the industrial shop, or in the home workshop. Tools and machinery have been developed to expedite fabrication of wood projects, but they can be safely used only if they are properly cared for, understood, and respected. Whether they are beneficial or detrimental depends upon you.

Facts regarding school-shop accidents reveal that more occur in the forenoon around ten o'clock than at any other time of day. We also learn that more accidents happen on Wednesday than on any other day, except on days immediately prior to or following vacation periods. It has been pointed out that the most hazardous area is woodworking; this is possibly owing to the types of hand tools, such as wood chisels, saws, knives, planes, hammers, and files which are used, or misused in woodworking. The wood chisel has been the cause of more injuries than all other hand tools. In machine-tool operations the jointer has been the cause of the largest number of accidents. The next most dangerous tools are the circular saw, wood lathe, grinder, band saw, and drill press, in this order. Hand-tool accidents have accounted for twice as many injuries as machine-tool accidents, and most of the injuries have been to the inexperienced person or the beginner because of negligence and improper use of the tools.

All shop accidents should be reported on a form such as the one given in Fig. 5-1. This is a standard form prepared by the National Safety Council. Any accident which causes an injury requiring first aid or medical attention should be reported on this type of form.

STANDARD STUDENT ACCIDENT REPORT FORM
Part A. Information on ALL Accidents

1. Name: ______ Home Address: ______
2. School: ______ Sex: M ☐; F ☐. Age: ____ Grade or classification: ______
3. Time accident occurred: Hour ____ A.M.; ____ P.M. Date: ______
4. Place of Accident: School Building ☐ School Grounds ☐ To or from School ☐ Home ☐ Elsewhere ☐

5. **NATURE OF INJURY**

Abrasion	____	Fracture	____
Amputation	____	Laceration	____
Bruise	____	Puncture	____
Burn	____	Scratches	____
Concussion	____	Sprain	____
Cut	____		
Other (specify) ______			

PART OF BODY INJURED

Ankle	____	Hand	____
Arm	____	Head	____
Back	____	Knee	____
Elbow	____	Leg	____
Eye	____	Nose	____
Face	____	Scalp	____
Finger	____	Tooth	____
Foot	____	Wrist	____
Other (specify) ______			

DESCRIPTION OF THE ACCIDENT

How did accident happen? What was student doing? Where was student? List specifically unsafe acts and unsafe conditions existing. Specify any tool, machine or equipment involved. ______

6. Degree of Injury: Death ☐ Permanent Impairment ☐
7. Total number of days lost from school: ____ (To be filled in when student returns to school)

Part B. Additional Information on School Jurisdiction Accidents

8. Teacher in charge when accident occurred (Enter name): ______
   Present at scene of accident: No: ____ Yes: ____

9. **IMMEDIATE ACTION TAKEN**

First-aid treatment	____	By (Name): ______
Sent to school nurse	____	By (Name): ______
Sent home	____	By (Name): ______
Sent to physician	____	By (Name): ______
		Physician's Name: ______
Sent to hospital	____	By (Name): ______
		Name of hospital: ______

10. Was a parent or other individual notified? No: ____ Yes: ____ When: ____ How: ______
    Name of individual notified: ______
    By whom? (Enter name): ______

11. **LOCATION**

		Specify Activity
Athletic field	____	______
Auditorium	____	______
Classroom	____	______
Corridor	____	______
Dressing room	____	______
Gymnasium	____	______
Home Econ.	____	______
Laboratories	____	______
Sch. grounds	____	______
______ shop	____	______
Showers	____	______
Stairs	____	______
Other	____	______

Remarks

What recommendations do you have for preventing other accidents of this type? ______

Signed: Principal: ______ Teacher: ______

FIG. 5-1. Standard student accident report form. (*Courtesy of National Safety Council.*)

Safety Rules

The listing of safety rules in this chapter pertains primarily to the performance of hand-tool processes. Safe practices with respect to the use of power machinery and machine-tool processes are included in the description of operations which can be performed on the various machine tools in Section III.

Physical. 1. Never depend upon your back muscles in lifting a heavy object. Get someone to help you, and then lift with your leg and arm muscles.

2. Test the sharpness of tools on wood or paper, not on your hand.

3. Be careful when using your thumb as a guide in crosscutting and ripping.

4. Always cut away from the body when using a knife.

5. Make sure your hands are not in front of sharp-edged tools while the tools are in use.

Clothing. 1. Dress appropriately for work in the shop. You should wear a shop apron or some other protective clothing, such as coveralls.

2. Tuck in your tie and roll up your sleeves so that they are out of the way.

Tools. 1. Lay tools to be used in an orderly arrangement on a bench top with the cutting edges away from you and in such positions that they will not rub against each other. Sharp tools should not be allowed to extend over the edges of the bench.

2. Screw-driver points must be kept properly pointed to prevent injury to hands and to wood fiber (Fig. 17-7).

3. Fasten handles securely on planes, hammers, and mallets.

4. Make certain that all files have handles.

5. Use tools only for their intended purpose and, then, properly. Do not attempt to pry with a file, screw driver, or wood chisel.

Materials. 1. Always fasten material securely in a vise, when practical, before working with it.

2. Put waste pieces of lumber in the scrap box or in the storage rack so that they will not be in anyone's way.

3. Keep oily rags used for finishing in closed metal containers to prevent fires.

Shop Courtesy

1. Report an accident immediately after it occurs so that first aid can be given.

2. Warn others to clear out of your way when you handle long pieces of lumber.

3. Do not run in the shop, laboratory, or home workshop; it is dangerous.

4. Carry only a few tools at a time.

Discussion Topics

1. Why is safety stressed in shops and laboratories?
2. Explain why hand tools are the cause of twice as many injuries as machine tools in woodworking.
3. Why should reports of accidents be made to school officials and to the National Safety Council?
4. Explain why the wood chisel is the cause of more accidents than any other wood tool used in woodworking.
5. What are at least three advantages in wearing some protective covering, such as a shop apron or coveralls?
6. What is your conception of shop courtesy?

Section II. HAND TOOL PROCESSES

Unit 6. Measuring and Laying Out

Accurate measurement is one of the basic skills to be mastered in working with wood. The foot and the inch are standard linear measurements used in most shops and industries. Practically all measuring tools used in woodworking are divided into marks of 1, $\frac{1}{2}$, $\frac{1}{4}$, $\frac{1}{8}$, and $\frac{1}{16}$ inch. Figure 6-1 illustrates these markings and divisions.

Tools

The tools commonly used for measuring and laying out are the 1- or 2-foot wooden bench rule (Fig. 6-2), steel square (Fig. 6-3), try square (Fig. 6-4), 2-foot folding rule (Fig. 6-5), zigzag rule (Fig. 6-6), flexible steel tape (Fig. 6-7), T bevel (Fig. 6-8), marking gauge (Fig. 6-9), and knife (Fig. 6-10).

Fig. 6-1. Divisions of an inch.

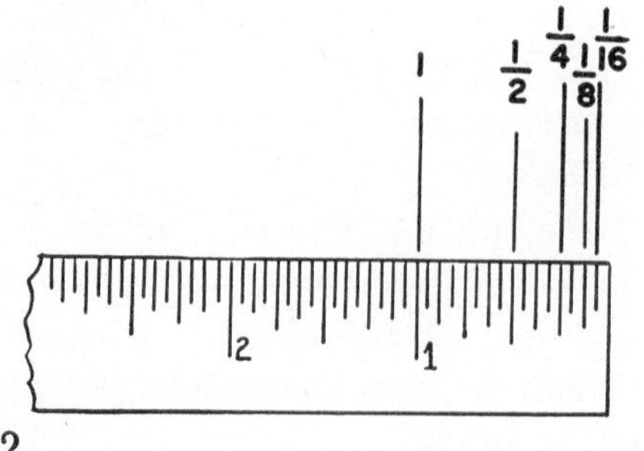

Two-foot wooden bench rule. One of the most frequently used tools is the 2-foot wooden bench rule (Fig. 6-2). One side has graduations of $\frac{1}{8}$ inch; the other is divided into markings of $\frac{1}{16}$ inch.

Steel square. This square has a 24-inch blade and a 16-inch tongue (Fig. 6-3). It is used in bench, cabinet, and carpentry work to measure, to square lines, to test large surfaces for *wind,* to test for squareness in assembly, and to laying out rafters, roof framing, and stairs. There are numerous tables on the two arms of the square which provide valuable information for use in carpentry. There are pamphlets, manuals, and books which describe the exact use for each of these tables.

Try square. The try square (Fig. 6-4) is one of the most used tools for squaring, testing, and measuring. It is usually

Fig. 6-2. One- and two-foot wooden bench rules.

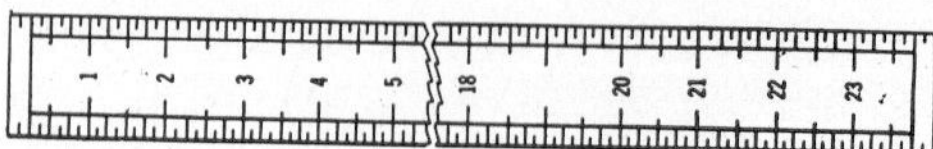

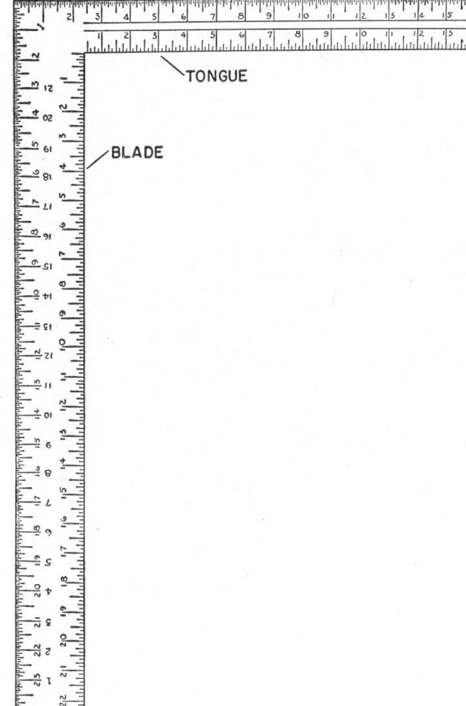

FIG. 6-3. Steel square.

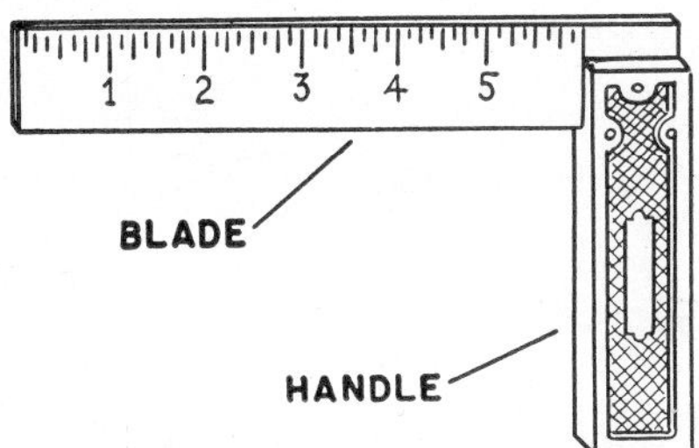

FIG. 6-4. Try square.

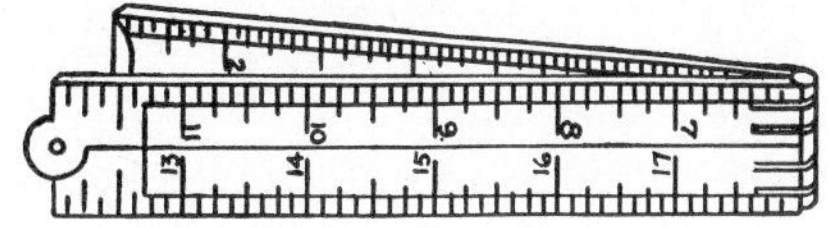

FIG. 6-5. Two-foot folding rule.

FIG. 6-6. Zigzag rule.

made of steel, but sometimes the handle is of wood.

Two-foot folding rule. This rule (Fig. 6-5) is so constructed that it folds into an over-all compact length of 6 inches. It is used for measuring.

Zigzag rule. The zigzag rule (Fig. 6-6) is built somewhat like the folding rule and usually extends to a 6-foot length. It is generally made of wood but sometimes is available in one of the lighter weight metals. It is useful for long measurements.

Flexible steel rule. A flexible steel rule which extends 6 feet in length is convenient for either outside or inside measuring (Fig. 6-7).

T bevel. This tool (Fig. 6-8) resembles the try square in appearance but has a movable blade which can be adjusted for laying out at any angle. It is also employed for testing chamfers, bevels, and angles.

Marking gauge. The marking gauge (Fig. 6-9) is used for scoring or for rolling a line parallel to a given space, edge, or end. It is made of either wood or metal, but most gauges are of wood. There is a metal spur point, which must be kept as sharp as a knife at all times.

FIG. 6-7. Flexible steel rule.

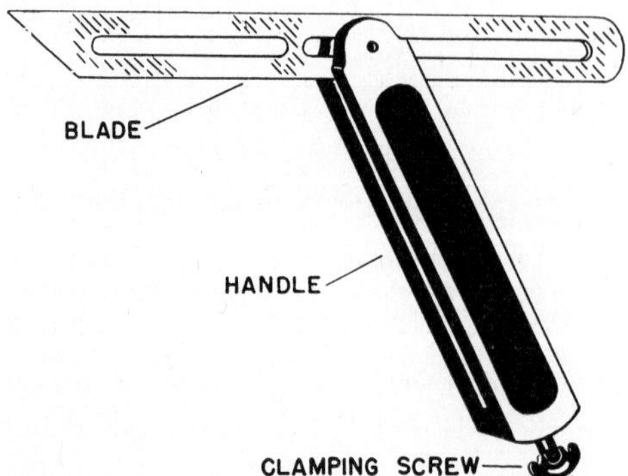

FIG. 6-8. T bevel.

One of the more popular all-metal gauges employs a small roller in place of the spur.

The beam, or main bar of the gauge, has measurements imprinted on it similar to those on a try square or rule. It is always advisable to check the measurement from the spur point to the movable head, as shown in Fig. 6-19, in order to ensure the most accurate measurement, because the spur point sometimes becomes bent or loose.

Knife. This tool (Fig. 6-10) may be used for accurate marking across the grain of the wood. It may also be used for cutting and whittling.

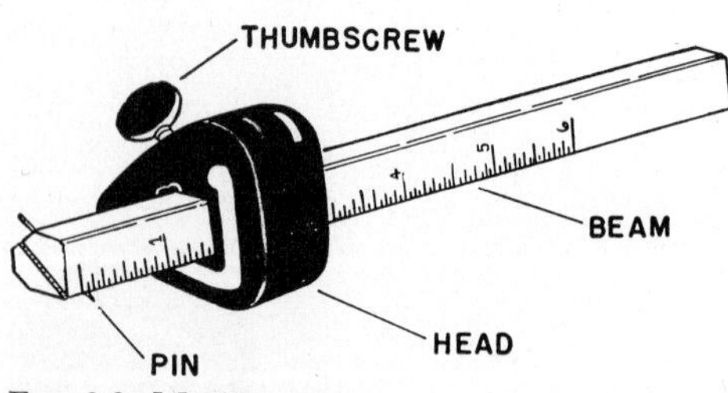

FIG. 6-9. Marking gauge.

FIG. 6-10. Knife.

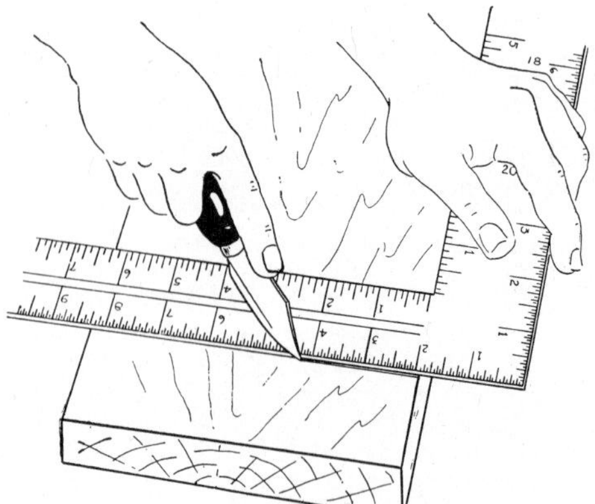
FIG. 6-11. Squaring a line across a board.

LAYING OUT LENGTHS

1. Select a board which has a minimum of imperfections such as cracks, checks, or blemishes (Fig. 6-12).

2. Square a line across the end of the board at a place which will avoid end checks and imperfections (Fig. 6-12). Place the blade of the square firmly against the edge of the board, and mark the line against the tongue of the square on the broad surface of the board (Fig. 6-11) so that the mark will be at 90-degree angle with the edge.

3. Lay out the desired length with a suitable measuring rule (Figs. 6-13 and 6-14), and mark with a sharp pencil or a knife. When using a rule,

FIG. 6-12. Board marked to avoid imperfections and checks.

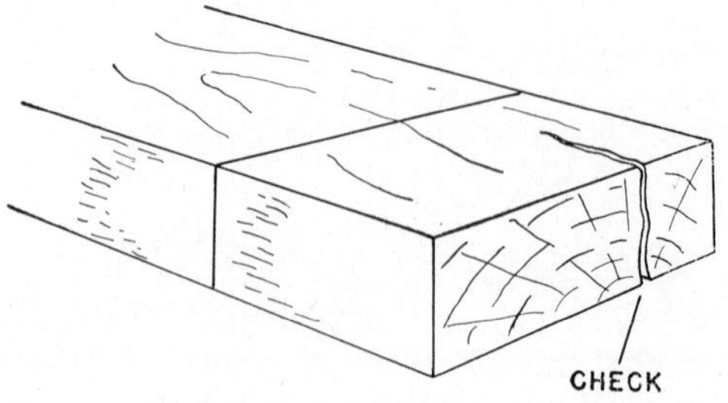

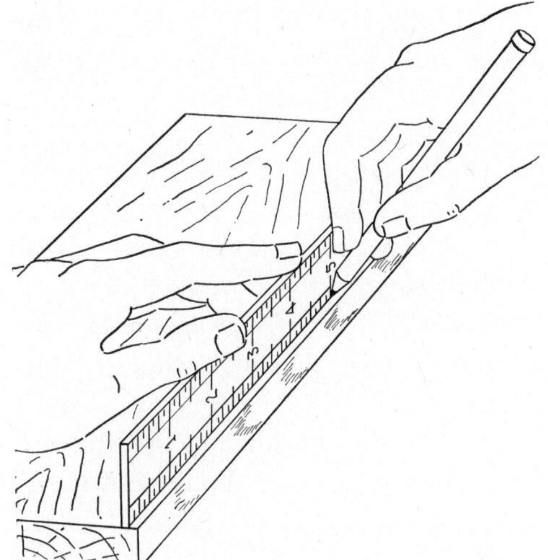

Fig. 6-13. Laying out measurement with rule on edge.

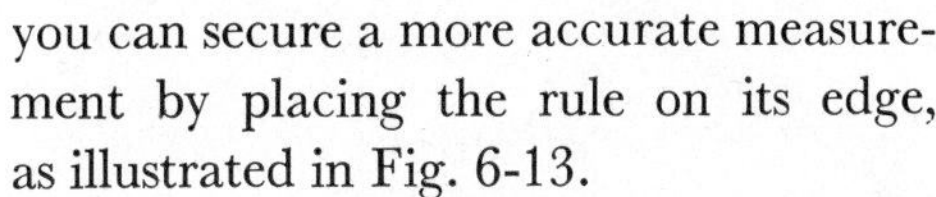

you can secure a more accurate measurement by placing the rule on its edge, as illustrated in Fig. 6-13.

4. Square the line just marked, by following the procedure described in step 2.

Fig. 6-14. Laying out measurement with flexible rule.

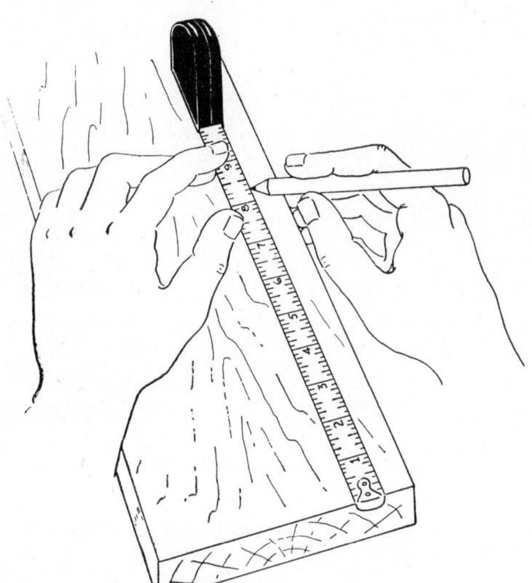

Fig. 6-15. Measuring for width.

Laying Out Widths

1. Measure and mark the desired width with any of the measuring tools (Figs. 6-15 and 6-13). A board may be divided and marked into any number of pieces of equal widths by laying the rule edgewise across the board in a diagonal position, as suggested in Fig. 6-16.

Fig. 6-16. Dividing a board into equal or proportional parts.

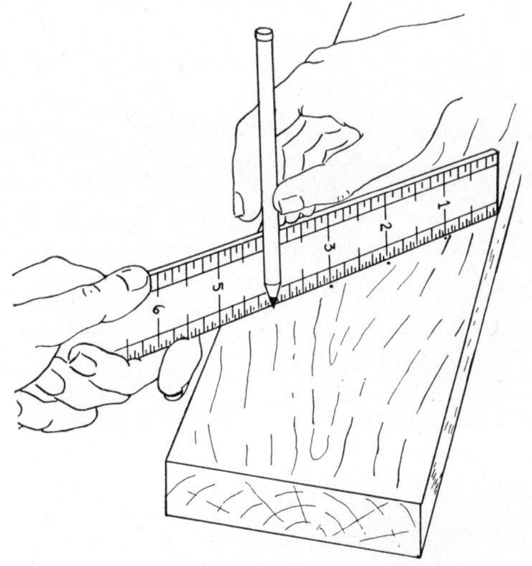

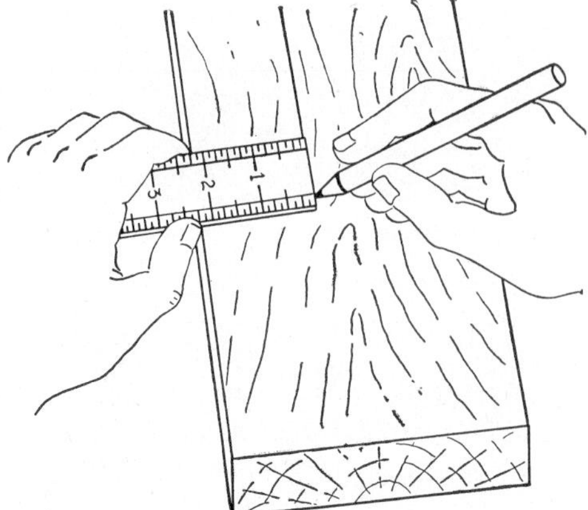

FIG. 6-17. Rule and pencil used as a marking gauge.

2. Mark the width layout on the board by either of the methods shown in Figs. 6-17 and 6-18.

GAUGING WIDTH AND THICKNESS

1. Adjust the marking gauge to the desired distance to be marked.

2. Check the setting against a rule to make certain that it is accurate (Fig. 6-19).

3. Push the marking gauge forward on the wood to make the desired marking (Fig. 6-20). Hold the head of the

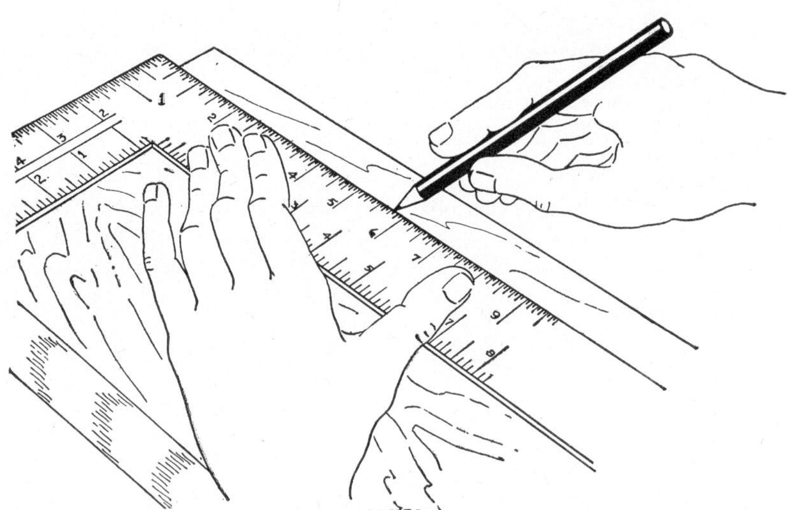

FIG. 6-18. Marking a line along a straightedge.

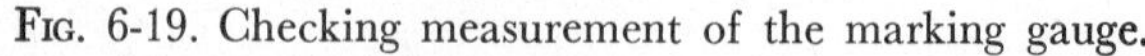

FIG. 6-19. Checking measurement of the marking gauge.

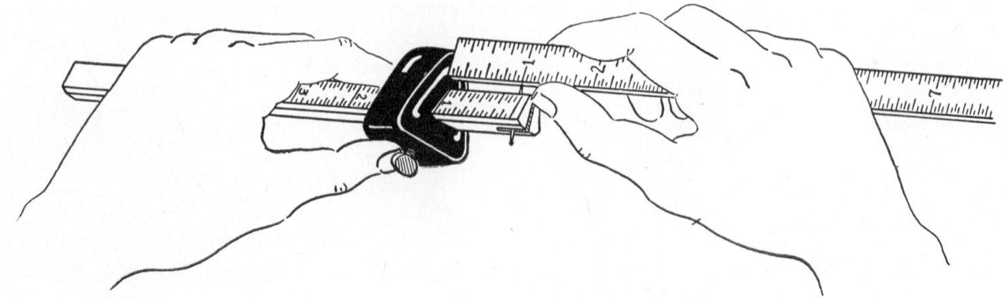

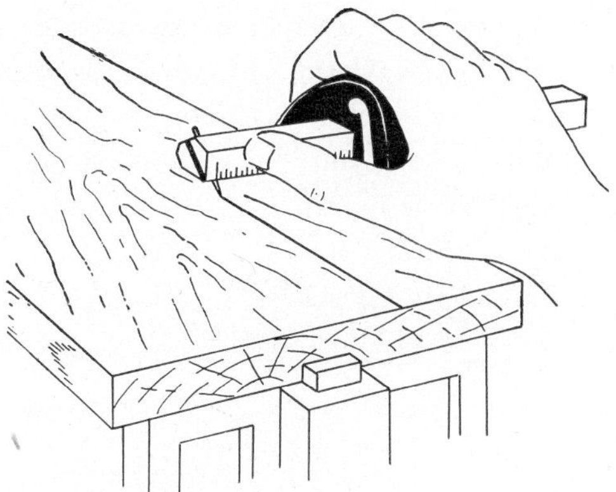

Fig. 6-20. Pushing the marking gauge to scribe a line.

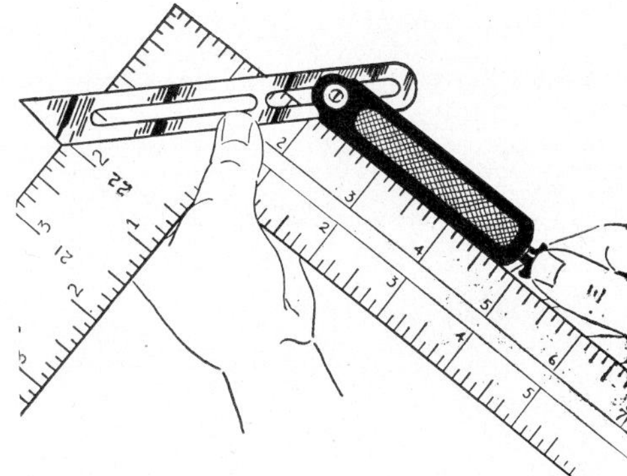

Fig. 6-22. Adjusting T bevel to desired angle against a square.

gauge firmly against the edge of the board while scribing a light line.

Laying Out Edges

Mark a line on the edge of the board extending the face line (Fig. 6-21). Hold the handle of the try square firmly against the broad side or face of the board while marking along the blade (Fig. 6-21).

Fig. 6-21. Extending the face line along an edge.

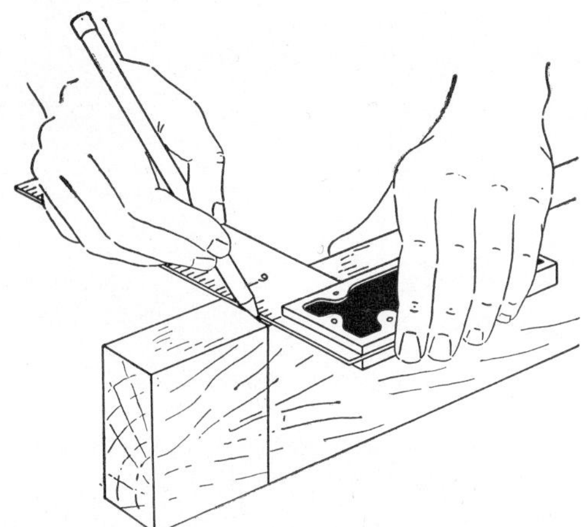

Laying Out Angles

1. Adjust the T bevel to the desired angle (Fig. 6-22) and tighten in position with the screw on the handle. This laying-out tool is especially useful for any acute (less than 90 degrees) or obtuse (over 90 degrees) angle. The degree setting of a T bevel may be obtained by the use of a protractor (Fig. 6-23).

2. Hold the handle firmly against the face or edge of the board and mark along the edge of the blade. This is similar to the method of marking with the use of a try square.

Fig. 6-23. Adjusting T bevel to desired angle with the aid of a protractor.

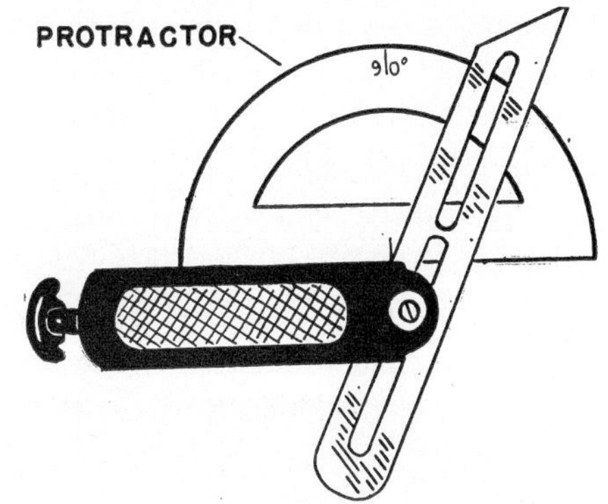

Discussion Topics

1. What are the linear standards of measurements?
2. How many eighths ($\frac{1}{8}$) are there in $1\frac{3}{8}$ inches?
3. Name six tools which might be used for measuring.
4. What is the advantage in placing a rule on its edge when measuring?
5. Describe at least two methods by which you would divide an 8-inch board into five equal lengths.
6. Why should you check the measurement of a marking gauge against a rule?
7. Should the marking gauge be pushed away from, or pulled toward, you? Explain.

Unit 7. Sawing Across or with the Grain of the Wood

The saw is one of the oldest tools known to mankind. The most primitive form dates back to the Stone Age when flint with ragged edges was used for cutting. Although the operation of the modern saw made of steel is very similar to that of the ragged flint one, refinements have developed the steel saw into a highly efficient cutting tool.

Tools

Saws common to woodworkers are the crosscut saw, the ripsaw, and the back or cabinet saw. Figure 7-1 shows a typical handsaw with the essential parts.

The size of a saw is determined by the length of the blade in inches. The more popular sizes are the 24- and 26-inch ones.

Fig. 7-1. Typical handsaw.

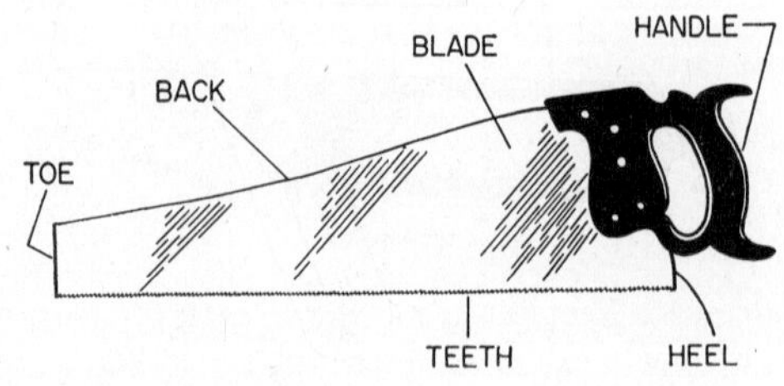

The coarseness or fineness of a saw is designated by the number of points per inch, as illustrated in Fig. 7-2. There will always be one more point than tooth per inch. For example, an eight-point saw will have seven teeth per inch. A coarse saw is better for doing fast work and for cutting green lumber; a fine one is more satisfactory for doing smoother, accurate cutting on dry, seasoned wood.

Crosscut saw. This is used to cut across the grain of the wood (Fig. 7-3). The teeth are set and filed, as shown in

Fig. 7-2. Points per inch on crosscut saw and on ripsaw.

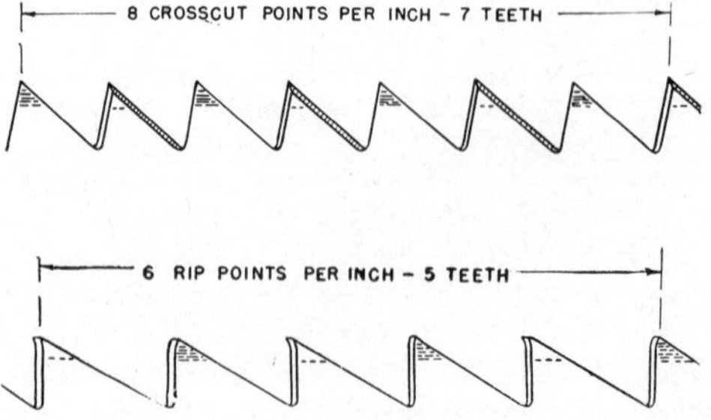

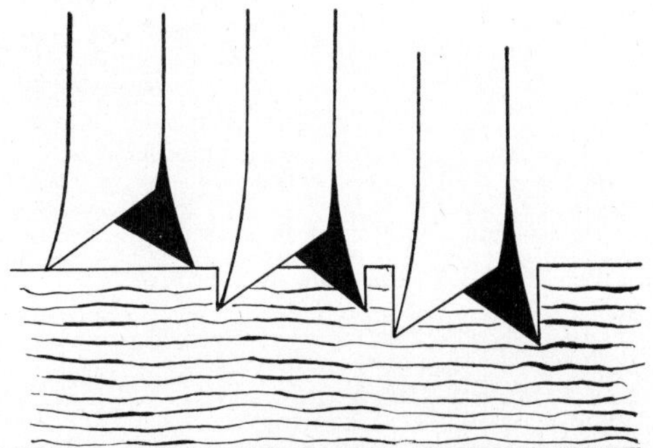

Fig. 7-3. Cutting action of crosscut-saw teeth.

Fig. 7-4. Top view of crosscut-saw teeth.

Fig. 7-2. They cut into the wood to make the *kerf* (saw cut), as shown in Fig. 7-3.

The teeth of saws are *set,* that is, bent alternately to the right and left, to make the saw kerf wider than the thickness of the saw blade. This prevents the saw from binding or sticking in the kerf. In addition to having the teeth set, high-grade quality saws are taper-ground and are thinner at the back than at the tooth edge. Saw teeth should always be kept sharp and properly set.

Fig. 7-5. Cutting action of ripsaw teeth.

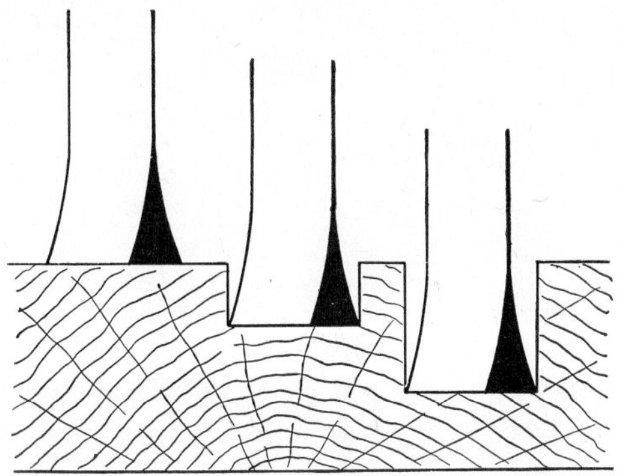

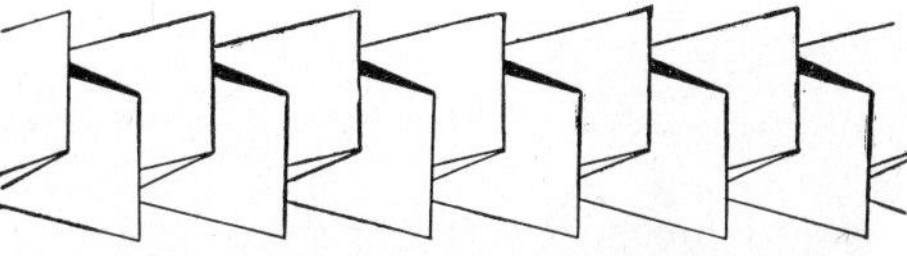

Fig. 7-6. Top view of ripsaw teeth.

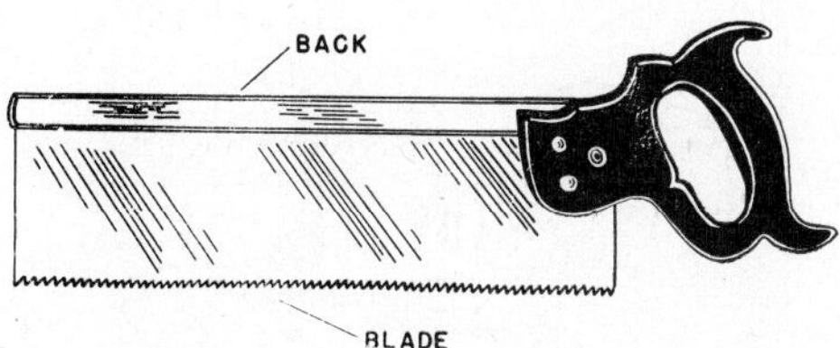

Fig. 7-7. Backsaw.

Ripsaw. The ripsaw is used for ripping or cutting with the grain of the wood (Fig. 7-5). The teeth are large and cut into the wood with short, chisel-like jabs. Figure 7-6 shows how the teeth of a ripsaw are filed and set, and Fig. 7-5 describes the manner in which this saw cuts into the wood to make the kerf.

Backsaw. Figure 7-7 is an illustration of a thin crosscut saw with fine teeth stiffened by a thick back. A popular length is 12 inches with fourteen points per inch. This type of saw is used for very fine work in cabinet construction and for making joints.

Vise. Much of the lumber to be sawed is held in a woodworker's bench vise. Before using this vise, it will be well to understand its mechanism (Fig. 7-8). Figure 7-9 shows an installed woodworker's vise being used.

Fig. 7-8. Woodworker's bench vise.

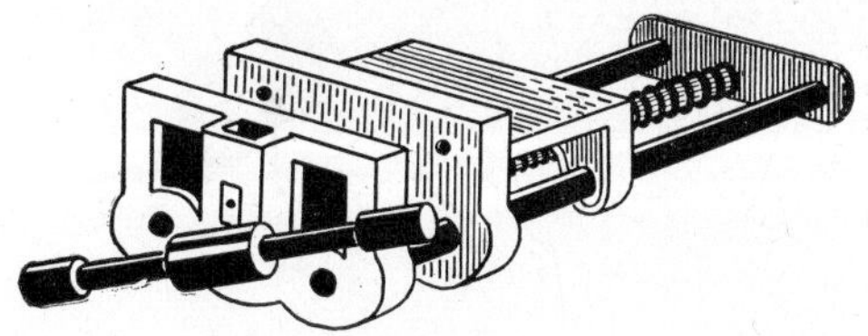

Fig. 7-9. Board held in woodworker's vise for crosscutting.

Crosscutting

1. Lay out and mark the board to be cut, as suggested in the preceding unit.

2. Fasten the board in a bench vise if it can be held securely by this means (Fig. 7-9). Wider or longer boards which cannot be held firmly in a vise should be placed across sawhorses (Fig. 7-12).

3. Place the heel of the crosscut saw near the cutting line on the *waste* side of the wood, and pull it, guiding it with the left thumb (Fig. 7-10). Figure 7-11 designates the waste portions of a board.

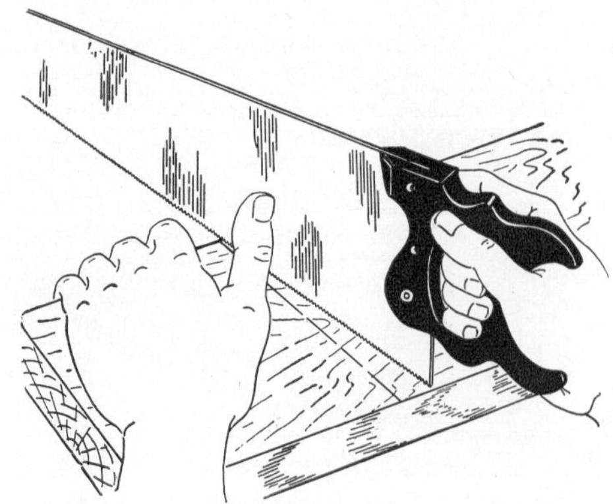

Fig. 7-10. Starting the cut across the grain.

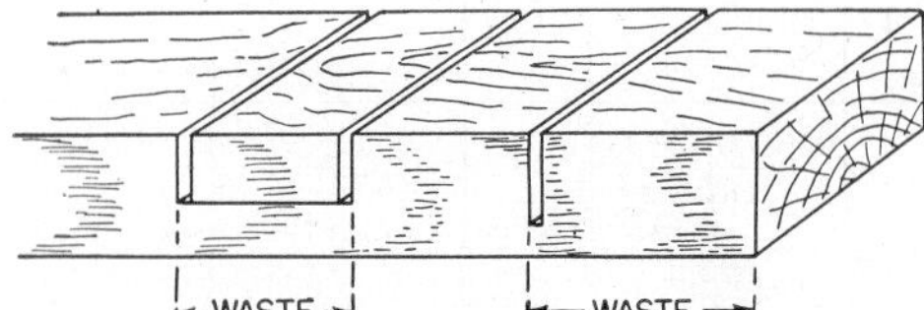

Fig. 7-11. Waste portions of a board.

4. Make short strokes until several cuts have been effected; then test with a try square to see that the saw blade is cutting at right angles to the surface of the board (Fig. 7-12).

5. Continue the cutting with long strokes. Have the saw cutting at about a 45-degree angle to the board (Fig. 7-13). The direction of the cut may be changed by twisting the handle slightly in the direction of the line.

6. Finish the cut with short, easy strokes (Fig. 7-14). Support the stock to be cut off with your left hand. This prevents the wood from splitting or breaking from its own weight.

Fig. 7-12. Testing saw cut with a try square.

Fig. 7-13. Proper angle of the saw for crosscutting.

Ripping

1. Mark the lumber to be sawed or ripped as described in the preceding unit.

2. Clamp the stock in a bench vise if possible (Fig. 7-15). Boards which cannot be handled in the bench vise should be placed on a sawhorse (Fig. 7-16).

3. Start the ripping procedure in much the same manner as that outlined in step 3 under "Crosscutting." Begin

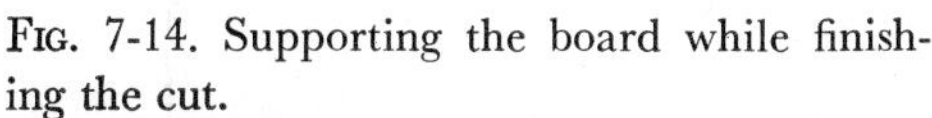

Fig. 7-14. Supporting the board while finishing the cut.

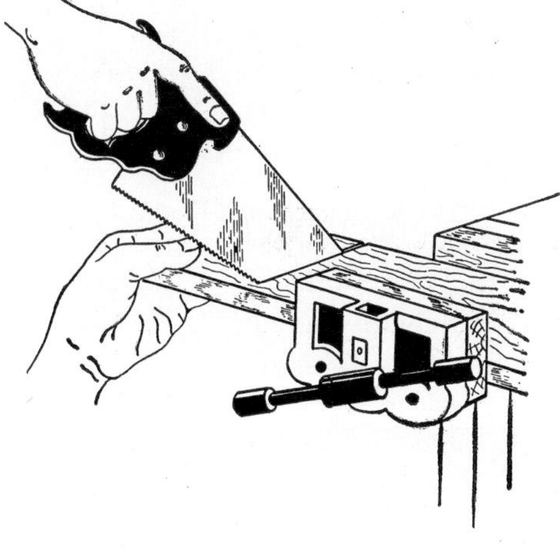

Fig. 7-15. Wood held in a bench vise while ripping.

Fig. 7-16. Starting to rip a board on a sawhorse.

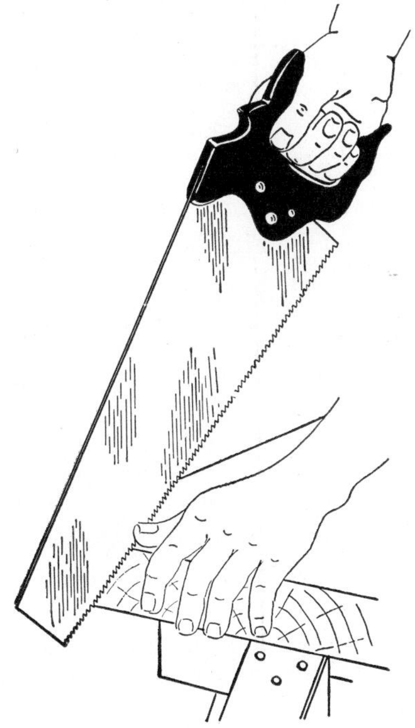

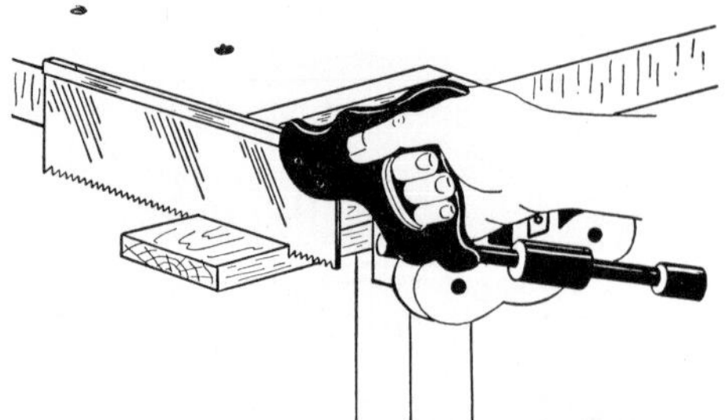

Fig. 7-17. Holding lumber in a vise while cutting with a backsaw.

the cut with the ripsaw on the backstroke, holding it so that the cutting edge is approximately 60 degrees with the surface (Figs. 7-15 and 7-16). Make certain that the cut is on the waste side of the board.

4. Continue ripping the stock with short, easy strokes to prevent splitting. If the board is held in a vise, hold the waste side with your left hand to steady it and to keep it from splitting on the finishing strokes (Fig. 7-15).

Fine or Cabinet Sawing

1. Lay out and mark the board for cutting.

2. Fasten the stock securely in a vise (Fig. 7-17) or hold it firmly against a bench hook (Fig. 7-18).

3. Start the cutting procedure with the backsaw in a manner similar to that used for crosscutting.

4. Continue cutting with short, easy strokes until the board has been cut. The waste portion must be held or protected with your left hand to prevent splitting in the final strokes, especially when the board is held in a bench vise.

Fig. 7-18. Holding lumber on a bench hook while cutting with a backsaw.

Discussion Topics

1. What are the essential differences between the crosscut saw and the ripsaw?
2. What does the number stamped on the heel of the saw indicate?
3. What is a saw "kerf?"
4. Why must the teeth of a saw have "set"?
5. Are there as many teeth as points per inch on a saw blade?
6. Name several possible causes for a saw blade binding or sticking.
7. Should the saw be pulled or pushed when starting a cut? Why?
8. Why should the final strokes in sawing be short and light?
9. Where does the backsaw get its name?
10. What are some of the features of the woodworker's vise that make it particularly adaptable for working with wood?

Unit 8. Assembling and Adjusting Planes

The plane is an indispensable tool to the woodworker. Although there are several types, the assembly, adjustment, and general operation of all are similar. The most common types of planes are the jack, smoothing, jointer, block, and rabbet. Figure 8-1 shows the essential parts of a plane.

Two other tools not mentioned in detail here, but which are often used to dress down and smooth wood, are the spokeshave and the several types of scraper. These are discussed in Unit 11, "Assembling and Adjusting a Spokeshave" and in Unit 14, "Assembling and Adjusting Scrapers."

Planes

The following descriptions and illustrations of planes will enable you to select the one most suitable for your needs.

Jack plane. This plane (Fig. 8-2) is the most universally used because of its size, utility, and versatility. It will perform the work of the smoothing, jointer, and block planes. It differs from the smoothing and jointer planes in length, having an approximate length of 14 inches.

Junior jack plane. The junior jack plane (not illustrated) is narrower and shorter but is proportioned like the jack. The bed is usually 10 inches long. It is of light-weight construction and is intended for children of grade and junior high school ages.

Smoothing plane. This plane (Fig. 8-3) is identical to the jack plane except that the bed is only about 8 inches long. It is primarily for fine work, particularly where ease of handling is important.

Jointer plane. The jointer plane (Fig. 8-4) resembles the jack plane except that the bed is from 22 to 30 inches long. It is used most often for planing the edges of boards preparatory to joining or for dressing down long flat surfaces.

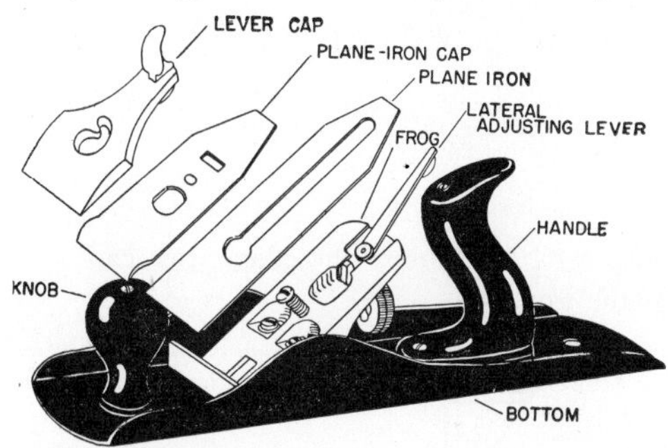

Fig. 8-1. Parts of a plane.

Fig. 8-2. Jack plane.

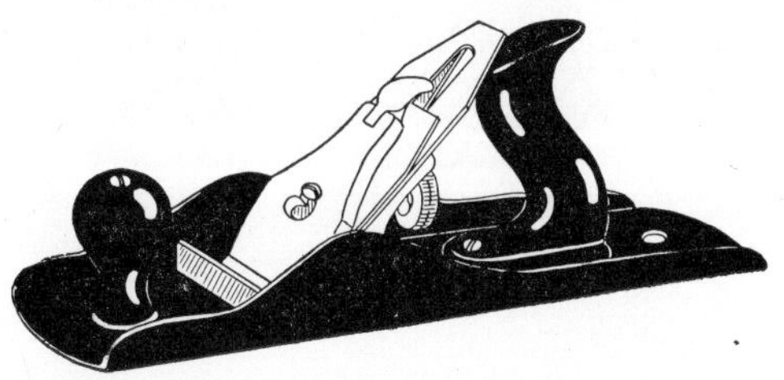

Fig. 8-3. Smoothing plane.

Fig. 8-4. Jointer plane.

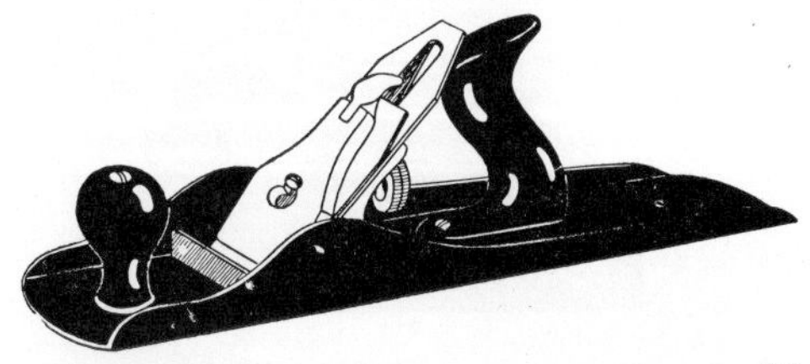

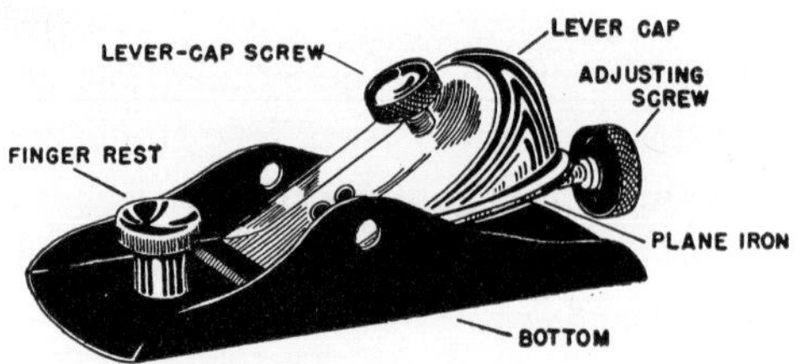

FIG. 8-5. Block plane.

Block plane. This plane (Fig. 8-5) is constructed somewhat differently from the jack plane but is adjusted in a similar manner. It is very convenient for planing end grain or for easy handling of many small jobs, because it is designed to fit the palm of the hand.

Rabbet plane. The rabbet plane, illustrated in Fig. 8-6, is described as "bullnose" because of its construction. It operates like the block plane but is narrower. The plane iron is located near the front of the bed for convenience in planing in close places. It will make a cut the full width of the bed and, therefore, is used for planing surfaces near corners, rabbets, and for general close work. It is ideal for dressing tenons to fit snugly into mortises. The bed on the plane is about 4 inches long.

Assembling and Adjusting

The assembling and adjusting of a plane is not difficult if the instructions presented here are carefully followed.

FIG. 8-6. Rabbet plane.

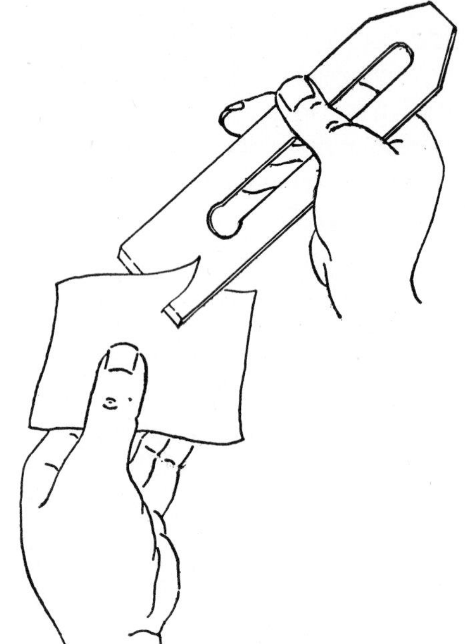

FIG. 8-7. Testing the cutting edge on a piece of paper to determine sharpness of plane iron.

Assembling. 1. Test the plane iron for sharpness (Fig. 8-7). If it needs to be sharpened, refer to Unit 27, "Sharpening tools," page 109.

2. Place the plane-iron cap on the flat side of the plane iron with the screw in the slot (Fig. 8-8).

FIG. 8-8. Assembling the plane-iron cap and plane iron.

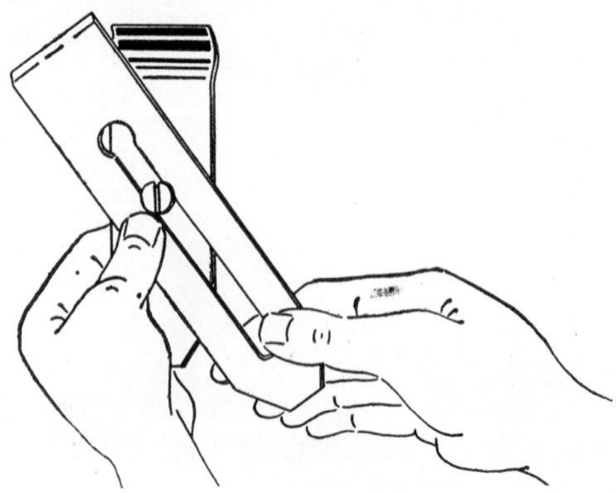

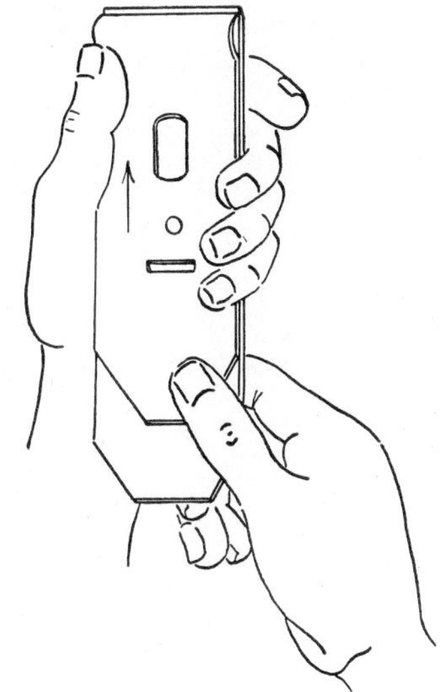

Fig. 8-9. Aligning the plane-iron cap and plane iron.

3. Pull the plane-iron cap back and turn it straight with the plane iron (Fig. 8-9).

4. Slide the cap toward the cutting edge of the plane iron. The cap should never be pushed over the edge of the blade. See Fig. 8-9 for this detail.

5. Adjust and fasten the plane-iron cap with a screw driver. The cap should be about $\frac{1}{16}$ inch from the cutting edge of the blade for average work.

6. Assemble the blade and plane-iron cap in the plane by placing the plane iron with its bevel side down on the frog (Fig. 8-10). Make certain that the plane iron is placed properly on the lateral adjusting lever.

Fig. 8-10. Assembling parts of a plane.

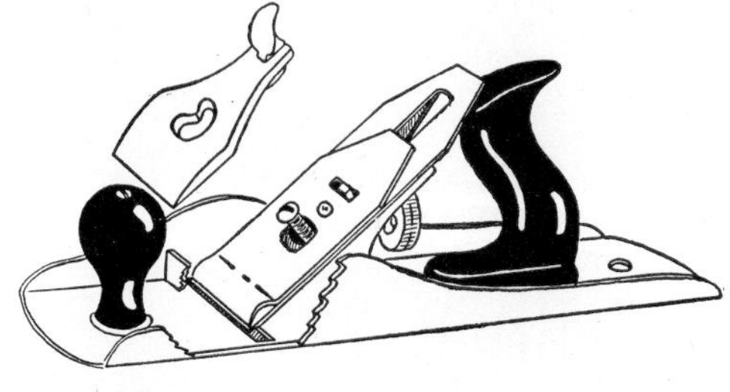

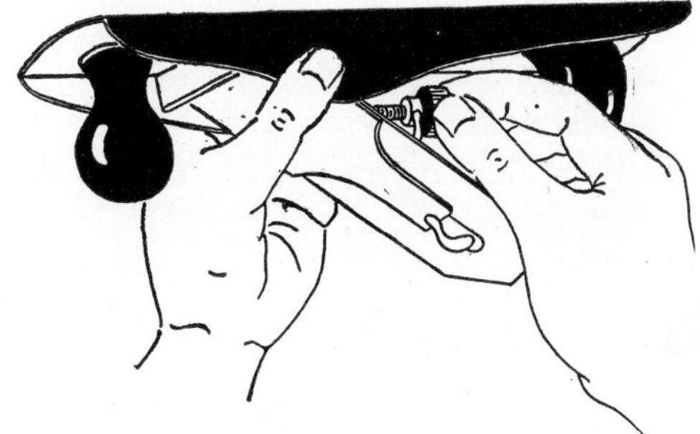

Fig. 8-11. Adjusting for cutting depth.

7. Place the lever cap over the plane-iron assembly so that the screw slides properly in the slot (Fig. 8-10).

8. Press the cam on the lever cap to hold the entire assembly securely. Figure 8-2 shows the lever cap in its proper position. If the cam does not press easily, re-check the assembly.

Adjusting. 1. Move the plane iron with the lateral adjusting lever until the cutting edge is parallel with the bed of the plane. Figure 8-1 shows the lateral adjusting lever.

2. Regulate the depth of cutting by manipulating the adjustment nut near the handle to the right or left until the desired depth is obtained (Fig. 8-11).

Discussion Topics

1. List six parts of a plane and describe the function of each.
2. What type of plane is the most popular with woodworkers?
3. Name at least five types of planes and give the intended purpose for each.

4. Make a demonstration of the assembly and proper adjustment of a jack plane.
5. What is the function of the lateral adjustment lever?
6. How far should the cutting edge of a plane iron extend beyond the plane-iron cap?
7. What is the function of the plane-iron cap?

Unit 9. Squaring Lumber

Squaring stock is one of the basic and fundamental procedures which all woodworkers must master early in learning the trade or in developing the hobby. It is essential to follow a definite sequence of steps for planing the surfaces, edges, and ends of each board. Squaring the different pieces in the process of planing all the surfaces of the stock until they are true and smooth, that is, until each is at right angles to the adjoining surfaces, edges, or ends. If all of the pieces in the project are squared to the exact dimensions specified in the drawing, they will fit together properly. Figure 9-1 indicates by number the sequence of steps for squaring a board.

Tools

The tools used in squaring lumber have been previously illustrated and described. Generally they are the jack plane, try square, framing square, marking gauge, rule, crosscut saw, ripsaw, and backsaw.

Squaring First Surface

1. Select the best surface or face of the board. It is assumed that the board has been cut to approximate length. If not, refer to Unit 6 "Measuring and Laying Out," page 12 and to Unit 7, "Sawing across or with the Grain of the wood," page 18.

2. Place the board on the bench and fasten it securely between the vise dog and a bench stop (Fig. 9-2). Arrange it so that you can plane with the grain.

3. Adjust the cutting depth of the plane iron so that it is uniform and not too deep.

Fig. 9-1. Sequence of steps in squaring a board.

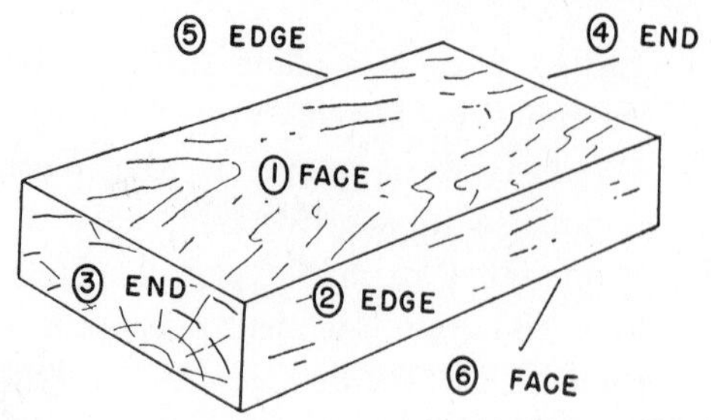

Fig. 9-2. Board fastened securely on bench ready for planing.

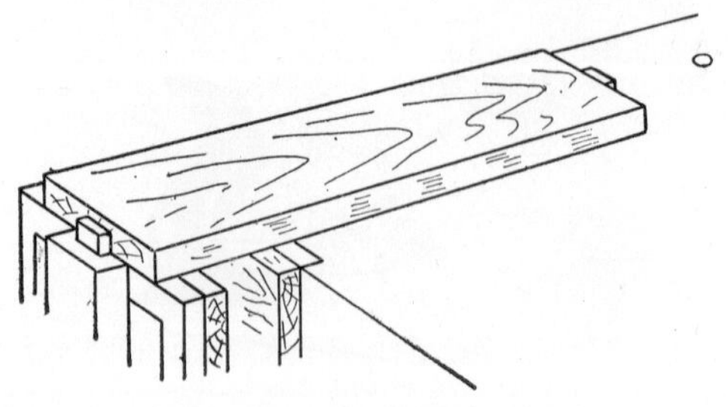

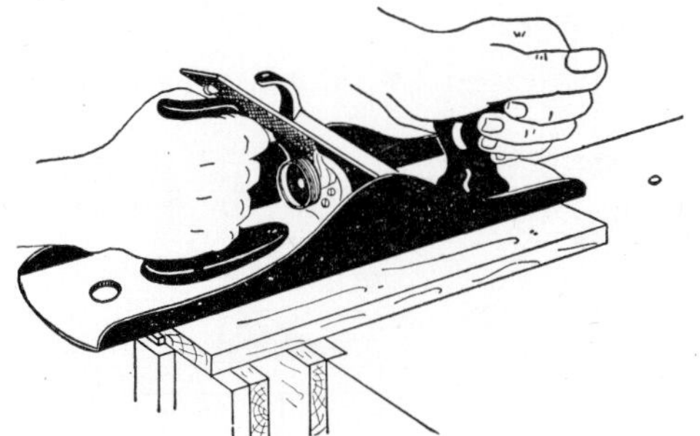

FIG. 9-3. Planing a surface.

4. Plane the surface until it is clean and smooth (Fig. 9-3).

5. Test the surface for flatness with the blade of a try square or with the tongue of a framing square (Fig. 9-4). The entire blade should be in contact with the surface throughout the complete length.

6. Test the surface across diagonals to detect a wind (Fig. 9-5). It may be necessary to use a longer straightedge, such as a framing square. Test across both diagonals.

FIG. 9-4. Testing for flatness.

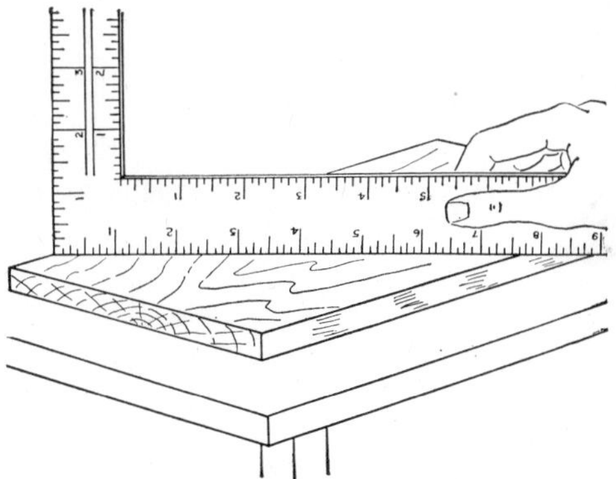

FIG. 9-5. Testing diagonally for a wind.

SQUARING THE FIRST EDGE

1. Select the best edge. This will probably be the one requiring the least amount of planing.

2. Fasten the board in a vise with this edge up and with the direction of the grain away from you (Fig. 9-6).

3. Plane the edge until it is square with the planed surface, or working face (Fig. 9-7). Notice when to put the pressure on the plane for starting and finishing the planing of an edge.

4. Test the edge with the face for squareness (Fig. 9-8).

FIG. 9-6. Placing a board in a vise for edge planing.

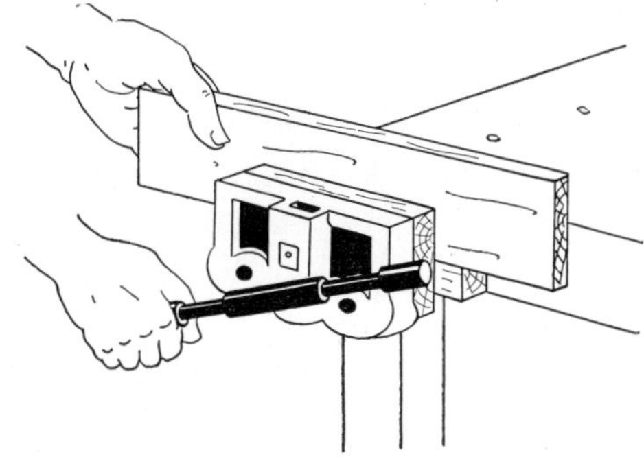

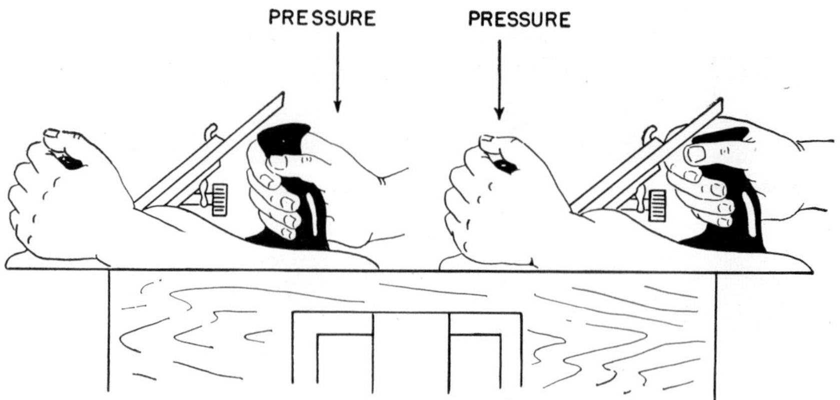

Fig. 9-7. Planing an edge.

Fig. 9-8. Testing an edge for squareness.

Squaring the First End

1. Select the best end.

2. Fasten the board in a vise with this end up (Fig. 9-12).

3. Select the procedure you will use in planing the end from one of the following three steps (Figs. 9-9, 9-10, and 9-11).

a. Chamfer the end as shown in Fig. 9-9. This chamfer should be from the unfinished edge. You may

Fig. 9-9. Chamfering an end for end planing.

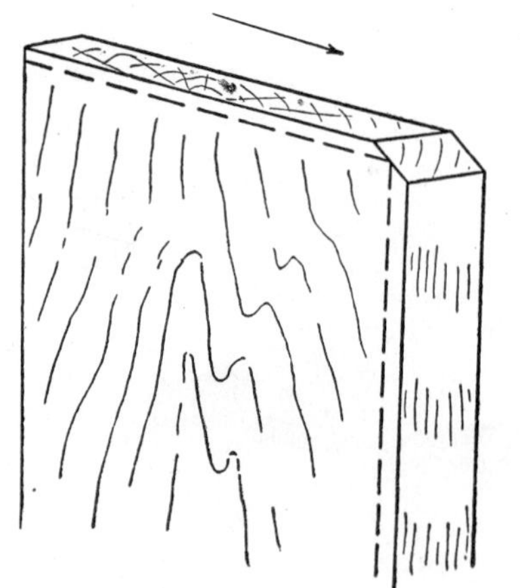

Fig. 9-10. Adding a piece of scrap stock for end planing.

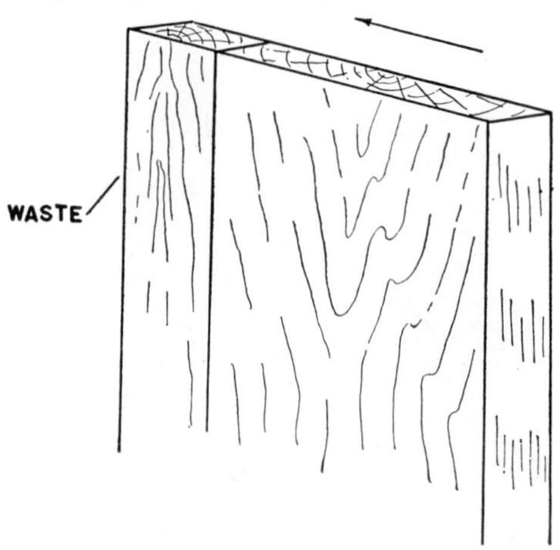

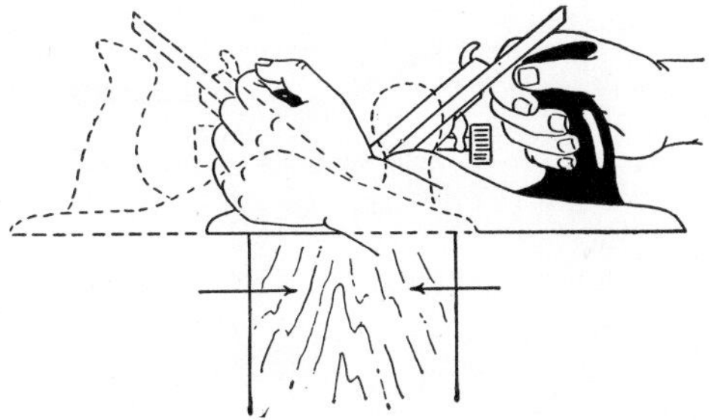

FIG. 9-11. Planing end grain from both directions.

plane in the direction of the arrow without splitting the edge.

b. Fasten a narrow piece of scrap wood against the unfinished edge, as shown in Fig. 9-10. Plane in the direction of the arrow to minimize the splintering of the outer edge.

c. Plane two-thirds of the distance across the end from one side and then reverse the direction. The opposite edge will not split off if the plane is lifted before going completely across Fig. 9-11).

4. Plane the end until it is square with the planed surface and edge (Fig. 9-12). A wide board may be held in a vise conveniently if it is supported with a hand-screw clamp which has been fastened to the board so that the clamp rests flat against the bench top.

FIG. 9-12. Planing the end of a wide board.

FIG. 9-13. Testing the squareness of an end with the surface.

5. Test the end for squareness with the working face and with the planed edge (Figs. 9-13 and 9-14).

FIG. 9-14. Testing the squareness of an end with the planed edge.

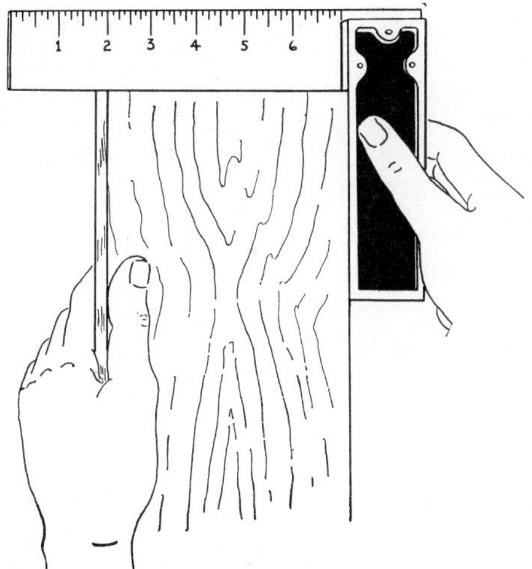

Fig. 9-15. Measuring a board for desired length.

Fig. 9-16. Sawing a board to length with a backsaw on a bench hook.

Squaring Opposite End

1. Measure the board for the exact desired length and mark it (Figs. 9-15).

2. Mark the length square with the planed edge.

3. Cut off the surplus with a crosscut saw or backsaw (Fig. 9-16). Allow $\frac{1}{8}$ inch for planing to the line.

4. Plane this end of the line so that it will be square with both the planed face and edge. Testing for squareness is similar to step 5 under, "Squaring the First End."

Squaring Opposite Edge

1. Measure and mark the board for the desired width. This will be similar to step 1 under "Squaring Opposite End."

2. Cut off the surplus stock, if necessary, with a ripsaw. This is desirable only when the waste to be removed is approximately $\frac{3}{8}$ inch or more. Allow $\frac{1}{8}$ inch for planing to the line.

3. Plane this edge to the line so that it is square with the working face or surface and with both ends.

Squaring Final Surface

1. Mark the board for thickness with the marking gauge. (Fig. 6-20). The gauge line should be put on both edges and ends.

2. Plane this last face or opposite surface to the gauge line. Test it frequently for squareness and for smoothness.

Discussion Topics

1. List the six general operations for squaring a board.
2. Describe a situation where the ends of a board would not have to be squared.
3. Is it possible to plane a board to the required thickness and still not have the faces true? Explain your answer.
4. How would you test a board to make certain that the surface was true?
5. Explain how you would hold a wide board in a vise while planing the end grain.
6. What are three methods of planing end grain properly?
7. What is meant by a "working face"?
8. What is meant by a "wind" in a board?
9. When placing a plane on a bench, why should it always be placed on its side?

Unit 10. Shaping a Chamfer and a Bevel

A chamfer and a bevel are often confused because both are formed edges which look somewhat alike. Figure 10-1 points out the difference. The chamfer is usually planed to a 45-degree angle, while the bevel may be any angle. The chamfer is a means of decorating an edge or of treating an *arris* (the meeting of two surfaces). The bevel may be either an edge treatment for decoration or a means of fitting two pieces together at an angle.

Tools

Tools commonly used for making either a chamfer or a bevel are the sliding T bevel and a jack or block plane.

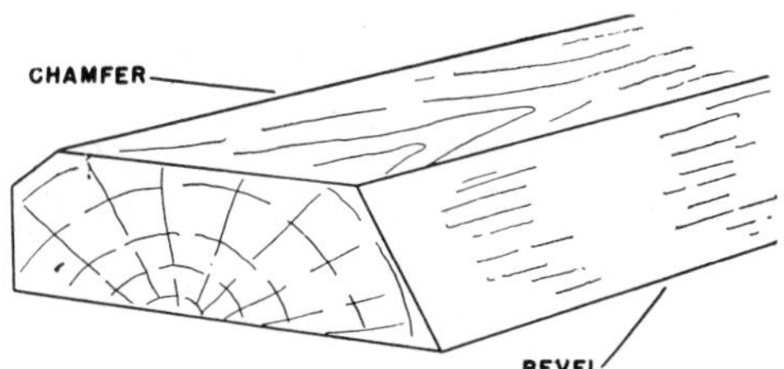

Fig. 10-1. Chamfer and bevel.

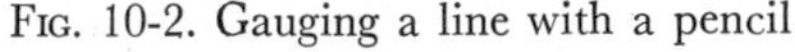

Fig. 10-2. Gauging a line with a pencil.

Laying Out Chamfer and Bevel

1. Gauge or mark the line or lines with the marking gauge or pencil to outline the chamfer or bevel. The pencil line is desirable for this purpose. Figure 10-2 shows how to gauge a line with a pencil.

2. Set the T bevel to the desired angle.

Planing and Testing

1. Fasten the board in a vise (Fig. 10-3).

Fig. 10-3. Planing a chamfer.

Fig. 10-4. Planing a chamfer on a small block of wood.

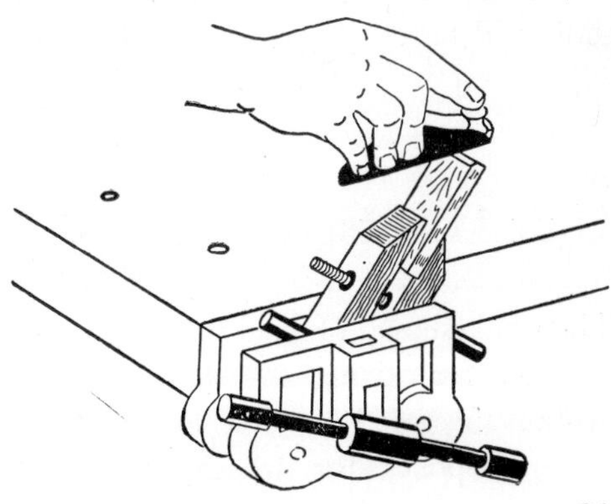

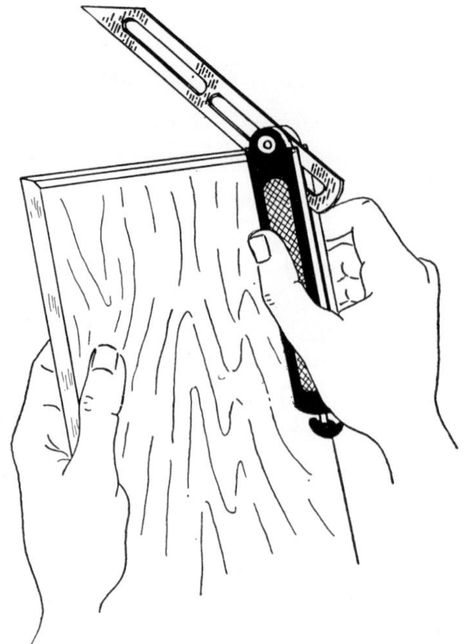

Fig. 10-5. Testing a chamfer with a sliding T bevel.

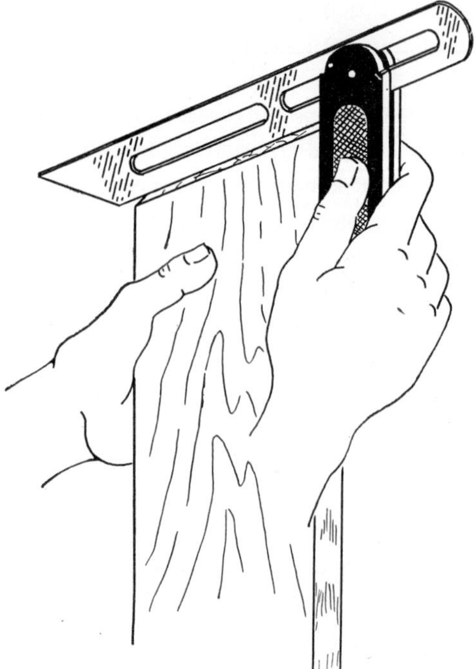

Fig. 10-6. Testing a bevel with a sliding T bevel.

2. Form the chamfer or bevel on the edges by planing (Fig. 10-3). If the board or block is small, fasten it in a hand-screw clamp which in turn may be secured in a vise (Fig. 10-4). It may then be planed with a small block plane.

3. Test the chamfer or bevel with a sliding T bevel (Figs. 10-5 and 10-6).

Discussion Topics

1. Illustrate the difference between a "bevel" and a "chamfer."
2. What tool is used to test the accuracy of a chamfer or a bevel?
3. What is the "arris" of a board?
4. What planes can be used most effectively in planing a chamfer or a bevel?

Unit 11. Assembling and Adjusting a Spokeshave

The spokeshave (Fig. 11-1) is a tool designed for cutting and shaping. Early artisans in wood used it expressly for making spokes for wheels, hence its name. Today it is used chiefly for forming concave and convex edges of stock and for making such projects as bows and the hulls for model boats. The cutter blade is sharpened very much as the plane iron is. Its general adjustment for cutting is controlled by adjusting nuts. The handles of the frame are built so that the spokeshave may be either pushed or pulled, depending upon the position and angle in making the forming stroke.

The following is the step-by-step procedure for assembling and adjusting a spokeshave:

1. Test the blade for sharpness. Refer to Fig. 8-7, since the cutting edge needs to be as sharp as that of a plane iron.
2. Put the blade into the frame so that the slots of the blade will seat on the adjusting nuts.
3. Place the lever cap over the blade so that the slot will slide under the lever-cap screw.
4. Hold the blade securely by tightening the lever-cap thumbscrew.

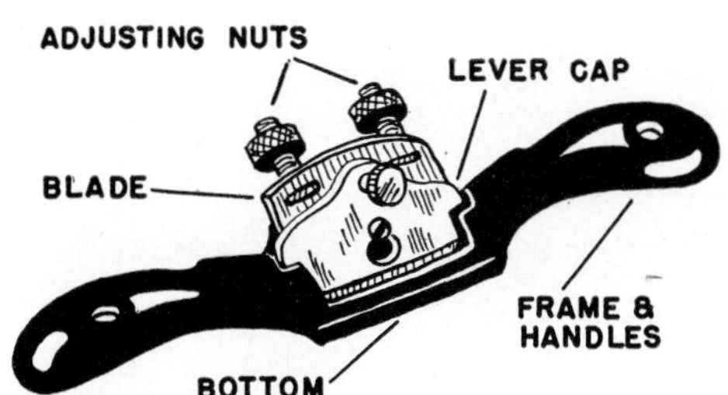

Fig. 11-1. Spokeshave.

5. Adjust for the proper cutting depth by means of the adjusting nuts.

Discussion Topics

1. How did the spokeshave get its name?
2. What is the spokeshave particularly adapted for?
3. How is the spokeshave similar to a plane?
4. Should you push or pull a spokeshave when using it?

Unit 12. Laying Out and Forming Irregular Pieces and Curves

It is often necessary to lay out and cut material into curved and irregular pieces to make up a project. Knowledge of the correct tools and skill in working with them entail considerable study of the best procedure and practice. It is advantageous, for example, to understand how to enlarge a pattern. Usually working drawings in books are drawn to a scale which fits the page, frequently to one-fourth of actual size; but the dimensions are given in full size. In order to make the irregular and curved pieces the correct size, it is therefore, necessary to enlarge the drawing. One should also learn how to draw a hexagon, an octagon, and an ellipse. It is likewise essential to know the general procedure for laying out distances and regular curves with dividers.

Tools

The following tools are essential for laying out and forming.

Dividers. This layout tool is common to both wood- and metalworking (Fig.

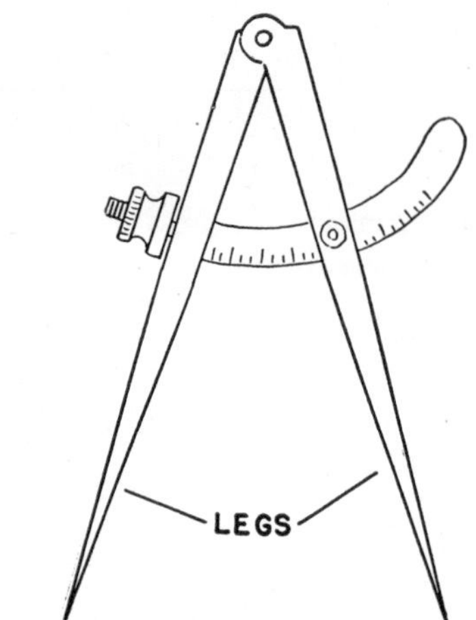

FIG. 12-1. Dividers.

12-1). It is suitable for laying out small circles, for dividing spaces equally, for scribing arcs, and for transferring measurements. The usual procedure in using this tool for obtaining distances is to place one leg on an inch mark of a rule and the other leg at 1 inch plus the distance desired. On most dividers this distance is maintained by the locking of a thumbscrew. An ordinary, inexpensive compass will accomplish the same results as the dividers in laying out arcs.

Trammel points. These are used for laying out large arcs and circles (Fig. 12-2).

FIG. 12-2. Trammel points.

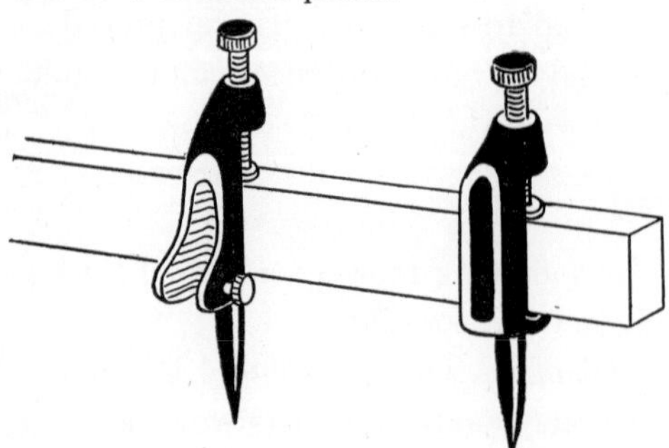

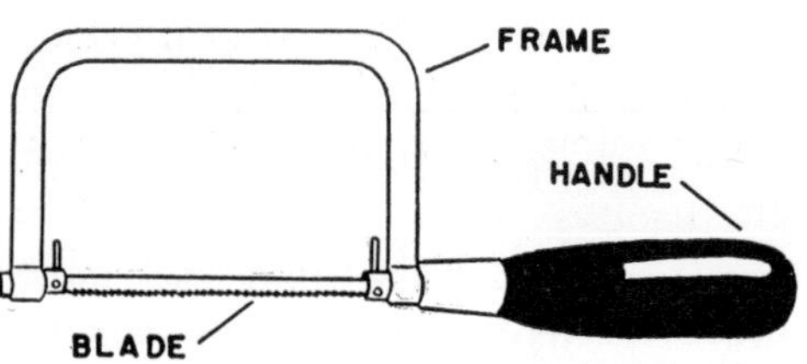

FIG. 12-3. Coping saw.

Another means of scribing a large arc is to tie a piece of string to a pencil which can serve as a compass.

Rule. This measuring device has been discussed in Unit 6, "Measuring and Laying Out."

Coping saw. The coping saw (Fig. 12-3) is especially useful for cutting small stock, such as thin boards or plywood. The thin blade and the adjustment on the frame allow it to be used in making short turns.

Turning saw. This hand tool, shown in Fig. 12-4, will do heavy, irregular cutting similar to that performed on the bandsaw in machine-tool work.

Keyhole or compass saw. Figure 12-5 pictures this saw, which is useful for cutting a design, particularly the inside curves where a turning or coping saw cannot be used because of the limitations of the frame. The cut is usually started by boring a hole near the line to be cut.

FIG. 12-4. Turning saw.

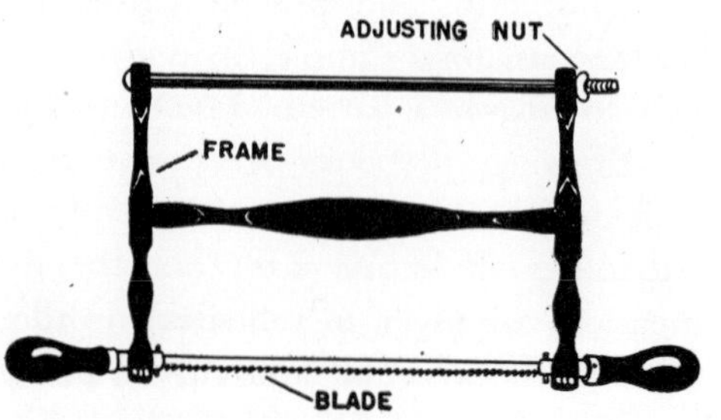

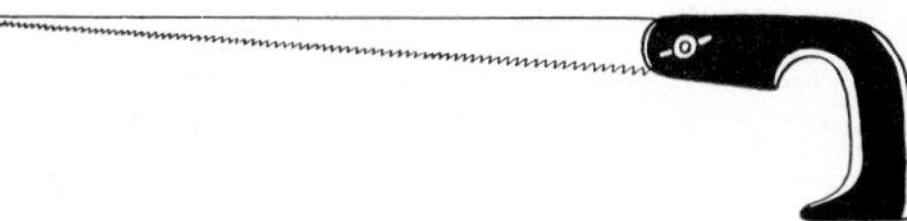

Fig. 12-5. Keyhole, or compass, saw.

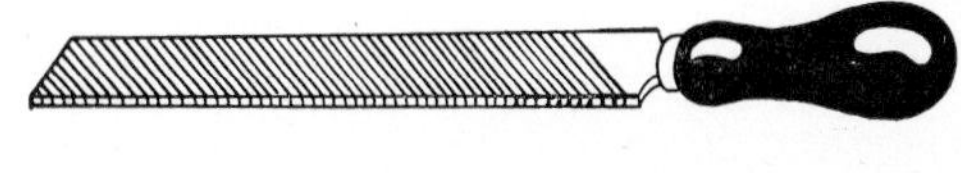

Fig. 12-7. Wood, or cabinet, file.

Spokeshave. This device has been illustrated and discussed in the preceding unit.

Drawknife. This tool (Fig. 12-6) has a blade approximately 10 to 12 inches long, supported by a handle on each end. The handles make it convenient to work with it. It is used effectively by skilled workmen for removing large amounts of stock rapidly. Its application to our work lies in trimming down stock on an irregular edge and in building model boats and canoe paddles. Because of its open blade, this tool should be handled very carefully.

Wood or cabinet file. The most commonly used file in woodworking is the cabinet file, which is available in varying degrees of coarseness of cuts and shapes (Fig. 12-7). The common shapes of files used by the woodworker are flat, half-round, round, and triangular. They are obtainable in many lengths from 4 to 14 inches. Files are used for smoothing edges and small curves which are difficult to reach with other tools. The cutting surface consists of rows of teeth which run in parallel lines diagonally across the surface (Fig. 12-8). Figure 12-8 illustrates the single- and double-cut pattern of teeth on a file.

Some pointers on the efficient use of files are: (1) see that there is a handle on every file, (2) keep oil on them

Fig. 12-6. Drawknife.

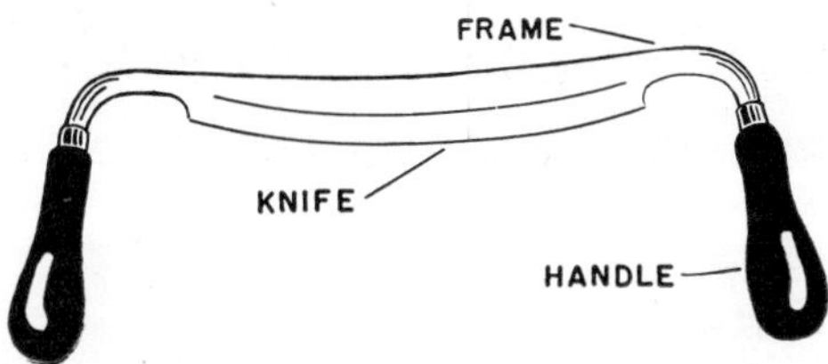

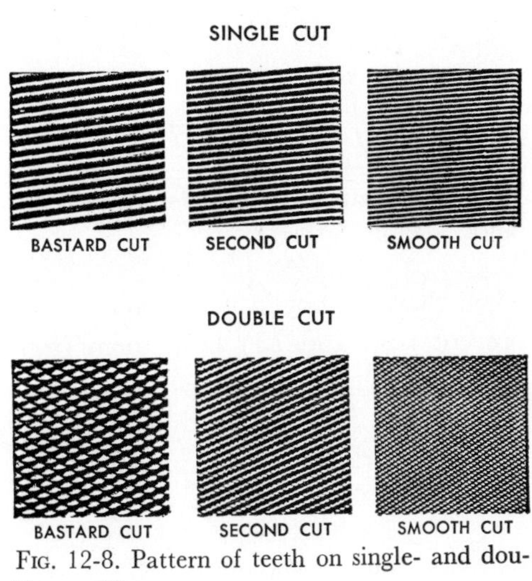

Fig. 12-8. Pattern of teeth on single- and double-cut files.

Fig. 12-9. File card.

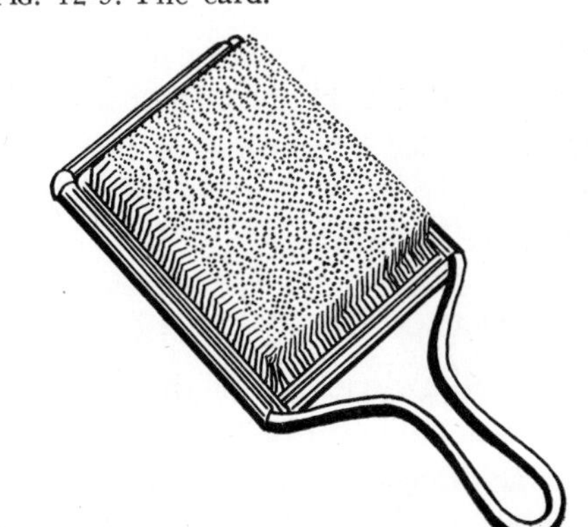

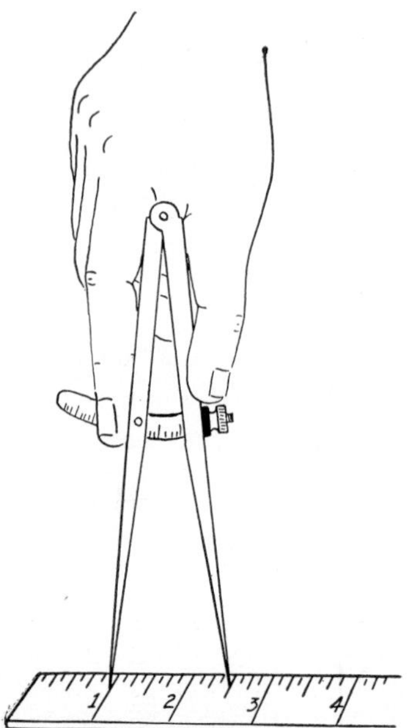

Fig. 12-10. Setting dividers for correct distance.

when they are not in continuous use to prevent rust, and (3) keep them from rubbing together or against other tools.

File card. The file card (Fig. 12-9) has steel bristles which are used for cleaning the teeth on a file.

Curves, Arcs, and Circles

1. Set the dividers or trammel points to the desired radius of the arc, curve, or circle (Fig. 12-10).

2. Scribe the arc, curve, or circle as shown in Fig. 12-11. Note that a heavy piece of paper or cardboard has been placed under the stationary leg to protect the wood surface.

Equal Distances

1. Set the dividers for the required distance to be duplicated or stepped off.

2. Lay out or step off these equal distances as shown in Fig. 12-12.

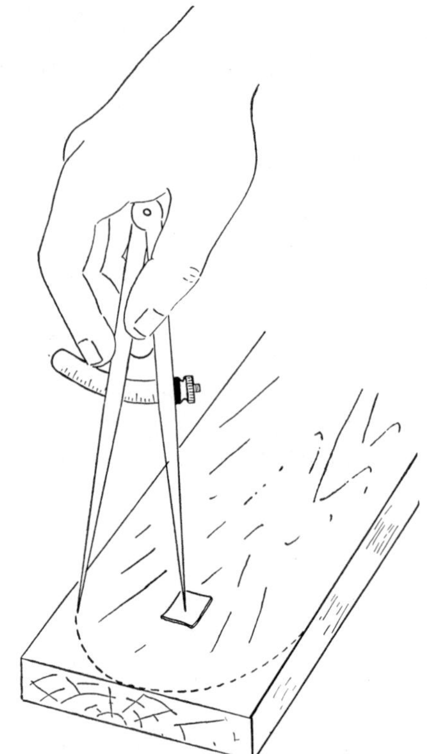

Fig. 12-11. Scribing an arc with dividers.

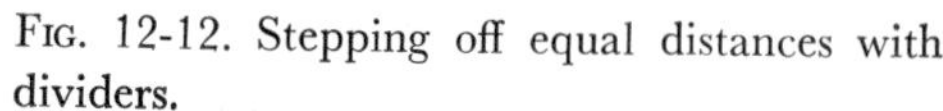

Fig. 12-12. Stepping off equal distances with dividers.

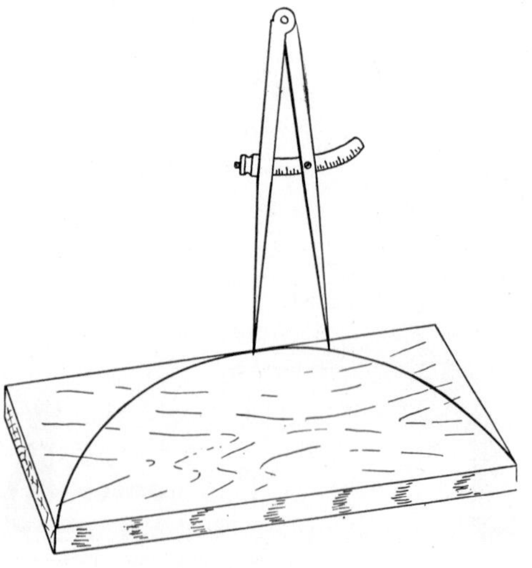

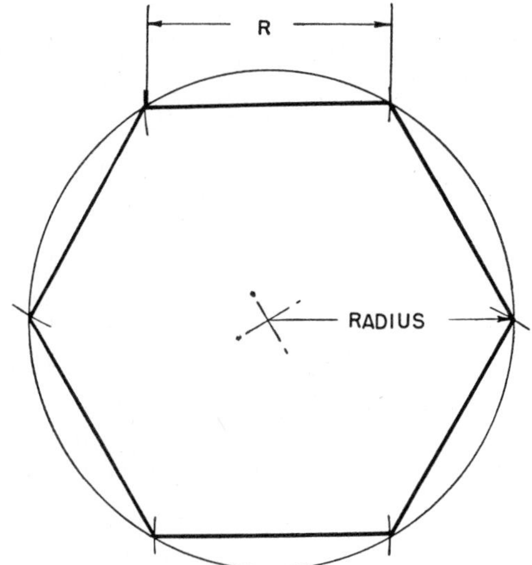

Fig. 12-13. Hexagon (R = radius).

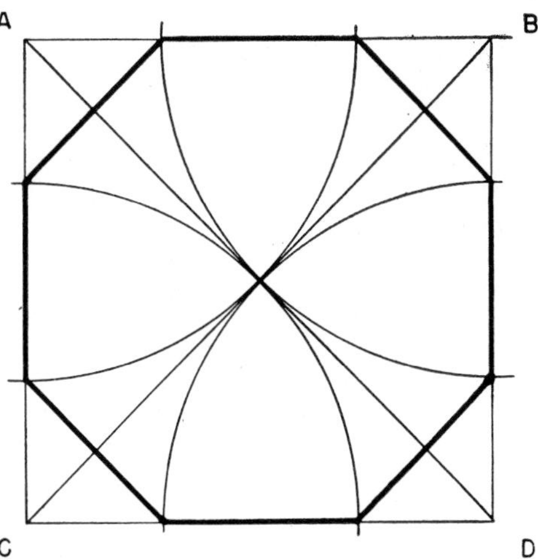

Fig. 12-14. Octagon.

Hexagon (Six Sided)

1. Determine the length of one side of the hexagon.

2. Set a compass or dividers so that the radius will be the same as the length of the side.

3. Draw a circle, using the radius set in step 2. This can be done directly on wood, paper, or cardboard, which may serve as a template (a temporary pattern).

4. Step off equal distances with the dividers on the circumference by using the same radius (Fig. 12-13).

5. Connect the points of intersection on the circumference with straight lines (Fig. 12-13). These will form the hexagon.

Octagon (Eight Sided)

1. Determine the over-all size of the octagon. This will be a distance from one side to the opposite one.

2. Lay out a square of this size.

3. Set dividers or a compass equal to one-half the length of a diagonal of the square. The diagonal is a line extending from opposite corners. In Fig. 12-14 the diagonals are *AD* and *BC*.

4. Set one point of the dividers at a corner of the square, and scribe arcs intersecting the sides of the square (Fig. 12-14).

5. Repeat step 4 from the other three corners of the square.

6. Connect or draw straight lines joining the intersecting points on the sides of the square. (Fig. 12-14). These will form the octagon.

Ellipse

1. Determine the desired width and length of the ellipse.

2. Draw a rectangle with sides representing the width and length of the ellipse (Fig. 12-15). This can be drawn directly on the wood or on a suitable template.

3. Draw two lines, *AB* and *CD*, equal to these two lengths and at right angles to each other.

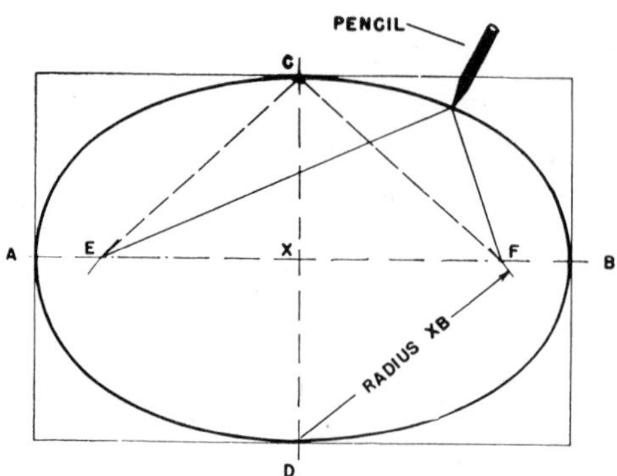

Fig. 12-15. Ellipse.

4. Set dividers to one-half the length of line *AB*. This now becomes radius *XB*.

5. Place the dividers on point *D* and make an arc which intersects line *AB* at *E* and *F*.

6. Place brads, thumbtacks, or pins at points, *C, E,* and *F*.

7. Fasten a string around points *C, E,* and *F* to form a triangle.

8. Remove the brad from point *C*.

9. Place a pencil against the string and draw the ellipse (Fig. 12-15).

10. Remove the brads, thumbtacks, and string. The ellipse has been formed.

Enlarging and Transferring

1. Determine the portion of the drawing which needs to be drawn full scale.

2. Draw vertical and horizontal lines $\frac{1}{4}$ inch apart over the section if it is not already graphed in this manner in the drawing. This is assuming that the drawing was made to the scale of $\frac{1}{4}$ inch equalling 1 inch. If the scale is different, the graph should be drawn accordingly (Fig. 12-16).

3. Lay out 1-inch squares on a large sheet of kraft or wrapping paper or on cardboard.

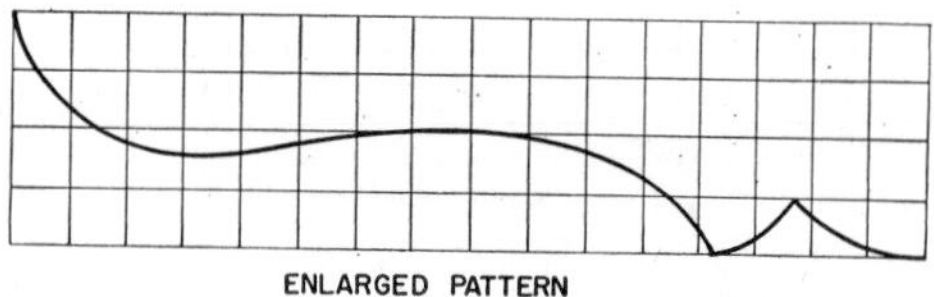

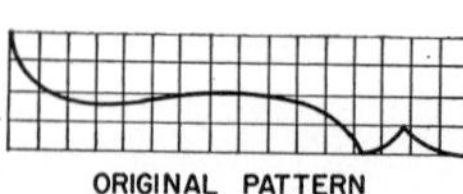

Fig. 12-16. Technique of enlarging a pattern.

4. Sketch on the full-size graph the points where the design intersects with the squares in the working drawing (Fig. 12-16).

5. Connect these points freehand until the full-size pattern resembles the reduced working drawing (Fig. 12-16).

6. Cut out the paper or cardboard for the full-size pattern.

7. Place the pattern on the board and trace around it with a pencil (Fig. 12-17) to get the exact pattern.

Cutting with Coping Saw

1. Lay out the irregular design or pattern. This may be a layout directly on the wood or a tracing round a template.

Fig. 12-17. Tracing a pattern on wood.

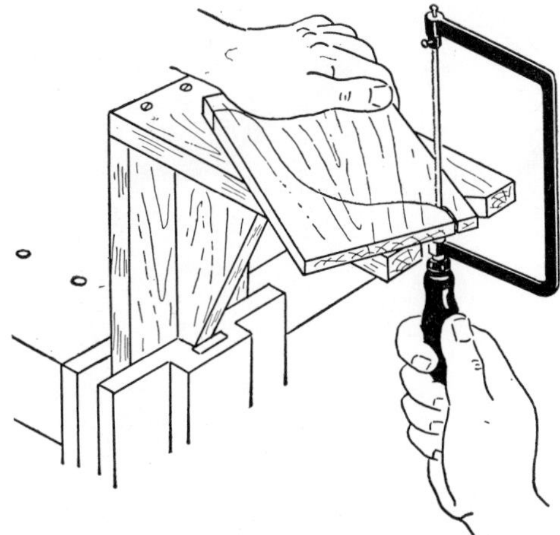

Fig. 12-18. Sawing on a V block.

2. For outline cutting place the wood on a V block or jig, and hold the wood securely on the jig with the left hand or with a hand clamp (Fig. 12-18). The V block or jig may be held in a vise or fastened directly to a bench top.

3. If heavier stock is to be cut, clamp it in a bench vise and cut as shown in Fig. 12-19.

4. Check the coping saw to make certain that the blade is inserted with the teeth pointing toward the handle. When the blade is fastened into the frame in this manner, it will not have a tendency to kink.

Fig. 12-19. Cutting with a coping saw.

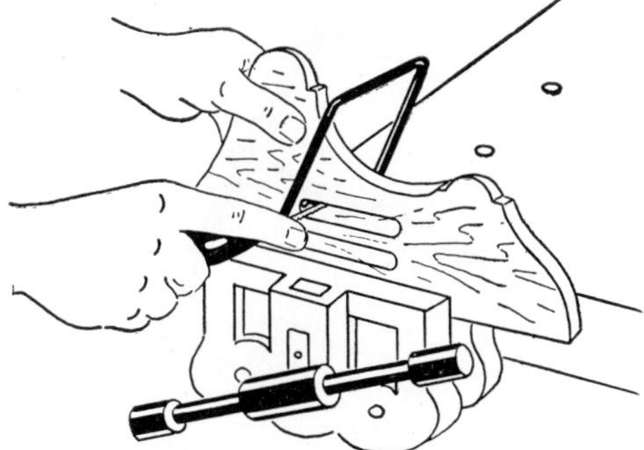

Fig. 12-20. Sawing a pierced design with a coping saw.

5. Grasp the stock securely with the left hand and saw with firm strokes. The first stroke will be a pull one.

6. In cutting a pierced design, bore or drill a small hole on the waste part of the stock near the line. Disassemble the blade from the frame, insert it through the hole, and fasten it securely to the frame again before attempting to saw.

7. Saw out the pierced design as shown in Fig. 12-20.

Cutting with Turning Saw

1. Transfer the pattern to the wood.

2. Clamp the stock in a vise (Fig. 12-21).

3. Adjust the turning saw for use. This saw is used to advantage where the stock is thicker than $\frac{1}{2}$ inch, particularly when cutting out duplicate parts simultaneously.

4. Cut the board on the outside of the pattern line to allow for smoothing (Fig. 12-21).

Cutting with Keyhole Saw

1. Transfer the design to, or draw it on, the wood.

FIG. 12-21. Cutting with a turning saw.

2. Start the saw kerf in a manner similar to that employed in crosscutting. The sawing should be slightly outside the line on the waste portion of the wood so that the stock can be dressed down to exact size.

3. Continue cutting. Use the narrow end of the blade for sharp turns.

4. When cutting inside curves and to irregular lines, bore a hole for starting the cut as shown in Fig. 12-22.

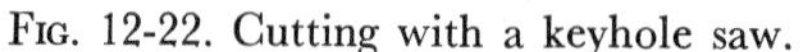

FIG. 12-22. Cutting with a keyhole saw.

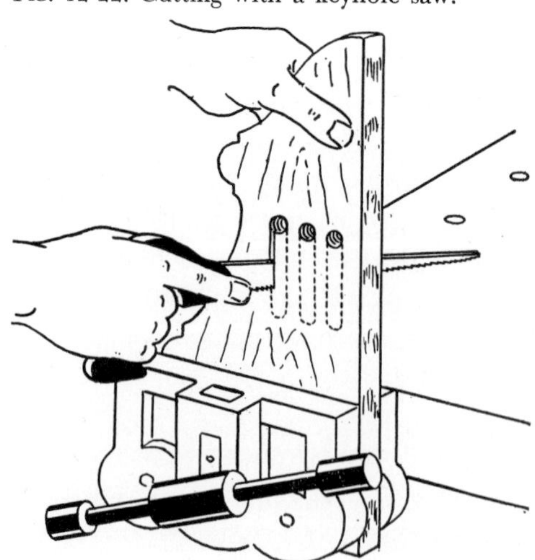

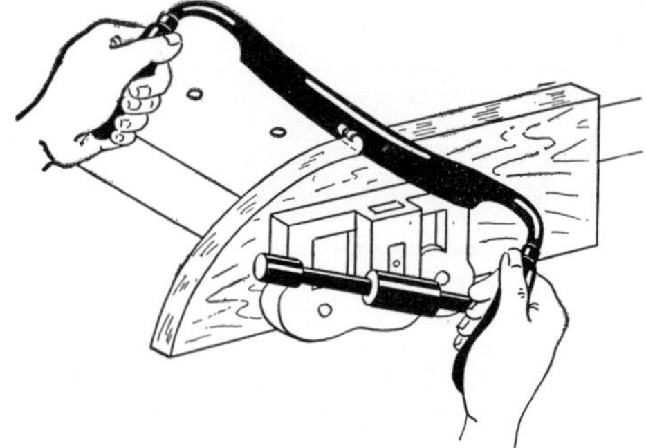

FIG. 12-23. Cutting with a drawknife.

SHAPING WITH DRAWKNIFE

1. Test the cutting edge of the drawknife for sharpness. This can be done in a manner similar to that for testing a plane iron.

2. Fasten the stock securely in a bench vise.

3. Look at the grain of the wood to determine in which direction you will cut.

FIG. 12-24. Pushing the spokeshave to smooth a curved edge.

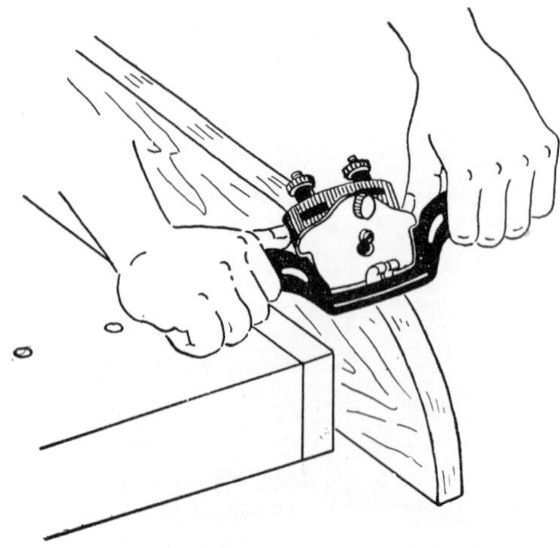

Fig. 12-25. Pulling the spokeshave to smooth convex and concave curves.

4. Hold the drawknife firmly with both hands with the bevel turned down.

5. Cut away the waste portion of the wood with short strokes pulled toward the body (Fig. 12-23). Adjust the depth of the cut by twisting the wrists. A cleaner cut may be obtained with a shearing stroke, that is, by holding one handle slightly ahead of the other.

6. Continue cutting until the waste stock has been almost entirely removed so that the stock itself can be shaped further in detail with a spokeshave or a file.

Forming with Spokeshave

1. Adjust the setting of the cutting edge for uniform depth.

2. Fasten the stock securely in a bench vise.

Fig. 12-26. Filing a curved edge.

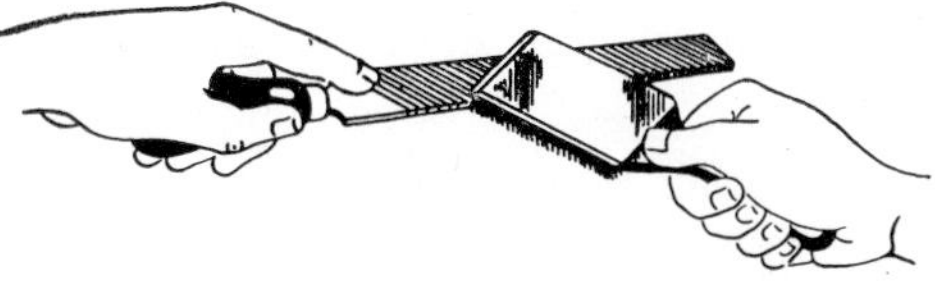

Fig. 12-27. Cleaning a file with a file card.

3. Smooth the curved edge with the spokeshave until the exact pattern line is reached (Figs. 12-24 and 12-25). You may use this tool effectively by either pushing or pulling it, whichever is convenient.

Forming with File

1. Select a medium-coarse wood file of the desired shape for the first smoothing.

2. Fasten the stock securely in a bench vise.

3. Push the file across the edge of the wood with a forward and side motion (Fig. 12-26). When handling a file in this manner you effect a shearing cut which prevents splintering the opposite edge. Take care in filing edges of plywood as they break and splinter easily.

4. Continue filing the irregular edge with the medium-coarse file until a semismooth finish is obtained.

5. Finish smoothing the edge curve with a smooth-cut file.

6. When necessary test the irregular edge with a try square for squareness with the smooth surface.

7. Clean the files with the file card (Fig. 12-27).

Discussion Topics

1. What is the difference between the "dividers" and the "compass"?

2. When scribing an arc or a circle on a piece of wood, why is it desirable to place a piece of cardboard under the stationary leg of the dividers?
3. Describe the procedure for drawing (*a*) a hexagon, (*b*) an octagon, (*c*) an ellipse, and for (*d*) enlarging a pattern.
4. List at least three uses for the dividers.
5. What are trammel points used for?
6. Name three hand-operated saws which can be used for cutting irregular curves.
7. What is the chief purpose of the drawknife?
8. How can the depth of cut be controlled when using a drawknife?
9. What is the essential difference between the single- and double-cut file?
10. What is the purpose of the file card?
11. Should the teeth point toward or away from the handle when a coping saw is being used?

Unit 13. Cutting and Trimming with a Chisel

Accurate cutting, fitting, shaping, and surface decoration may be accomplished with sharp and correctly beveled wood chisels. A wood chisel is pictured in Fig. 13-1.

Tools

Cutting and trimming with chisels and gouges should be done with the greatest care. Remember that the wood chisel has been the cause of more injuries than all other hand tools.

Chisels. Chisels are generally classified as the socket, or firmer, chisel and the tang chisel. These designations indicate the manner in which the handle is fastened to the blade. Both types employ a beveled cutting edge. The size of the wood chisel is determined by the width of the blade, the sizes commonly range from $\frac{1}{8}$ to 1 inch by eighths and from 1 to 2 inches by fourths.

Gouges. Gouges are chisels which are used for grooving, for shaping edges, and for modelmaking. They are classified in two groups: one with the bevel on the inside of the blade (Fig. 13-2) and one with it on the outside (Fig. 13-3). The latter are used more often. The blades of all gouges are concave but vary in size from $\frac{1}{4}$ to 2 inches in width.

Fig. 13-1. A firmer wood chisel with reinforced handle.

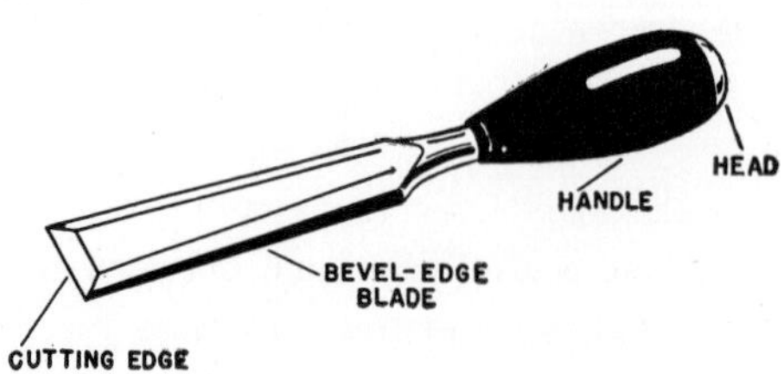

Fig. 13-2. Inside-bevel gouge.

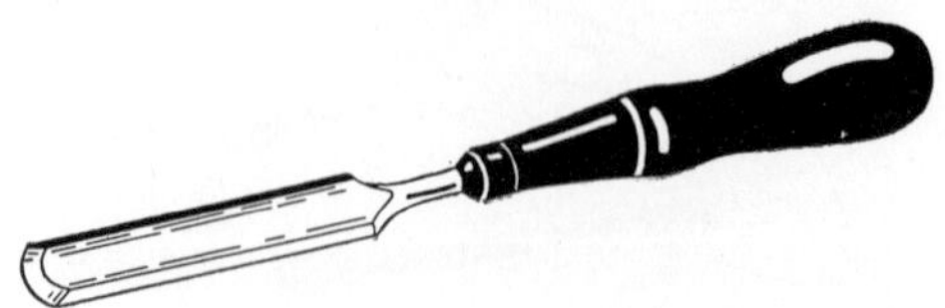

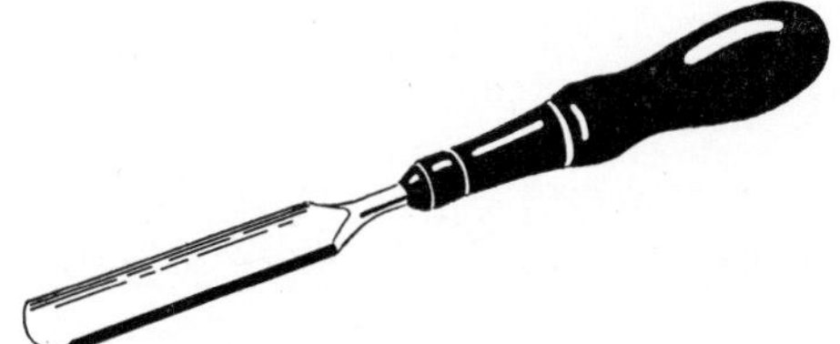

Fig. 13-3. Outside-bevel gouge.

Fig. 13-4. Mallet.

Occasionally the chiseling process requires additional pressure, which may be applied by using wood or fiber *mallet* (Fig. 13-4).

Horizontal Chiseling

1. Fasten the wood firmly in a bench vise.

2. Push the chisel with one hand while using the forefinger and thumb of the other hand as a brake (Fig. 13-5). Make certain that the bevel of the chisel is turned up when it is used in this manner.

3. Continue to make thin cuts, taking care to stop each time before reaching the opposite side. The inset on Fig. 13-5 illustrates the procedure for cutting across the board to protect the grain on the opposite side.

Fig. 13-5. Horizontal chiseling.

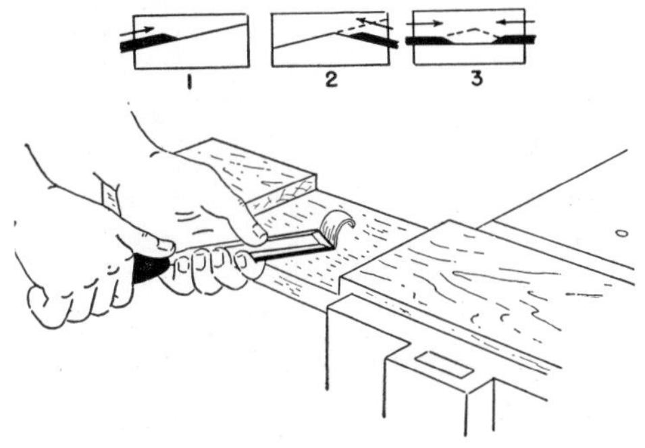

Fig. 13-6. Holding wood securely in bench vise for vertical chiseling.

Vertical Chiseling

1. Fasten the wood securely in a bench vise (Fig. 13-6) or hold it firmly on a bench hook.

2. Hold the flat side of the chisel against the wood in a vertical position.

3. Hold the chisel with one hand and guide the blade with the other (Fig. 13-6). The left hand will serve as a brake.

4. Push the chisel and apply a shearing cut, as shown in Fig. 13-6.

5. Use a wooden or fiber mallet, if necessary, to drive the chisel in cutting out mortises.

Cutting Stop Chamfers

1. Mark the width and length of the stop chamfer with a pencil on the edge of the board.

2. Fasten the board firmly in a bench vise.

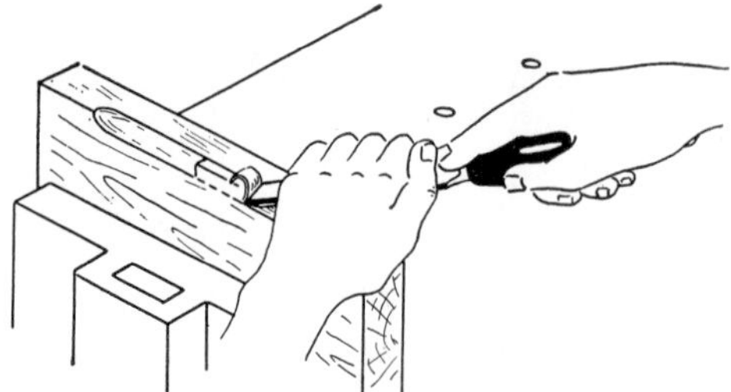

FIG. 13-7. Cutting a stop chamfer with a chisel.

3. Cut or pare by starting at one end of the stop chamfer (Fig. 13-7). Take thin cuts about one-half the length of the chamfer.

4. Continue with light cuts until the pencil line is reached.

5. Reverse the lumber in the vise and cut the other half of the chamfer from the opposite end in a similar manner.

CURVED CHISELING

1. Fasten the wood securely in a bench vise.

2. In cutting a round corner, move the chisel in a shearing cut across the work by making a series of short strokes (Fig. 13-8). Make certain that the bevel edge of the chisel is up.

3. In trimming a concave edge, hold the bevel side of the chisel against the wood while pushing it with the right hand. Use the left one to hold the chisel against the work (Fig. 13-9). Always work with the grain.

FIG. 13-8. Trimming a convex curve with a chisel.

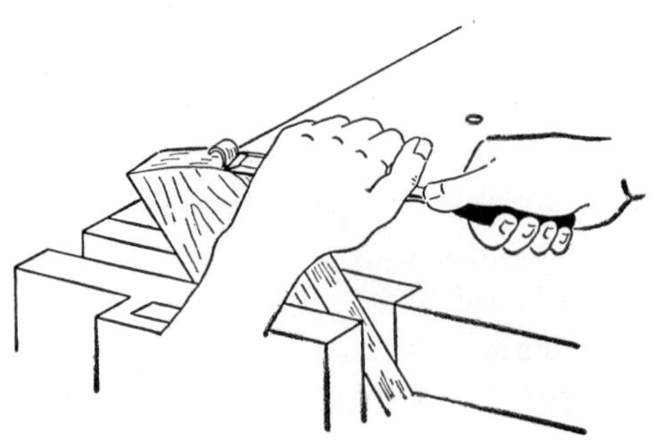

FIG. 13-9. Trimming a concave edge with a chisel.

GROOVING

Grooves may be cut in surfaces, or blocks hollowed out with gouges as shown in Fig. 13-10.

Discussion Topics

1. How are chisels generally classified?
2. What is the purpose of a gouge?

FIG. 13-10. Cutting a groove in a surface.

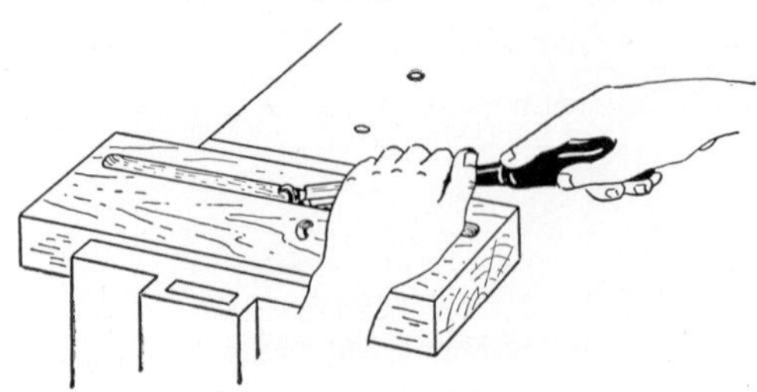

3. Why should small nicks be ground out of chisels and gouges?
4. Are the wood and cold chisels used for the same purpose? Explain their differences.
5. In trimming a concave cut, should the bevel edge of the chisel be against the work or away from it?
6. Explain the difference between concave and convex.

Unit 14. Assembling and Adjusting Scrapers

Scrapers are used to smooth wood which is difficult to dress with a plane. They are particularly effective on irregular-grained, knotty, and burly lumber. The action of the scraper edge differs from the cut made by a plane or spokeshave in that it scrapes by means of a burred edge. Refer to Unit 27, "Sharpening Tools," page 109.

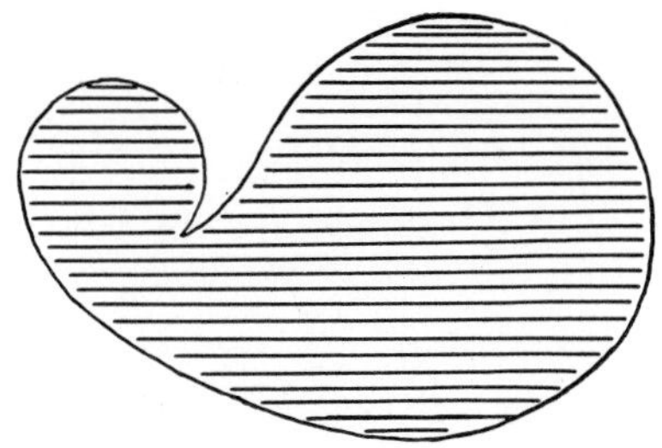

Fig. 14-2. Swan-neck scraper blade.

Tools

The scraping tools described here are relatively simple to adjust and to operate.

Hand scraper. There are varying shapes of hand scrapers ranging from the rectangular (Fig. 14-1) to the swan neck (Fig. 14-2). They are thin, flexible pieces of high-grade steel which, when sharpened properly, will remove very thin shavings like those from a plane. They may be pulled or pushed and are particularly useful for smoothing stock in corners where cabinet scrapers will not reach. Since the blade is held in the hand, there is no assembly for the hand scraper.

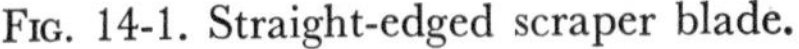

Fig. 14-1. Straight-edged scraper blade.

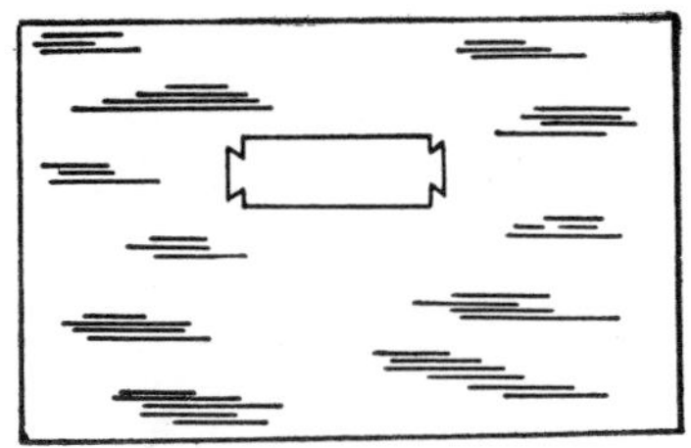

Cabinet scraper. This is a metal frame with two handles which holds a scraper blade (Fig. 14-3). It is perhaps the most common scraper frame. It is pushed, as illustrated in the following unit on smoothing by scraping.

Fig. 14-3. Cabinet scraper.

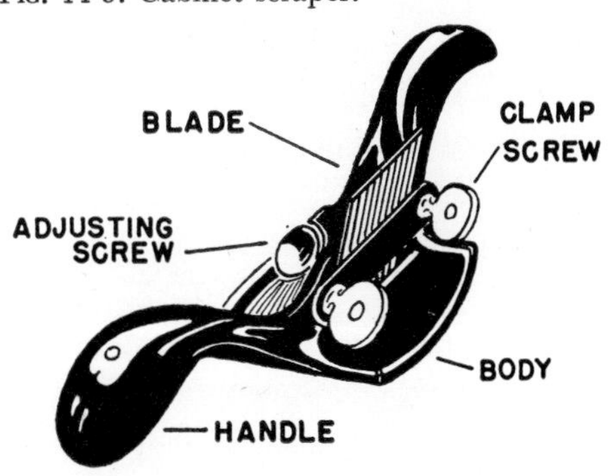

Fig. 14-4. Pull, or box, scraper.

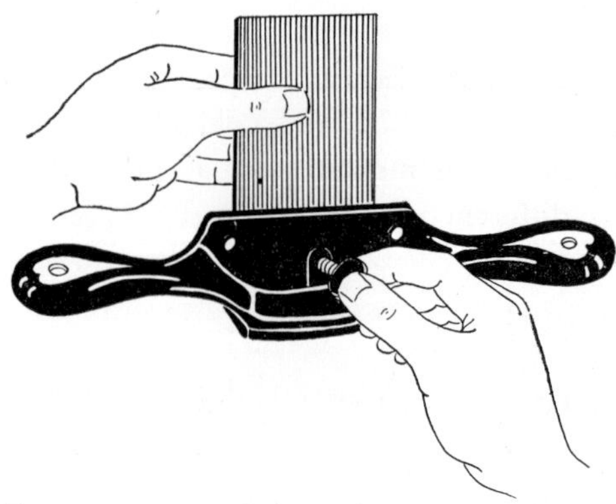

Fig. 14-5. Adjusting a cabinet scraper for depth of scraping action.

Pull scraper. The pull scraper, sometimes referred to as the *box scraper,* is shown in Fig. 14-4. It is pulled rather than pushed on the wood.

Scraper plane. Perhaps the least used of the three scraper frames mentioned here is the scraper plane. It is worth citing, however, because it looks like a smooth plane except that the blade is held forward so that it will produce a scraping action. Personal preference and availability will determine which scraper is used for a job; the effectiveness of each is about the same.

Assembling and Adjusting

The following instructions are typical for any of the scraper frames.

1. Test the blade for properly burred edge. Refer to Unit 27, "Sharpening Tools," page 109, to determine the correct burr.

2. Place and tighten the blade in its proper position in the frame (Fig. 14-5). This will vary slightly with each of the three types of scrapers. The blade should be placed so that the burred edge will produce a shaving. Since this procedure is a very simple mechanical adjustment, it will not be necessary to go into detail with each frame.

3. Adjust the blade for depth of scraping action with the thumb nut or thumbscrew, depending upon the type of scraper being used (Fig. 14-5).

Discussion Topics

1. What are scrapers used for?
2. Where are they especially effective?
3. Name two shapes of scrapers.
4. Is the scraper blade pulled or pushed?
5. What is the most common scraper frame?
6. Name three kinds of scraper frames.
7. What is a "burred" edge?
8. How is the blade adjusted for scraping action?

Unit 15. Smoothing a Surface by Scraping.

It is often necessary to scrape surfaces of wood and, occasionally, edges, particularly if the grain in the material is burly or knotty. The scraper will produce a very fine surface on open-grain wood, such as mahogany, oak, and walnut, and it will remove any irregularities or blemishes which may have been left by the plane. The action of the scraper differs from that of the chisel or plane in that it does the work with a scraping burr.

In making built-up cedar panels without power equipment—for the parts of a cedar chest or for the back and bottom for a cedarized walnut, mahogany, or other type of chest—it is usually advisable to dress the cedar across the grain with a sharp plane and then to scrape the panels lengthwise with any/or a combination of the scrapers described in the preceeding unit. The effectiveness of the smoothing action will depend upon the care exercised in sharpening the scraper edge. The sharpening procedure is described in Unit 27, "Sharpening Tools," page 109.

Handscraping

1. Grasp the scraper blade firmly between the thumb and the fingers so that it can be sprung to a slight curve with the thumb and forefinger (Fig. 15-1). More effective scraping action will result if the blade is held to the approximate angle of 45 degrees (Fig. 15-2).

2. It is sometimes convenient to pull the scraper blade toward you (Fig. 15-3).

Fig. 15-1. Scraping a surface with a hand scraper.

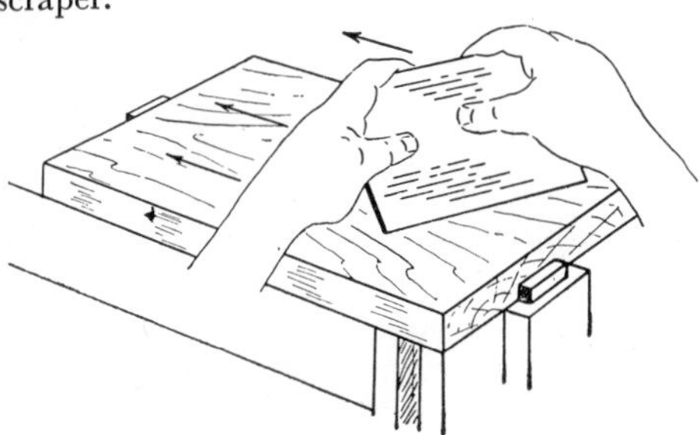

Smoothing with Cabinet Scraper

1. Assemble and adjust the blade in its proper place in the cabinet-scraper body. See the preceding unit for correct adjustment. The action of the box scraper plane is very similar to that of the cabinet scraper. Refer to the preceding unit for the description of these scrapers.

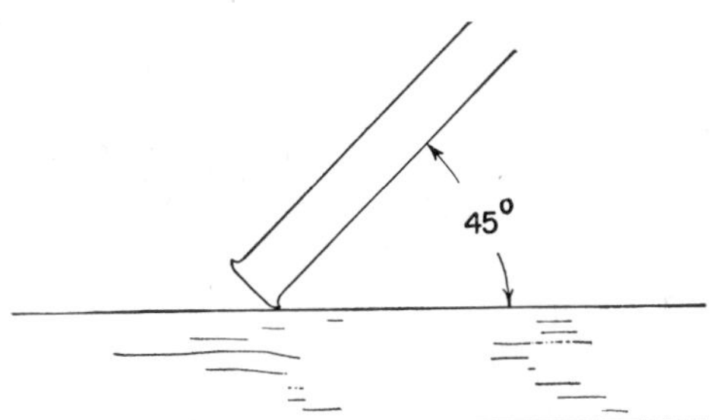

Fig. 15-2. Angle for handscraping.

Fig. 15-3. Pulling a scraper blade.

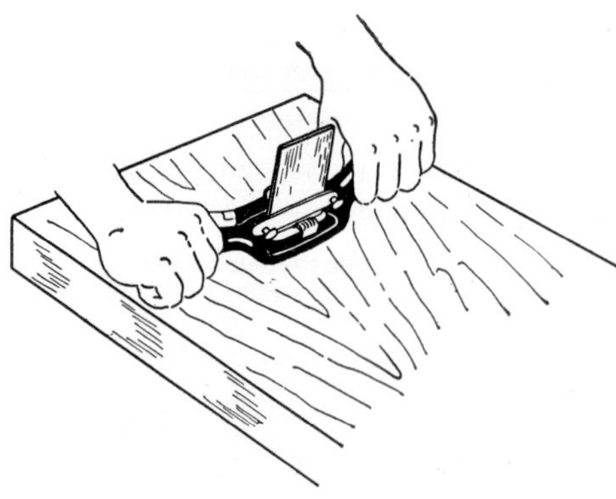

FIG. 15-4. Smoothing a surface with a cabinet scraper.

2. Grasp the scraper handles firmly in your hands, with the thumbs pressing on the frame back of the blade (Fig. 15-4).

3. Try the scraper on a piece of wood and adjust it further, if necessary, until it produces a fine, thin, even shaving.

4. Scrape the surface of the wood with long, even strokes and with the grain, preferably with the cabinet scraper turned slightly so that it will produce a shearing cut.

5. Continue scraping until the entire surface has been smoothed evenly.

Discussion Topics

1. Why is it often necessary to scrape surfaces of wood?
2. Upon what condition of the scraper blade does the effectiveness of the scraping action depend?
3. How does the action of the scraper differ from that of a chisel or plane?
4. At what approximate angle will effective scraping action result?
5. Describe the ideal type of shaving to get from a scraper blade.

Unit 16. Boring and Drilling Holes

Holes are bored or drilled in wood for screws, bolts, dowels, inside sawing, and ornamentation. Some of the more common types of bits for boring or drilling are the auger bit, twist drill, iron drill, gimlet, expansive bit, foerstner bit, straight-shank drill, and automatic drill.

A depth gauge is a supplementary tool which is very useful in boring holes to a given depth.

TOOLS

The descriptions and illustrations which follow will guide you in the proper selection of bits and other tools.

Brace. The brace (Fig. 16-1) is used with any of the bits which have the square *tang* (shank).

FIG. 16-1. Brace.

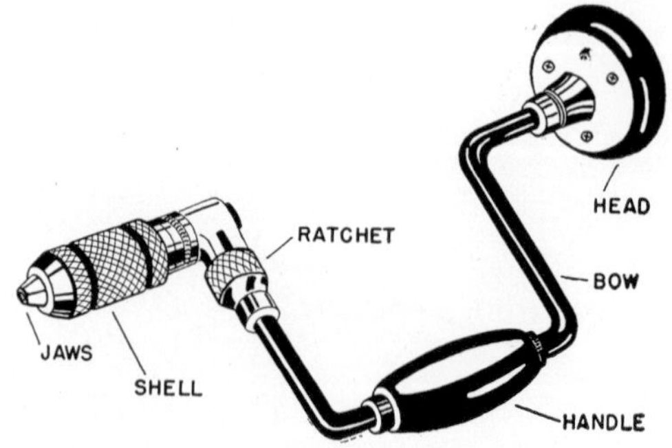

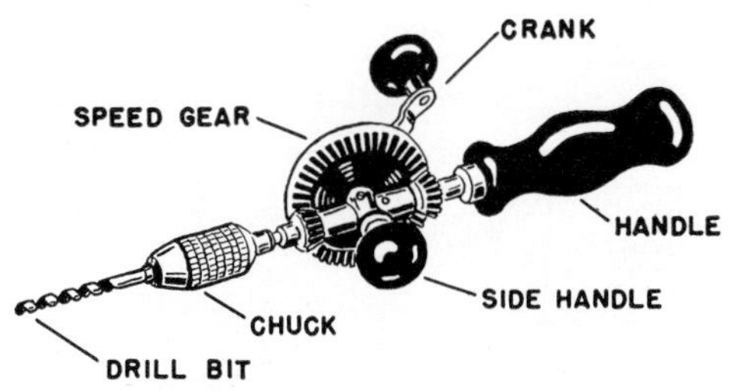

FIG. 16-2. Hand drill.

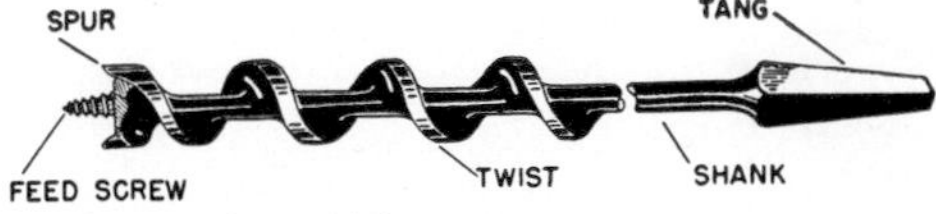

FIG. 16-4. Auger bit.

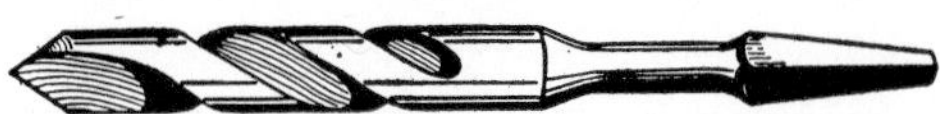
FIG. 16-5. Twist drill.

FIG. 16-6. Iron drill.

Hand drill. For holes less than $\frac{1}{4}$ inch in diameter, the hand drill (Fig. 16-2) and a straight-shank bit are usually used in combination, but the brace and twist drill may be used.

Automatic drill. The automatic drill (Fig. 16-3) is often employed instead of the hand drill, the choice depending upon personal preference.

Auger bits. Auger bits (Fig. 16-4) are sized by sixteenths of an inch, ranging in measurement from $\frac{1}{4}$ to 1 inch in diameter, that is, in the diameter of the hole each will make. These bits vary in length from 7 to 10 inches with the exception of the dowel bits, which are auger bits about $5\frac{1}{2}$ inches long. The number stamped on the square tang usually indicates the size in sixteenths of an inch. For example, a bit with "11" stamped on it will cut a hole $\frac{11}{16}$ inch in diameter, one marked "6" will cut a $\frac{3}{8}$-inch hole, because it is listed at $\frac{6}{16}$ inch.

Twist drills. Twist drills (Fig. 16-5) for wood are used to make holes for screws, nails, and bolts. They are sized by thirty-seconds of an inch and range from $\frac{1}{8}$ to $\frac{1}{2}$ inch.

Iron drill. The iron drill (Fig. 16-6) may be used for drilling holes in metal as well as in wood. They are sized in thirty-seconds of an inch and range from $\frac{1}{16}$ to $\frac{5}{8}$ inch.

Gimlet bit. The gimlet bit (Fig. 16-7) is for drilling holes for screws. It bores rapidly and leaves a reasonably smooth hole. It is sized by thirty-seconds of an inch and ranges from $\frac{1}{8}$ to $\frac{3}{8}$ inch.

Expansive bit. The expansive bit (Fig. 16-8) has a scale on the movable spur or cutter. Holes larger than 1 inch in diameter are bored with the adjustable expansive bit. These bits are available

FIG. 16-3. Automatic drill.

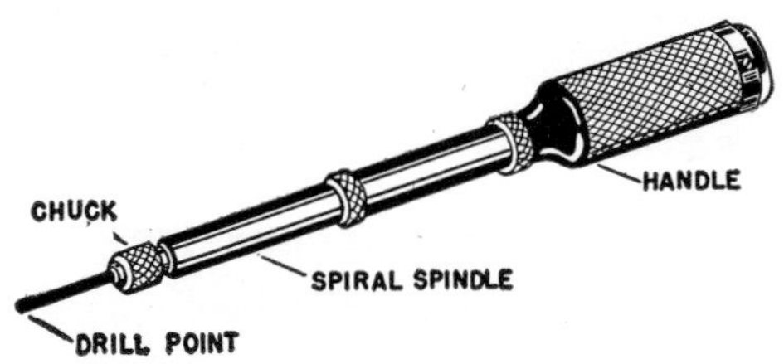

FIG. 16-7. Gimlet bit.

FIG. 16-8. Expansive bit.

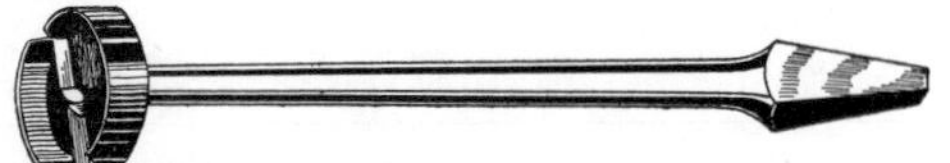

FIG. 16-9. Foerstner bit.

with various size cutters to bore holes from 1 to 4 inches in diameter.

Foerstner bit. The foerstner bit (Fig. 16-9) can do many boring operations which the auger bit cannot. Because of its construction it can bore a hole to any depth desired without breaking through the wood. These bits are available in sizes ranging from $\frac{1}{4}$ to 2 inches in diameter and are numbered in the same way as auger bits.

Straight-shank drill. The straight-shank drill (Fig. 16-10) is gauged for the diameter of holes to be drilled under any one of three systems: fractional, decimal, and numerical. The fractional is the most common for woodworking and is the most easily read. Fractional-size drills are designated by sixty-fourths of an inch, the smallest size being $\frac{1}{16}$ inch. Woodworkers generally have an assortment up to $\frac{1}{2}$ inch.

Automatic-drill bit. An automatic-drill bit (Fig. 16-11) fits into the automatic drill and is used for drilling small holes.

A necessary tool in boring holes to specified depth is the *depth gauge* (Fig. 16-12). A very simple gauge can be made by boring a hole lengthwise through a piece of wood, as shown in Fig. 16-13.

FIG. 16-10. Straight-shank drill.

FIG. 16-11. Automatic-drill bit.

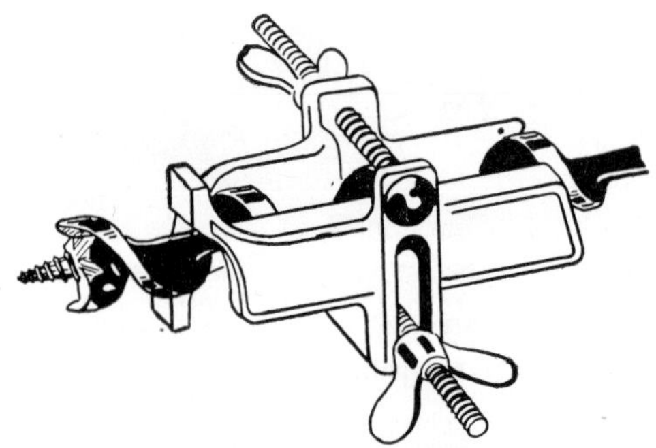

FIG. 16-12. Adjustable metal depth gauge.

FIG. 16-13. Wooden depth gauge.

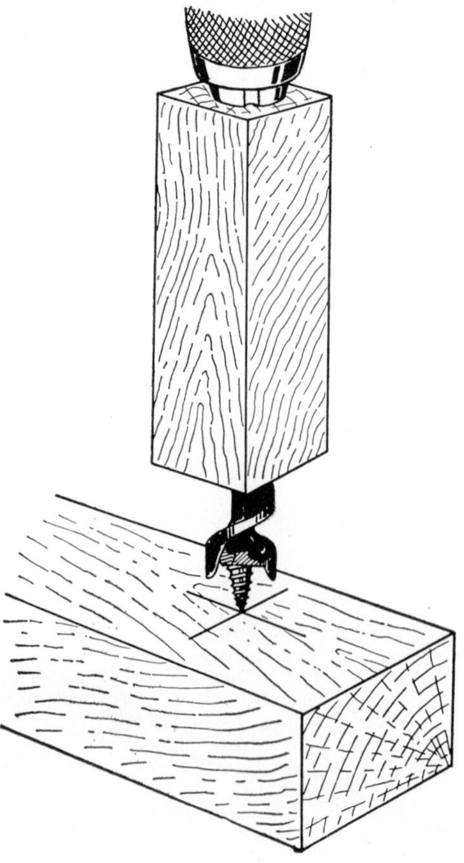

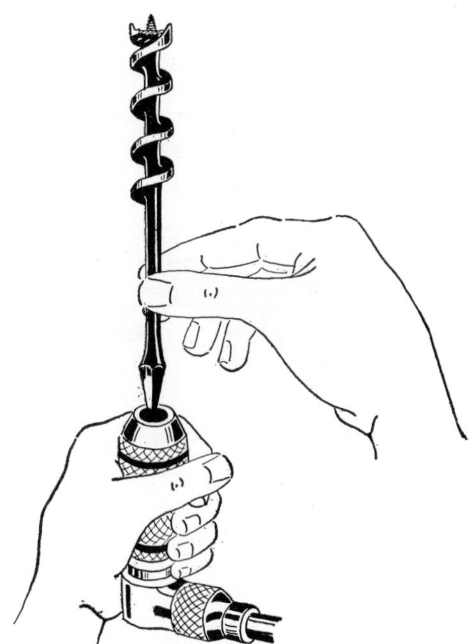

Fig. 16-14. Inserting auger bit into brace chuck.

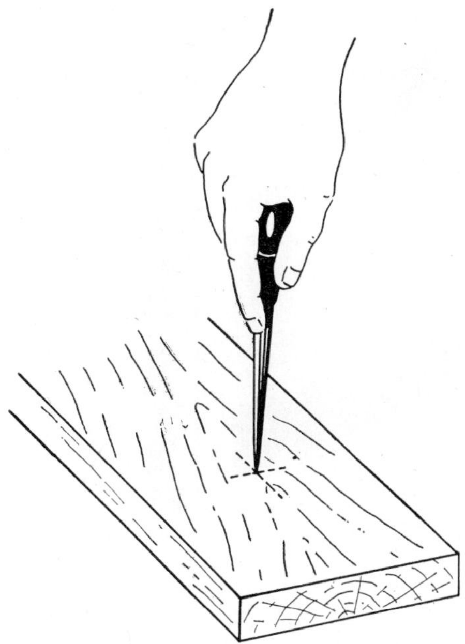

Fig. 16-15. Starting the hole with an awl.

Boring a Hole

1. Select the correct size square-shank auger bit or other bit for boring into wood.

2. Place the bit in the chuck of the brace (Fig. 16-14). To place the bit in the chuck, grasp the chuck shell and turn the handle to the left until the jaws open wide enough for the taper shank of the bit to pass the ends of the chuck jaws.

3. Fasten the bit firmly in the chuck by turning the handle to the right until the bit is held securely.

4. Mark the location for boring the hole. If possible, start the hole with an awl to give the feed screw a definite hold (Fig. 16-15).

5. Place the feed screw at the spot marked for the center of the hole, and with a firm pressure of the arm make a few turns with the brace to start the hole (Fig. 16-16).

6. Test the boring by holding a try square on the wood and against the bit to make certain that the hole is being

Fig. 16-16. Boring a hole vertically.

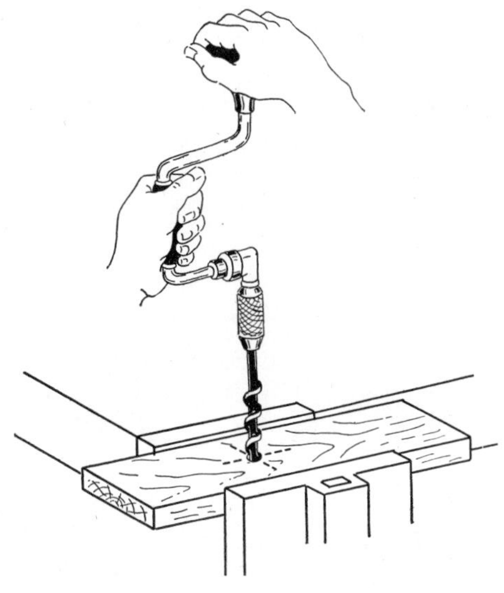

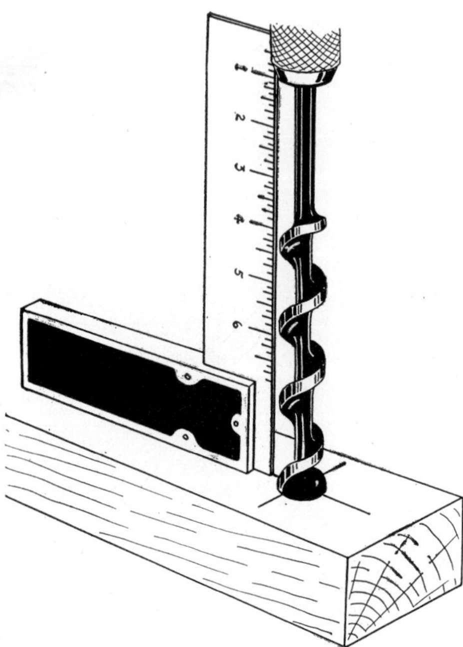

FIG. 16-17. Testing boring for accuracy.

bored at right angles to the surface of the work (Fig. 16-17).

7. Bore carefully until the point begins to come through on the back side (Fig. 16-18, Step 1).

8. Remove the bit from the hole by reversing the direction of the boring (Fig, 16-18, Step 2).

9. Bore through from the back side to make the hole clean-cut and without splinters (Fig. 16-18, Step 2). Figure 16-19 shows what will happen if the bit goes clear through the wood. Another method of boring a hole without splintering the back side of the board is to have a piece of scrap wood behind the board, as shown in Fig. 16-20. Holes bored with an expansive bit should be backed up with a piece of scrap wood to prevent splintering.

In boring holes for dowel joints, use a regular shortened dowel auger bit with the dowel jig.

FIG. 16-18. Step 1: Correct procedure in boring a hole. Step 2: Boring a clean-cut hole.

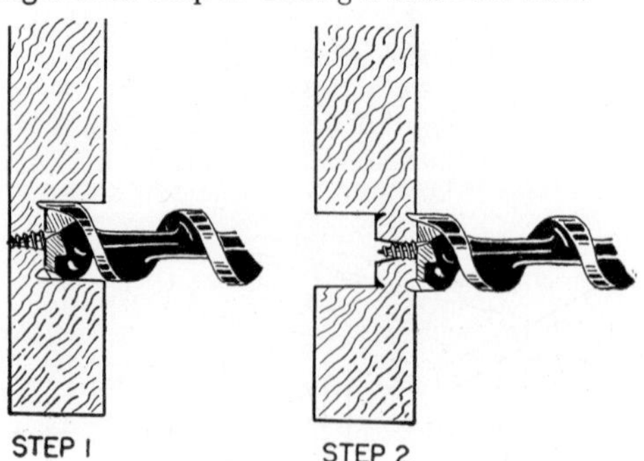

FIG. 16-19. Incorrect boring of a hole.

FIG. 16-20. Boring a hole with the aid of a piece of scrap wood.

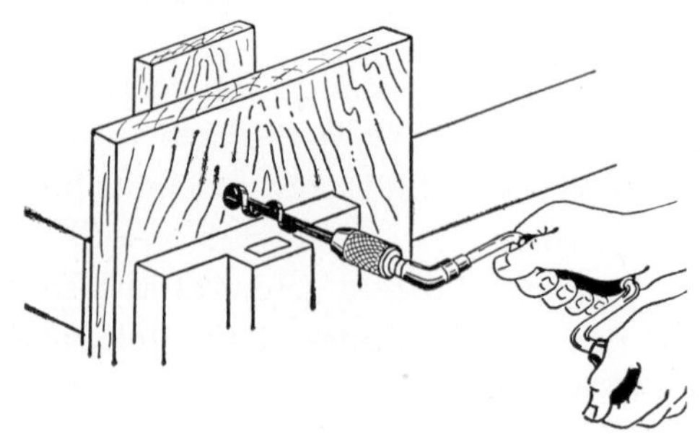

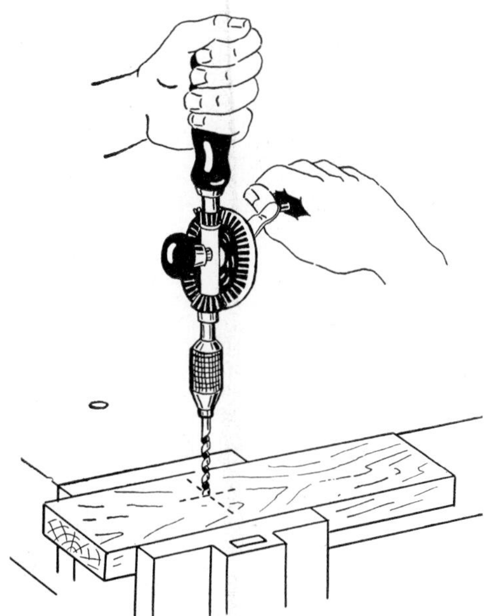

Fig. 16-21. Drilling a hole with a hand drill.

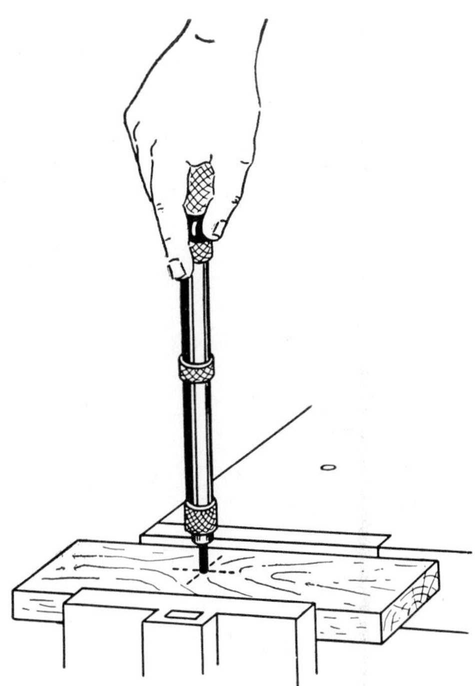

Fig. 16-22. Drilling a hole with the automatic drill.

Boring to a Specified Depth

1. Fasten an auger bit of the desired diameter in a brace, as described in steps 2 and 3 of the preceding section.

2. Fasten the adjustable metal depth gauge (Fig. 16-12) on the bit to regulate the depth the bit is to bore. The wooden depth gauge, illustrated in Fig. 16-13, is also suitable to use.

3. Check this depth against the rule.

4. Proceed in boring the hole until the depth gauge stops the boring action.

5. Remove the bit and shake out the loose wood particles in the hole.

Drilling a Hole

1. Select the straight-shank drill bit or the automatic drill of the desired diameter.

2. Fasten the straight-shank drill bit in the hand-drill chuck, much as you fasten an auger bit in the brace. The automatic drill is held in a special chuck. It is advisable to refer to the instructions which accompany the automatic drill for fastening as well as for using automatic bits.

3. Locate and mark where the hole is to be drilled.

4. Place the bit on the mark, and hold the drill steady in the direction desired while turning the crank at a constant, but not too fast, speed (Fig. 16-21).

A hole is drilled with an automatic drill in the manner illustrated in Fig. 16-22.

Discussion Topics

1. What is the difference between an "auger bit" and a "drill bit"?
2. Does the number stamped on the

shank of an auger bit denote the numerator or denominator of the fraction determined by that size bit?
3. What are the sizes of auger bits which have the following numbers stamped on the shank: 5, 6, 7, 10, 11, and 16?
4. What kind of a bit is used for boring holes larger than 1 inch in diameter?
5. List four other types of bits and give their primary uses.
6. How can you bore a hole through a board without splitting the back side?
7. What three methods are used to list sizes of drill bits?
8. How might you make a depth gauge?

Unit 17. Fastening with Screws

Screws are used for fastening boards and for assembling projects. A project which has been fastened with screws can be easily dismantled and reassembled without injury.

The three most common types of screws for joining wood are illustrated in Fig. 71-1. They are the round-head, flat-head, and oval-head screw. The first two are used most often in woodworking. The screw with the slotted head which will accommodate an ordinary screw driver has been used for a long time.. A more recent trend in screw-head designs is the Phillips-head screw (Fig. 17-2). This type is also available with the round, flat, or oval head.

Screws vary in length from $\frac{1}{4}$ to 6 inches and in gauge sizes from 0 to 24. Most are made of mild steel; however, they are also manufactured from brass for use where humidity is a problem as in the assembly of boats. Flat-head screws of mild steel generally have a bright finish, while the round-head are often finished in a dull blue. Screws are also available with various plated finishes.

They are usually sold in variety stores and hardware stores by the dozen. The factory packages them in boxes of one gross (144). A box marked "1 gross, $1\frac{1}{4}$ inch, No. 10, F.H.B. Screws" means that it contains: 144 screws, $1\frac{1}{4}$ inches in length, gauge 10 (diameter of the

FIG. 17-1. Round, flat-, and oval-head wood screws.

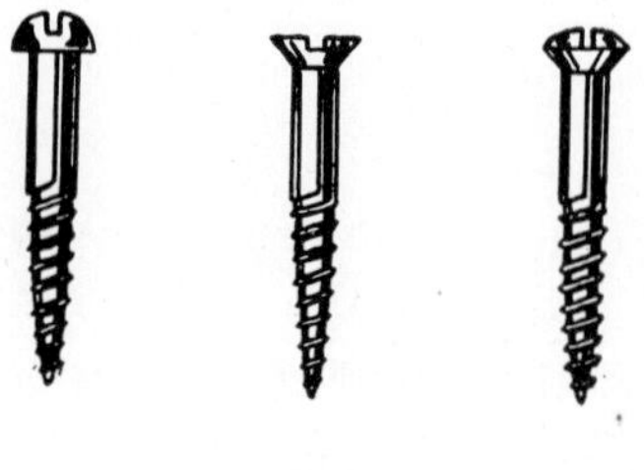

FIG. 17-2. Round-, flat-, and oval-head Phillips-head screws.

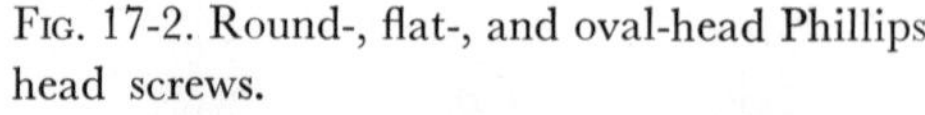

Fig. 17-3. Factory package for screws.

Fig. 17-5. Screw-driver bit.

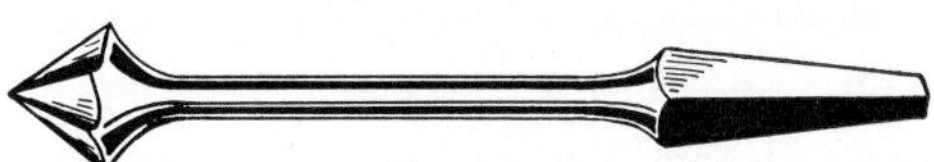

Fig. 17-6. Countersink bit.

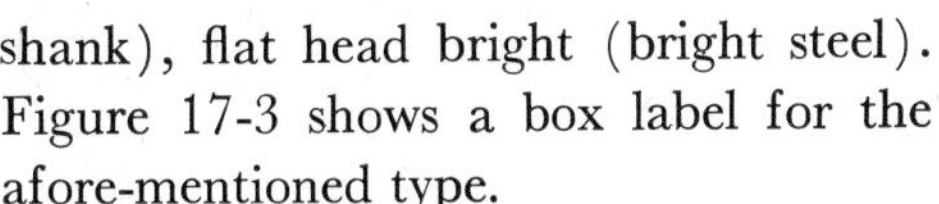

shank), flat head bright (bright steel). Figure 17-3 shows a box label for the afore-mentioned type.

Screws are superior to nails as wood fasteners because they are more permanent, hold better, may be tightened easily, and allow the project to be readily dismantled. However, they do require much time in planning and care for proper insertion.

Tools

In fastening with screws, the following tools are needed: hand-drill and straight-shank drill bits, brace and auger bits, awl, screw driver (Fig. 17-4), screw-driver bit (Fig. 17-5), and countersink bit (Fig. 17-6). The tip of the screw driver should be shaped to fit the slot of the screw, as shown in the right view in Fig. 17-7. The screw driver used for the Phillips-head screw

Fig. 17-4. Screw driver.

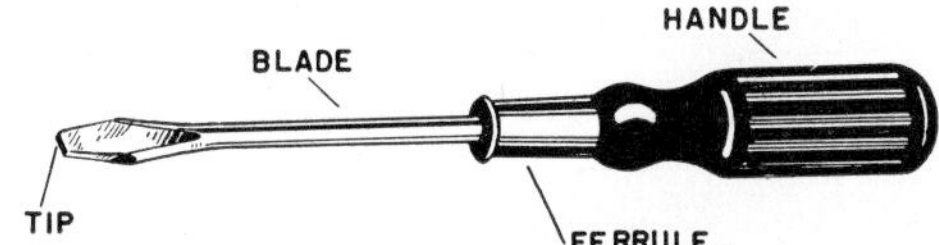

Fig. 17-7. Incorrectly and correctly shaped screw-driver tips.

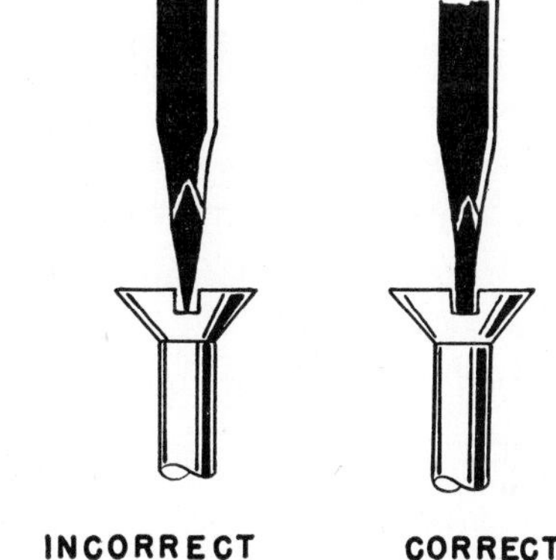

TABLE 17-1. SIZES OF BITS OR DRILLS TO BORE HOLES FOR WOOD SCREWS

	Number of screw	1	2	3	4	5	6	7	8	9	10	12	14	16	18
	Approximate body dia. of screw	$\frac{5}{64}$	$\frac{3}{32}$	$\frac{3}{32}$	$\frac{7}{64}$	$\frac{1}{8}$	$\frac{9}{64}$	$\frac{5}{32}$	$\frac{11}{64}$	$\frac{11}{64}$	$\frac{3}{16}$	$\frac{7}{32}$	$\frac{15}{64}$	$\frac{17}{64}$	$\frac{19}{64}$
First hole (pilot)	Twist-drill size	$\frac{5}{64}$	$\frac{3}{32}$	$\frac{7}{64}$	$\frac{7}{64}$	$\frac{1}{8}$	$\frac{9}{64}$	$\frac{5}{32}$	$\frac{11}{64}$	$\frac{3}{16}$	$\frac{3}{16}$	$\frac{7}{32}$	$\frac{1}{4}$	$\frac{17}{64}$	$\frac{19}{64}$
	Auger-bit number	..	..	..	..	..	..	3	3	3	3	4	4	5	5
Second hole (anchor)	Twist-drill size	..	$\frac{1}{16}$	$\frac{1}{16}$	$\frac{5}{64}$	$\frac{5}{64}$	$\frac{3}{32}$	$\frac{7}{64}$	$\frac{7}{64}$	$\frac{1}{8}$	$\frac{1}{8}$	$\frac{9}{64}$	$\frac{5}{32}$	$\frac{3}{16}$	$\frac{13}{64}$
	Auger-bit number	..	..	..	..	..	..	..	..	..	..	..	3	3	4

is very similar to the standard one except that it has a specially processed tip to fit the cross slots.

Table 17-1 provides the necessary information for the selection of screws, drills, auger bits, and pilot and anchor holes. Exact sizes cannot be given for the holes for wood screws. Variations in hardwood and in softwood and snug or loose fits should be considered. A trial fit in scrap wood is a practical solution.

Fastening with a Screw

1. Mark the location for the screw hole. A dent with an awl makes an excellent beginning for boring or drilling a hole.

2. Select the bit of the correct size for drilling or boring the pilot hole (Table 17-1). The size of the bit should be large enough to clear the shank of the screw.

3. Fasten the bit in the brace or the drill in the hand drill, and make the pilot hole (Fig. 17-8).

4. Place boards for the joint in position, and mark the location of the anchor hole with an awl (Fig. 17-9).

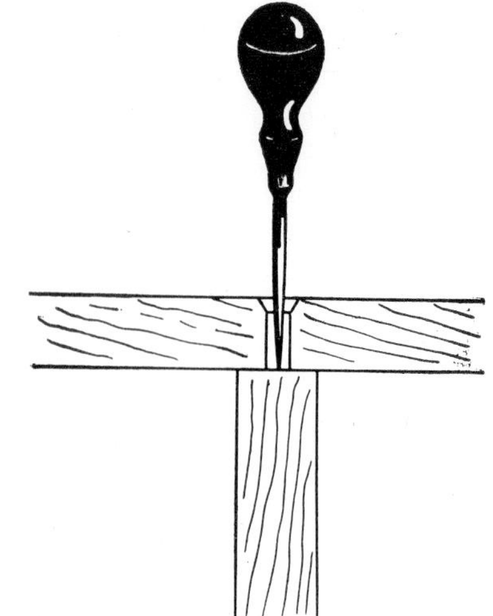

Fig. 17-9. Marking for anchor hole.

5. Bore or drill the anchor hole. If a drill bit is not available for making this hole, a nail with the head cut off may be used in a hand drill for this purpose. A nail can be made to cut a larger hole by flattening it near the point.

6. Countersink the pilot hole slightly if a flat- or oval-head screw is to be

Fig. 17-8. Pilot and anchor holes.

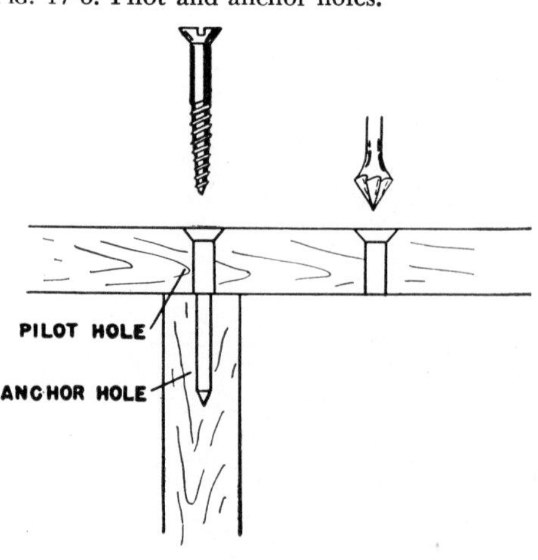

Fig. 17-10. Countersinking a pilot hole.

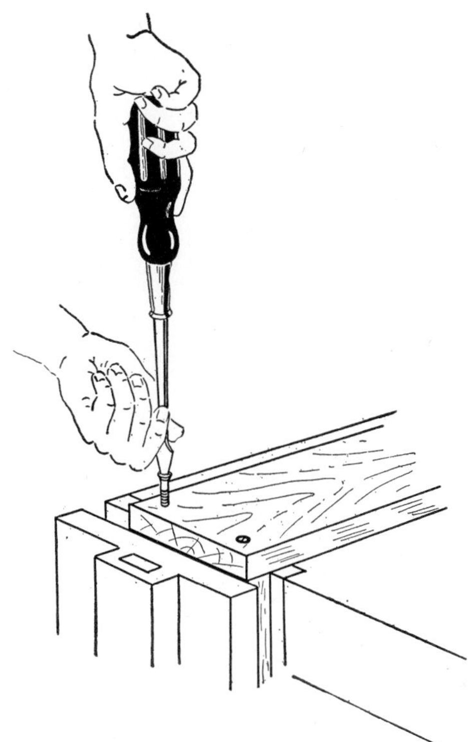

Fig. 17-11. Driving a screw wth a screw driver.

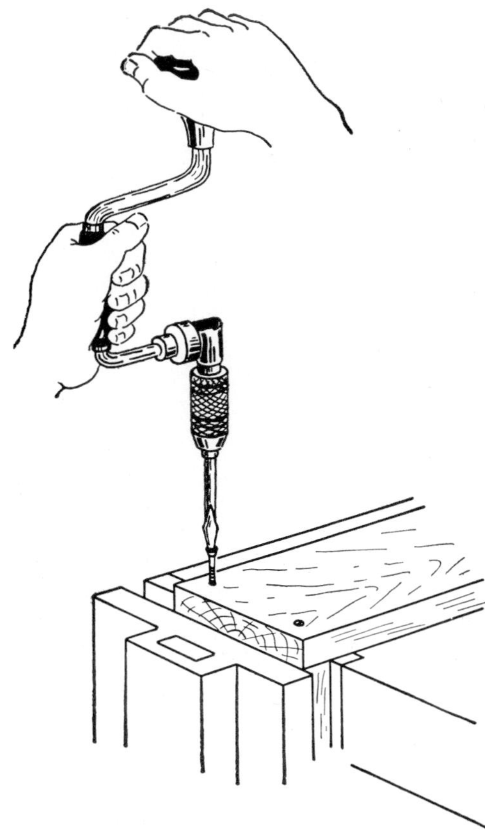

Fig. 17-12. Driving a screw with a screw-driver bit and brace.

used (Fig. 17-10). Make sure that you do not countersink too deeply, or the head will pull into the wood. A counter-sink bit fitted into a file handle serves excellently for this purpose.

7. Select the screw driver which fits the slot of the screw snugly. The tip should be ground properly (Fig. 17-7).

8. Fasten the screw with a screw driver (Fig. 17-11) or with a screw-driver bit and brace (Fig. 17-12). Hold the screw driver firmly and in line with the screw to prevent it from slipping out of the screw slot. If the screw turns too hard, unscrew it and coat it with hand soap.

9. If the screw is to be hidden or to be covered with a wooden button or plug, it will be necessary to set the head in the wood, as shown in Fig. 17-13. Standard-size wooden plugs are available commercially, or you may make them.

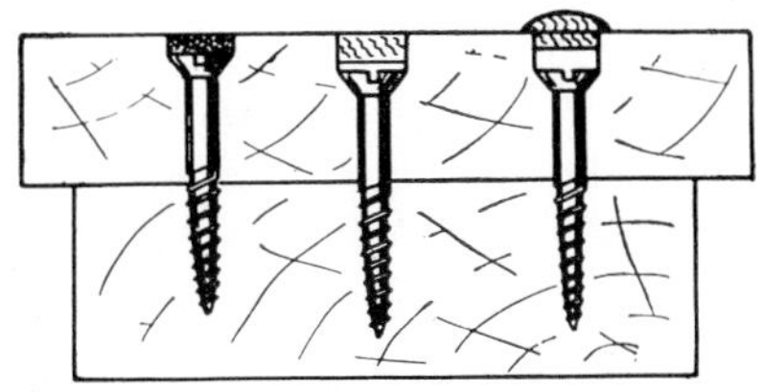

Fig. 17-13. Methods of recessing flat-head screws.

Discussion Topics

1. Name three of the most common types of slotted screws used in woodworking.
2. What are two advantages in using the Phillips-head screws?
3. When should brass screws be used?
4. What information must you know before buying screws for a particular job?
5. List three advantages in using screws instead of nails.
6. Illustrate the correct shape of the tip of the screw driver with relation to the screw slot.
7. What is the purpose of the pilot and anchor holes?
8. What tool is used on the pilot hole for making a flat-head screw flush with the surface of the wood?

Unit 18. Driving and Pulling Nails

A great deal of skill is involved in driving, setting, and pulling nails correctly. Almost everyone has occasion to drive and pull nails; it is, therefore, essential to know how to use a hammer and how to select the correct nail to use for the particular job.

Nails that are used most extensively in woodworking are termed *box, common, finishing, brads,* and *casing* (Fig. 18-1.) *Box nails* are relatively thin with flat heads. They were originally made for nailing together boxes where wood was thin and easily split. *Common nails* have heavy, flat heads and are slightly larger in diameter than box nails. The *finishing nail* has a small head, and is used on finished surfaces where the head is to be set with a nail set and covered with putty or a wood plastic. The *brad* is actually a small finishing nail which varies in length from $\frac{1}{4}$ to 1 inch and is used to nail thin stock to-

Fig. 18-1. Kinds of nails: (*A*) box, (*B*) common, (*C*) finishing, (*D*) brads, and (*E*) casing.

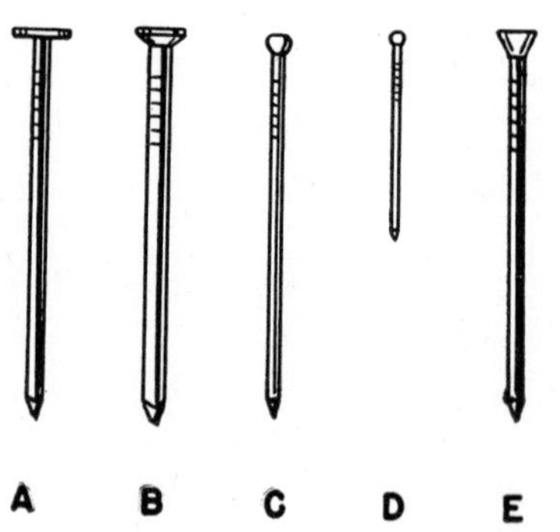

TABLE 18-1. NAIL CHART

Size (penny)	*Length (inches)*
2	1
3	$1\frac{1}{4}$
4	$1\frac{1}{2}$
5	$1\frac{3}{4}$
6	2
7	$2\frac{1}{4}$
8	$2\frac{1}{2}$
9	$2\frac{3}{4}$
10	3
12	$3\frac{1}{4}$
16	$3\frac{1}{2}$
20	4
30	$4\frac{1}{2}$
40	5

gether. The *casing nail* has a cone-shaped head which gives good holding power and is used mostly for interior trim and cabinet work.

The size of nails is usually indicated by *penny* or *d*. It is believed that this terminology was derived from the weight of a thousand nails. As an example, one thousand 10-penny nails would weigh 10 pounds. It may be seen from the nail chart, Table 18-1, that a 2-penny (or 2d) nail is 1 inch long. For each additional penny add $\frac{1}{4}$ inch up to 3 inches. Beyond that the length cannot be figured in this manner.

Tools

The most convenient tool for driving nails is the *claw hammer* (Fig. 18-2). The size of this type of hammer is designated by the weight of the head, which ranges from 7 to 20 ounces. The popular size has a 10- to 20-ounce head.

A *nail set* (Fig. 18-3) is used in setting the head of a finishing nail or casing nail. The tip is built with a slightly concave surface so that it will not slide off the nailhead too easily. Nail sets are available in a variety of tip sizes.

Fig. 18-2. Claw hammer.

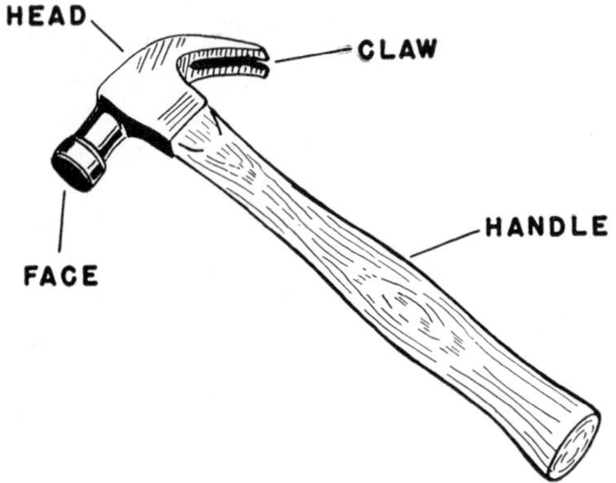

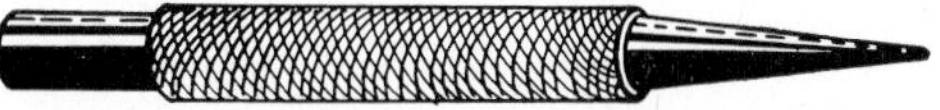

Fig. 18-3. Nail set.

Important rules to remember when nailing are: (1) the length of the nail should be three times the thickness of the first board the nail goes through; (2) the size of the nail should not be too large or it may split the wood; and (3) it is desirable when driving nails through hardwood to drill a very small pilot hole through the first board.

Driving Nails

1. Select the proper type and size of nail for the job.

2. Hold the nail firmly with one hand making the first light blow (Fig. 18-4). Grasp the handle of the hammer firmly near the end.

3. Remove the hand which holds the nail, and continue to strike the nail directly on the head until it is driven flush with the wood. Try to avoid bending the nail.

Fig. 18-4. Starting to drive a nail.

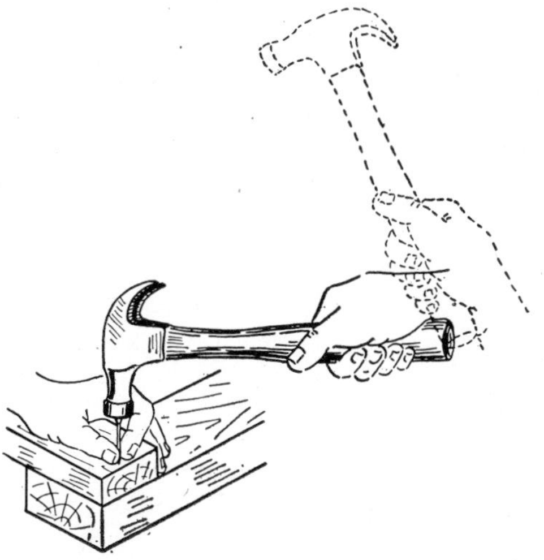

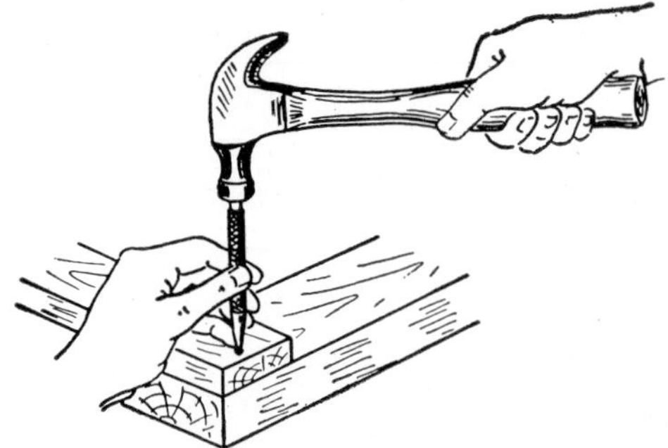

Fig. 18-5. Setting a nail.

4. Where necessary, set the head of the nail about $\frac{1}{16}$ inch below the surface of the wood (Fig. 18-5), especially if it is a finishing or casing nail.

5. Fill the hole with putty, wood plastic, or dough if the nail has been set (Fig. 18-6).

6. Figure 18-7 illustrates how nails may be driven in order to produce what is termed *toenailing.*

7. Nails which are driven at an angle have a greater holding power than those driven straight (Fig. 18-8).

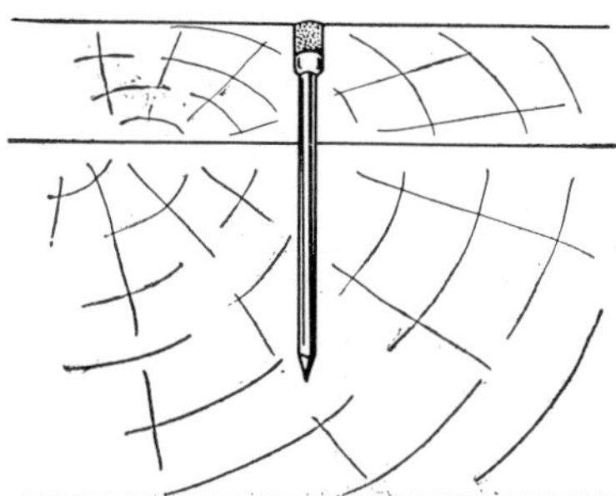

Fig. 18-6. Covering a nailhead.

Fig. 18-7. Toenailing.

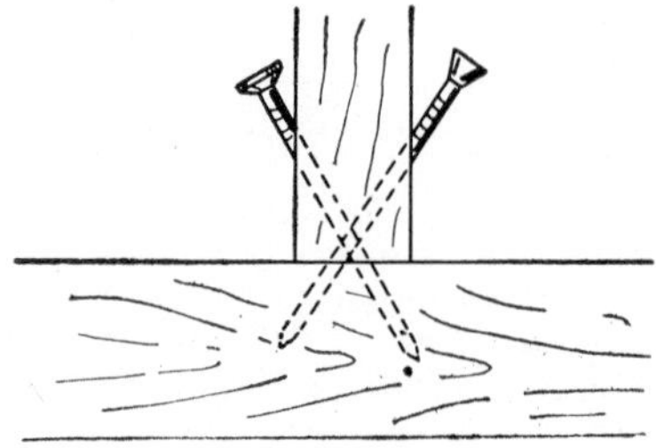

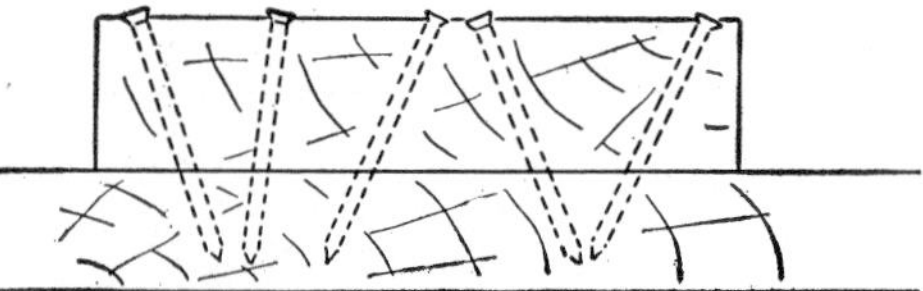

Fig. 18-8. Driving nails at an angle to increase holding power.

8. To clinch nails in holding two or more boards securely, see Fig. 18-9.

Pulling Nails

1. Slip the claw of the hammer under the head of the nail and pull the handle

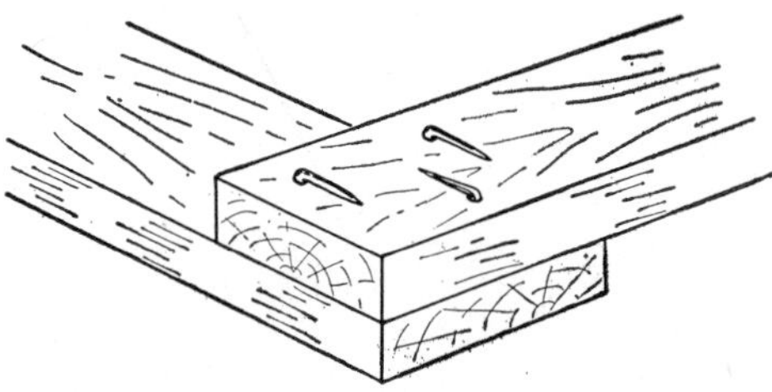

Fig. 18-9. Clinching nails to hold boards securely.

Fig. 18-10. Pulling nail with claw hammer.

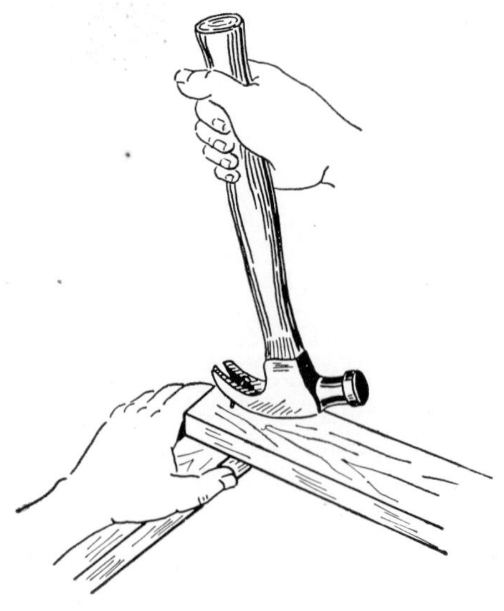

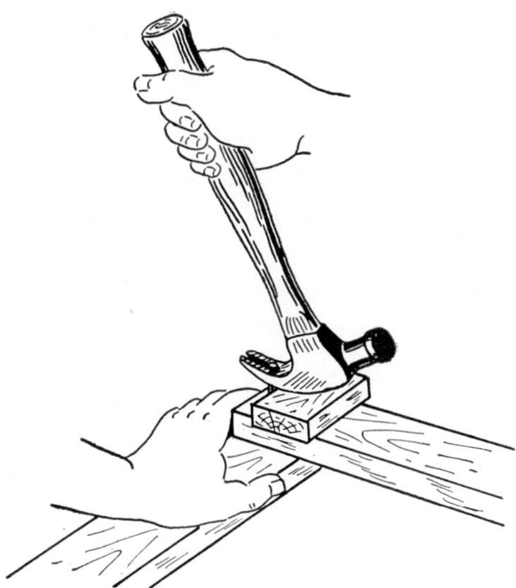

Fig. 18-11. Pulling nail with increased leverage.

until it is at nearly 90 degrees with the board (Fig. 18-10). Put a piece of heavy cardboard or a thin piece of wood under the hammer head to protect the surface of the board.

2. To pull a nail which is too long to come out as outlined in step 1, slip a block of wood under the head of the hammer (Fig. 18-11). This will increase the leverage and lessen the strain on the hammer handle.

Discussion Topics

1. List the five common types of nails and brads and explain their uses.
2. What tool is used to set the head of a finishing or casing nail?
3. What must you know about nails before purchasing them?
4. Give three important rules to remember when nailing.
5. What might it be necessary to do before driving a nail through hardwood?
6. How can you secure greater leverage when pulling a nail?

Unit 19. Joining

One or more types of joints are often included in the making of a piece of furniture or in cabinet work. There are many kinds of joints, some of them variations of the few basic types; however, all have a definite application which involves layout, cutting, fitting, and assembling. In order to understand each, it is desirable to study the several types and then to make the application or adaptation most suitable.

The basic types of joints which will possibly be the most suitable for your use will be the butt, dowel, dado, rabbet, lap, mortise and tenon, and miter. Each of these has numerous variations which adapt it for specific situations. A few of these variations and additional less used ones are shown in Figs. 19-1, 19-8, and 19-27.

Tools

Some of the more special tools, which have not been discussed in previous units and which are employed in the construction of some of the joints, are the commercial miter box with stiff-back saw, a homemade miter box, a

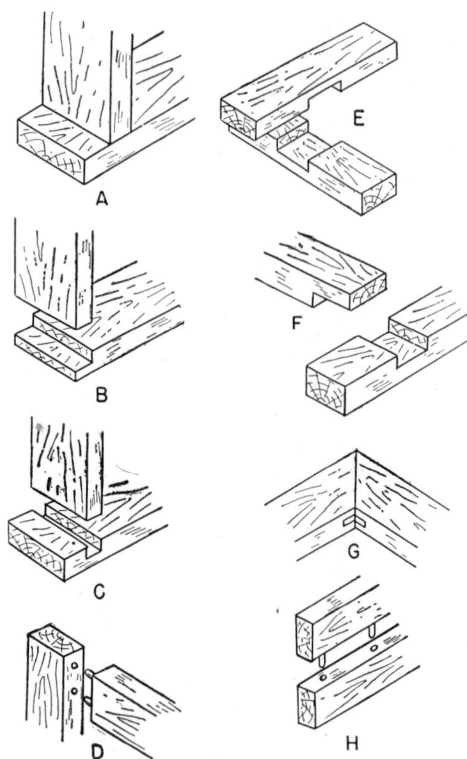

FIG. 19-1. A few of the common joints: (*A*) butt, (*B*) rabbet, (*C*) dado, (*D*) doweled-butt, (*E*) cross-lap, (*F*) middle-lap, (*G*) splined-miter, and (*H*) doweled-edge.

doweling jig, and the dowel pointer.

Miter box. The commercial miter box with stiff-back saw (Fig. 19-2) is a regular piece of equipment for practically all woodcraftsmen. The saw can be adjusted to cut at any angle desired. A small wooden miter box may be made

FIG. 19-2. Miter box with stiff-back saw.

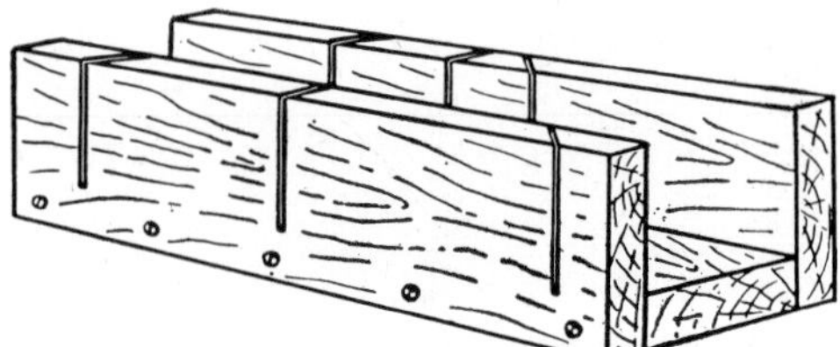

FIG. 19-3. Homemade miter box.

when the worker desires only a few set angular cuts, as shown in Fig. 19-3.

Doweling jig. The doweling jig (Fig. 19-4) is preferred by many workmen for boring holes in dowel joining. A special bit, known as a *dowel bit,* is often used in conjunction with this jig. The dowel bit is a shortened auger bit and is of the proper length so that a bit stop is not required when it is being used. The jig may be adjusted to practically any position for boring holes at right angles to the stock.

Dowel pointer. The dowel pointer (Fig. 19-5) was designed for trimming the point of dowels used in joining. This allows easier insertion of the dowel in the joint. Although the bit was made for fastening in a brace, it may be fastened conveniently in a wooden file handle, as indicated in Fig. 19-5. This makes it easy to handle.

FIG. 19-4. Doweling jig.

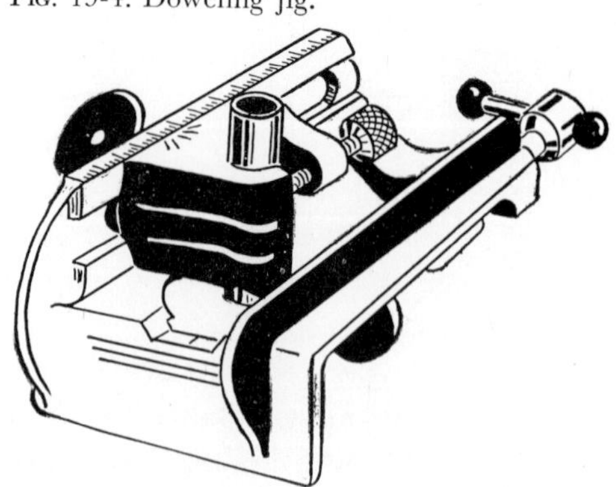

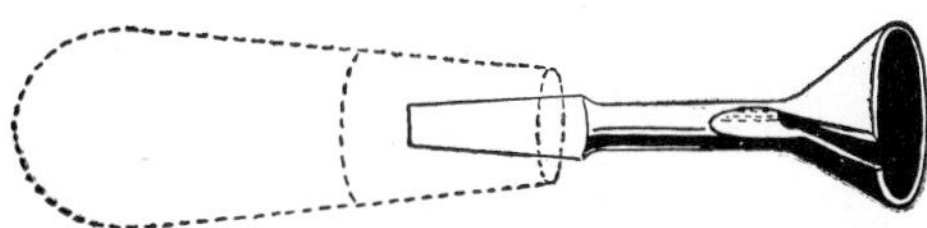

Fig. 19-5. Dowel pointer.

Butt Joint

The butt joint (Fig. 19-6) is one of the simplest types which can be held securely with nails, screws, or dowels. It should be used where the fasteners will not be exposed to view. A variation of the butt joint held together with corrugated fasteners is shown in Fig. 19-7.

To make a butt joint.

1. Square the end of the stock which is to be butted against the other surface.
2. Mark the exact location on the surface where the butt joint is to be made.
3. Select the type of fastening you will employ: nails, screws, dowels, or corrugated fasteners.
4. If nails are used, select the type most suitable and drive them so that they go through the surface piece with the points barely protruding.
5. Hold the pieces to be joined in their respective position, and finish driving the nails into the piece which is being butted. Refer to the preceding unit for nailing procedure. Check the construction with a try or framing square to ensure the 90-degree angle, or use the sliding T bevel if an acute or obtuse angle is desired. For fastening with screws, refer to Unit 17, "Fastening with Screws," page 54.

Fig. 19-6. Butt joints.

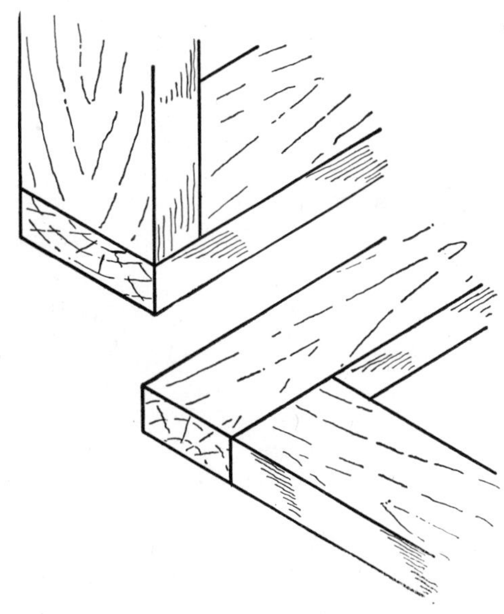

Fig. 19-7. Butt joint held with corrugated fasteners.

Dowel Joint

Dowels are frequently used in furniture and cabinet construction (Fig. 19-8). They are very often employed when gluing edge-to-edge joints, and they may also be utilized as substitutes for mortise-and-tenon joints. The latter is a common practice in furniture construction, especially in making the inexpensive type. Miter joints may be held securely with dowels also.

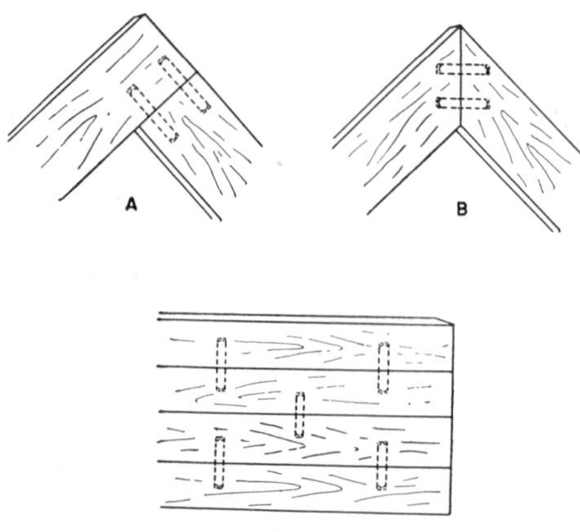

FIG. 19-8. Three types of dowel joints: (*A*) doweled-butt, (*B*) doweled-miter, and (*C*) doweled-edge.

The better grades of dowels are made from hardwood, such as birch or maple. They are round pieces of wood available in many lengths and diameters, generally starting at $\frac{1}{4}$ inch (Fig. 19-9). A special grooved dowel pin is available, as shown in Fig. 19-9. Grooves retain glue better than smooth pins.

To make the edge joint:

1. Plane the edges of the pieces to be fastened together. Check to see that these edges are square with the surface (Fig. 19-10) and that they are straight and true (Fig. 19-11).

FIG. 19-9. Two types of dowel pins.

FIG. 19-10. Squaring the edge for a joint.

FIG. 19-11. Checking the edge with a steel straightedge for trueness.

2. Arrange the boards to be joined so that the grain on the surfaces is in the same direction. The end grain should also be arranged so that it will alternate (Fig. 19-12). This tends to relieve warping of the glued-up stock.

3. Place the boards as they will join and mark these joints as indicated in Fig. 19-12. This prevents interchanging of pieces.

4. Assemble the pieces for the edge

FIG. 19-12. Proper arrangement and marking of boards for edge gluing.

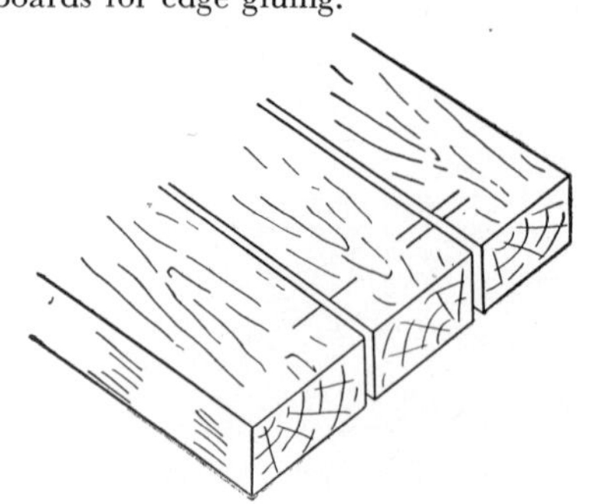

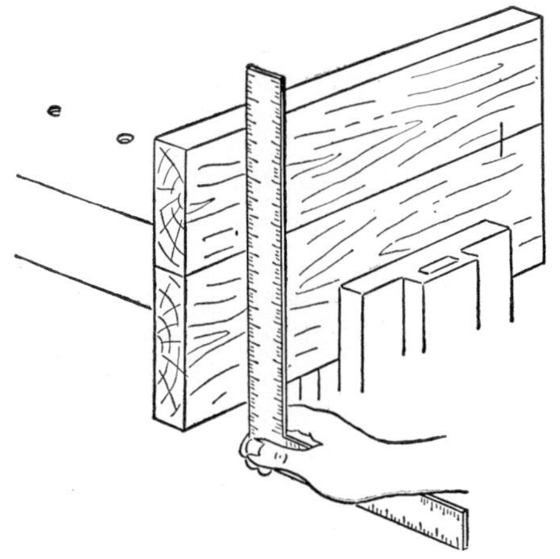

FIG. 19-13. Aligning boards with a straightedge.

joints and test them for proper alignment (Fig. 19-13).

These steps are all that are required if you wish to glue up an ordinary edge joint or joints *without* dowels.

5. Clamp the boards that are to be glued.

6. Mark lines across the edges at intervals of 12 to 18 inches with the aid of a try square (Fig. 19-14). These lines indicate the markings for the dowel centers. Dowels should be at least 4 to 6 inches in from the ends of boards.

7. Set the marking gauge at half the thickness of each board.

FIG. 19-14. Marking edges for location of dowels.

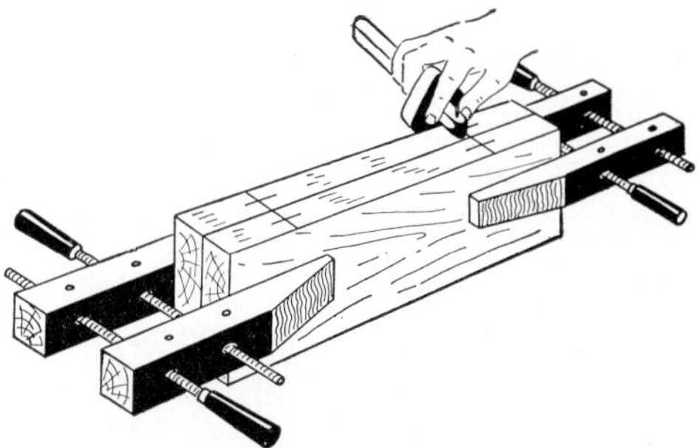

FIG. 19-15. Locating centers for dowels with marking gauge.

8. Intersect the lines made in step 6 with the marking gauge (Fig. 19-15). Keep the head of the gauge against the matched working surfaces.

9. Select the auger bit for the desired diameter of the dowel and fasten it in the brace. For edge joints this will usually be $\frac{5}{16}$ or $\frac{3}{8}$ inch.

10. Bore holes to the desired depth for the dowel rods with the auger bit. This may be done with or without the aid of a doweling jig. Dowels for edge joints are usually 2 to 3 inches long; therefore, the hole in each piece will be a trifle deeper than half the length of the dowel. The depth may be controlled with the depth gauge (Figs. 16-12 and 16-13).

11. In using the dowel jig (Fig. 19-16), place the proper size dowel guide (metal cylinder), as shown in Fig. 19-4, and fasten it into place with the thumb nut.

12. Adjust the sliding piece which holds the guide so that the centers for all holes will be the same distance from the surfaces of the boards (Fig. 19-4). Center this alignment as marked in step 8.

13. Place the doweling jig on the

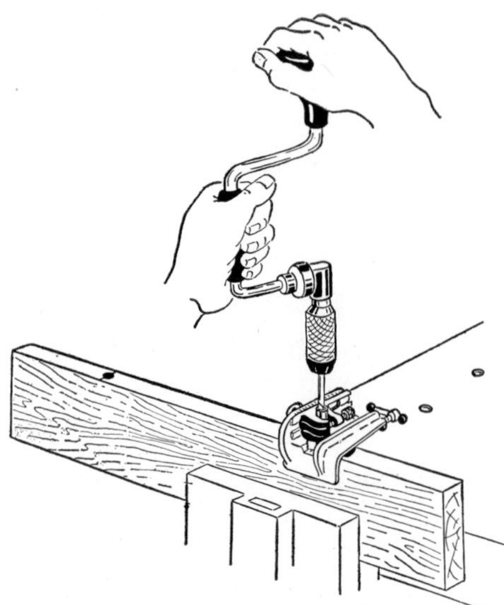

FIG. 19-16. Boring edge holes with the aid of a doweling jig.

edge of the board so that the index marking on the jig is in line with the marks put on in step 6.

14. Select the proper size auger bit and fasten it in the brace as indicated in step 9.

15. Bore all holes to uniform depth. Usually $1\frac{1}{4}$ to $1\frac{3}{4}$ inches is sufficient.

16. Cut the dowels to the proper length. This can be $\frac{1}{4}$ inch shorter, generally, than the combined depths of both corresponding holes.

17. Taper the ends of the dowels with dowel points (Fig. 19-17).

18. Place the dowels in the holes and trial-assemble the joint to see if it fits (Fig. 19-18).

FIG. 19-17. Pointing a dowel pin.

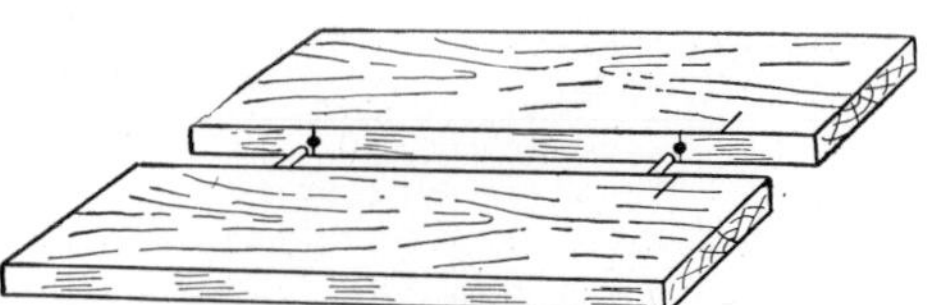

FIG. 19-18. Trial assembly of doweled-edge joint.

19. In gluing the edge joint for final assembly, apply glue in the holes, on the dowels, and on the edges of the boards. Assemble and clamp as described in Unit 22, "Gluing and Clamping," page 81.

RABBET JOINT

The rabbet joint (Figs. 19-1 and 19-22) is similar to the dado joint except that the pieces are joined together at the ends. It is ideal for some types of corner construction and is particularly adaptable in the construction of drawers.

To make a rabbet joint:

1. Make and square the pieces to be joined to the given dimensions.

2. Place the two pieces in their respective positions and mark the location of the rabbet joint (Fig. 19-19). The piece to be rabbeted should be marked back the thickness of the piece which fits it.

FIG. 19-19. Marking for a rabbet joint.

FIG. 19-20. The first cut in making a rabbet joint.

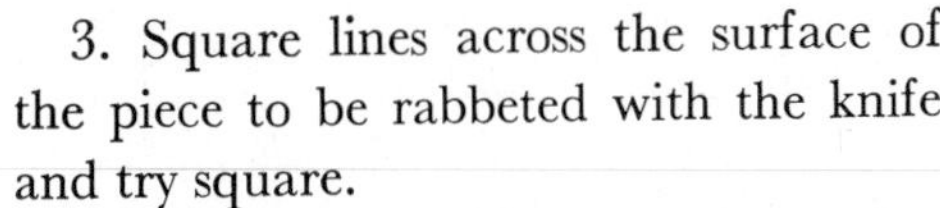

3. Square lines across the surface of the piece to be rabbeted with the knife and try square.

4. Extend the lines across the edge with a try square and sharp pencil.

5. Mark the depth of the rabbet on the end and the edges with the try square and pencil or with the marking gauge.

6. Place the piece to be cut in a vise, and saw just inside the edge of the knife-drawn line to the desired depth (Fig. 19-20). A backsaw is desirable.

7. Cut away the remaining waste stock by making an end cut, as shown in Fig. 19-21.

8. Fit the two pieces for a trial assembly. If necessary, pare the edge of the rabbet with a sharp wood chisel.

9. Assemble the rabbet joint with nails or screws (Fig. 19-22).

FIG. 19-21. The final cut in a rabbet joint.

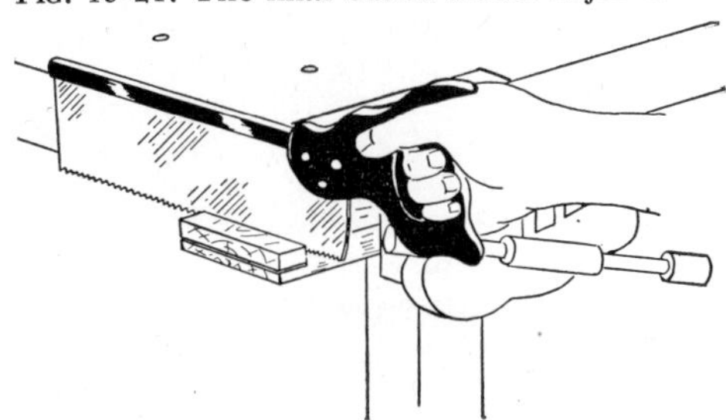

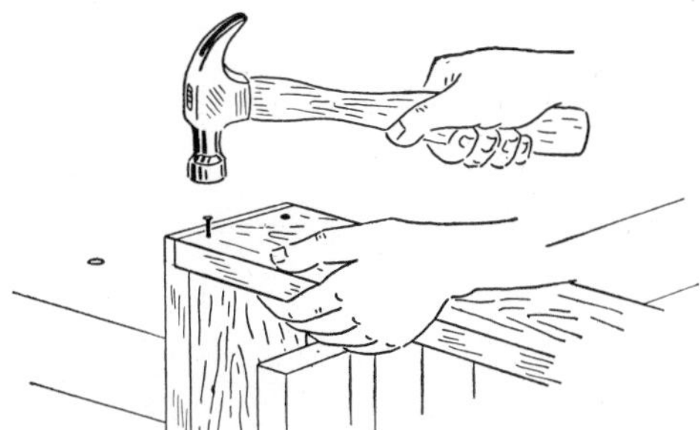

FIG. 19-22. Assembling a rabbet joint with nails.

DADO JOINT

This type of joint is a groove cut across the grain of a piece of wood into which is fitted another piece (Figs. 19-1 and 19-23). Dado joints are used in such wood construction as drawers, shelves, bookcases, and stepladders.

To make a dado joint:

1. Make and square the pieces to be joined to the given dimensions.

2. Place the two pieces in their respective positions and mark the location for making the dado joint (Fig. 19-23).

FIG. 19-23. Marking a dado joint.

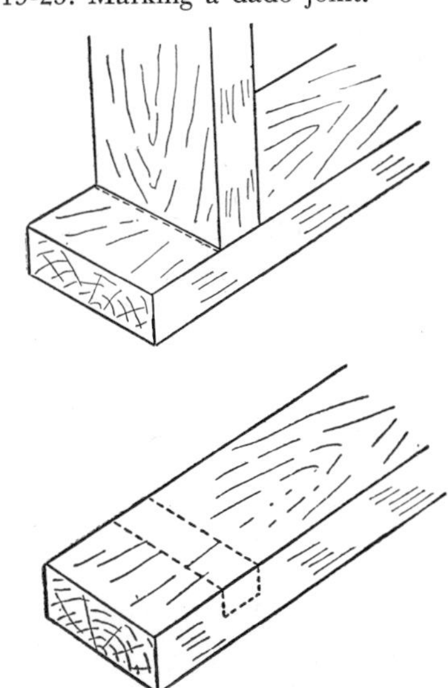

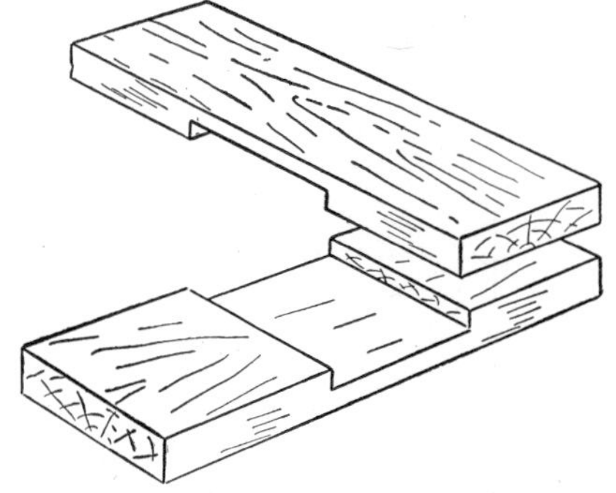

FIG. 19-24. Cross-lap joint.

3. Square lines across the surface of the piece to be dadoed with the knife and a try square.

4. Extend the knife lines across the edges with a try square and sharp pencil.

5. Mark the depth of the dado with the marking gauge.

6. Saw just inside the edges of the knife-drawn lines to the desired depth (Fig. 19-21). A backsaw is desirable.

7. Remove the wood between the saw cuts with a wood chisel (Fig. 19-26).

8. Fit the two pieces for a trial assembly. If the joint is too tight, pare the edges of the dado carefully with a sharp wood chisel. The pieces should fit snugly but without having to be driven in place.

9. Make the final assembly with glue and clamps, nails, or screws.

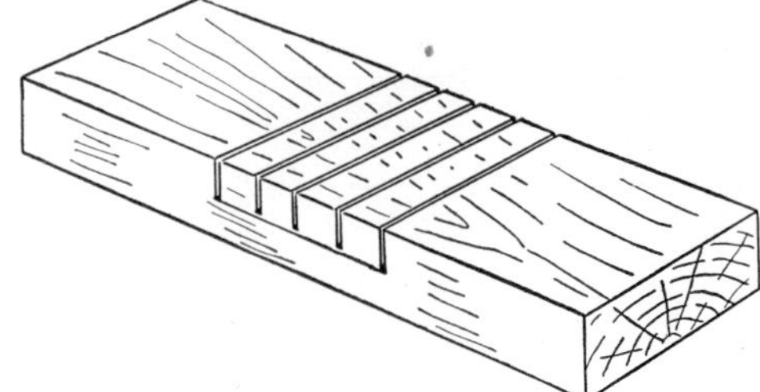

FIG. 19-25. Saw cuts in cross-lap joint.

LAP JOINT

There are numerous kinds of lap and notched joints, but one of the most common in furniture making and carpentry is the cross lap (Figs. 19-1 and 19-24).

To make a cross-lap joint:

1. Make and square the pieces to be joined to the given dimensions.

2. Place the two pieces in their respective positions and mark the locations of the cross-lap joint (Fig. 19-24).

3. Square lines across the surfaces of both pieces to be fitted with the knife and try square.

4. Extend the knife line on the edges of both pieces with a sharp pencil and a try square.

5. Mark the depth of the notch with the marking gauge. The depth should be one-half the thickness of the pieces, because the surfaces are to be flush when fully assembled.

6. Saw just inside the knife-drawn lines on the surfaces of both pieces to the proper depth. A backsaw is desirable.

7. Make a few extra saw cuts inside the marked lines to approximately the same depth (Fig. 19-25). This will facilitate chiseling.

8. Remove waste stock with a wood

Fig. 19-26. Removing waste stock with a wood chisel.

chisel (Fig. 19-26). Also refer to Fig. 13-5, page 43.

9. Fit the two pieces for a trial assembly. If the joint is too tight, pare the edges of the piece carefully with a sharp wood chisel. The pieces should fit snugly but without being driven.

10. Make the final assembly with glue and clamps, nails, or screws.

Mortise-and-Tenon Joint

Mortise-and-tenon joints (Fig. 19-27) are used extensively in furniture and in interior cabinet work, particularly on doors, window sash, and other places where added strength is needed. There are many kinds. A few of them are shown in Fig. 19-27. The procedure described for making the blind mortise and tenon is practically the same as for the others.

To make the *mortise:*

1. Make and square the pieces to be joined to the given dimensions.

2. Determine the thickness and width of the mortise from your working drawing. If the drawing does not give detailed dimensions, the following rules will assist you:

a. A mortise and tenon $\frac{3}{8}$ inch thick is desirable when the rail stock measures $\frac{3}{4}$ or $\frac{13}{16}$ inch in thickness.

b. The face of the rail should be at least $\frac{1}{8}$ to $\frac{1}{4}$ inch recessed from the outer face of the leg.

c. Take advantage of the location of the mortises by having them as deep as possible so that the tenons can meet or cross-lap (Fig. 19-33).

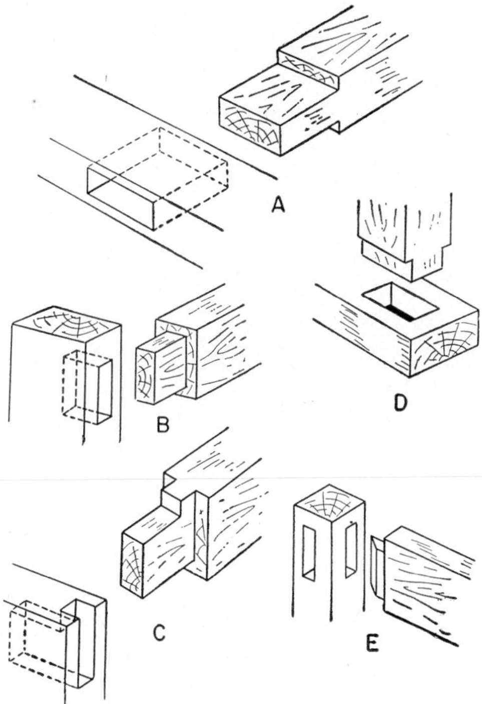

Fig. 19-27. Mortise-and-tenon joints: (*A*) through mortise-and-tenon, (*B*) blind mortise-and-tenon, (*C*) haunched mortise-and-tenon, (*D*) stub mortise-and-tenon, and (*E*) mitered mortise-and-tenon.

3. Lay out the mortise on the leg in a manner similar to that shown in Fig. 19-28. Note that where possible it is advisable to drop down from the top $\frac{3}{4}$ inch and to allow for a shoulder of $\frac{1}{4}$ inch at the bottom. The layout can be

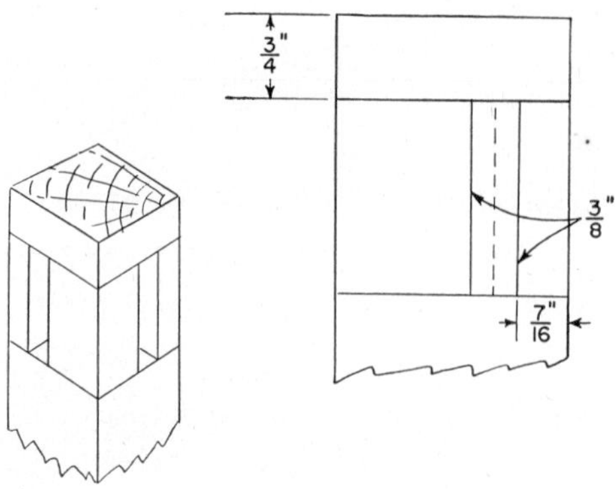

Fig. 19-28. Layout for a mortise on a leg.

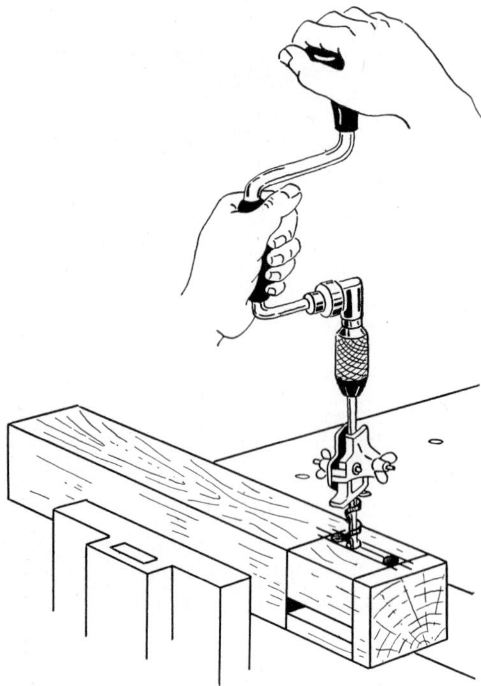

Fig. 19-30. Boring holes for a mortise.

done most efficiently with the try square and pencil and with the marking gauge.

4. When marking identical mortises, such as would be the case in making a stool or table, it is advisable to mark all four legs simultaneously, as shown in Fig. 19-29.

5. Fasten the piece to be mortised securely on a bench or in a vise.

6. Select an auger bit slightly smaller than the width of the mortise and fasten it in a brace.

7. Bore a series of holes to the depth necessary, placing the spur of the auger bit on a center line of the mortise (Fig. 19-30). A depth gauge should be used to bore holes of uniform depth.

8. Chisel and pare the sides of the mortise with a sharp wood chisel to the gauge lines. The ends of the mortise can be cut easily with a chisel of the proper width. The narrow chisel is ideal for removing the waste stock and for cleaning the mortise. Refer to Unit 13, "Cutting and Trimming with a Chisel," pages 42 to 44.

To make the *tenon:*

1. Lay out the tenon on the rail according to the dimensions of the working drawing (Fig. 19-33) so that it will fit the mortise. The try square and marking gauge are used in this operation.

2. Fasten the rail securely in a vise so that it can be cut (Fig. 19-31).

Fig. 19-29. Laying out mortises on four legs at one time.

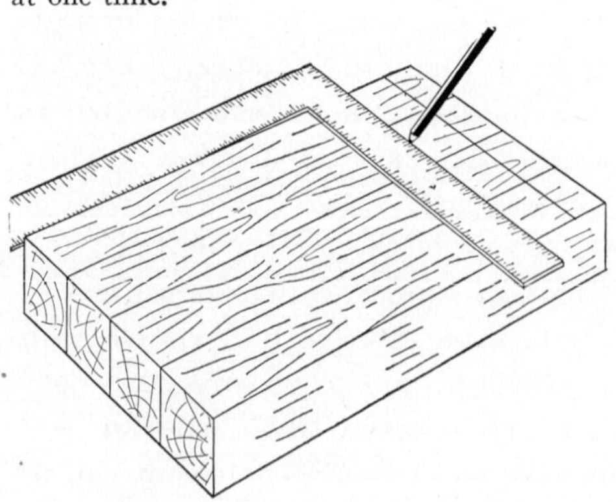

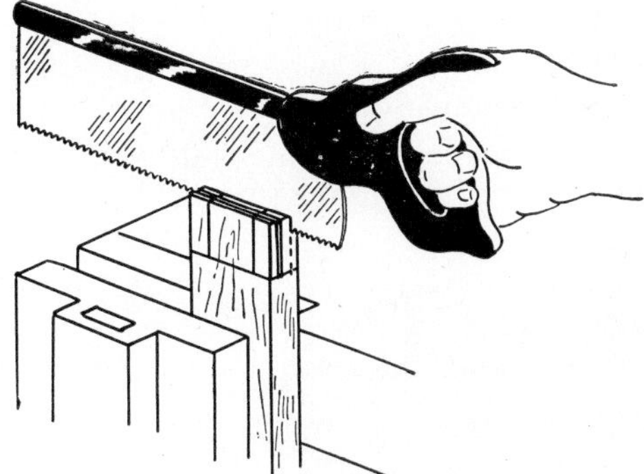

Fig. 19-31. First step in cutting a tenon.

3. Cut the tenon as shown with a backsaw, making certain that the saw line is barely outside of the gauge line (Fig. 19-31).

4. Place the rail horizontally in a vise or bench hook, and cut on the waste side of the marked lines on the surface to remove the surplus stock (Fig. 19-32).

5. Make the remaining cuts on the tenon until it is completed.

6. Fit the mortise-and-tenon pieces for a trial assembly. The pieces should fit snugly without being driven. If necessary, pare the sides of the mortise or the tenon until a proper fit is obtained (Fig. 19-33).

Fig. 19-32. Second step in cutting a tenon.

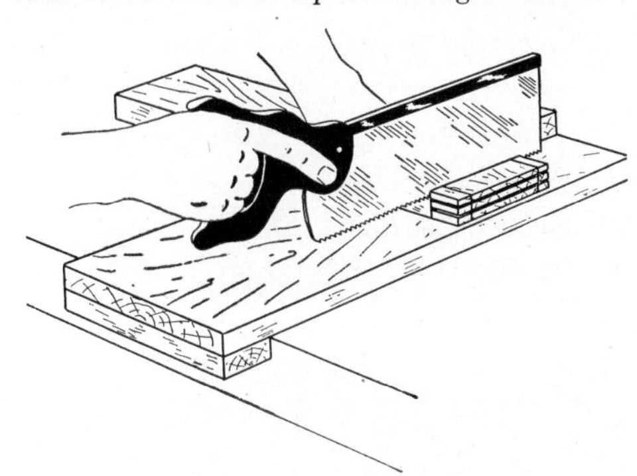

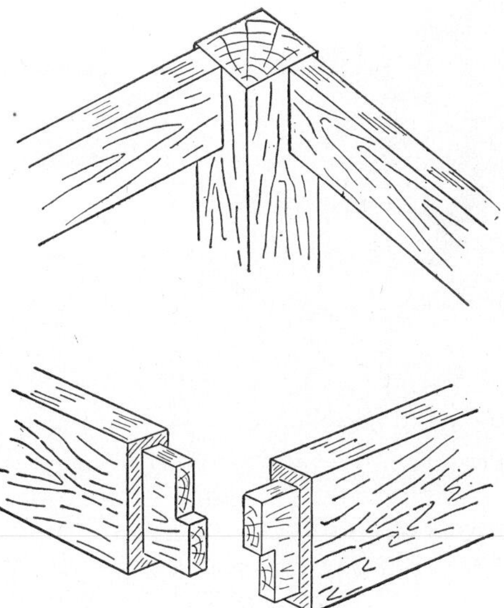

Fig. 19-33. Cross-lap tenon.

7. Make final assembly of the mortise-and-tenon joint by gluing and clamping. Refer to Unit 22, "Gluing and Clamping," page 81.

Miter Joint

The miter joint is commonly used in making picture frames, door molding, and other pieces where it is undesirable to have the end grain of the wood exposed.

Miter joints are most satisfactorily cut on the metal miter box (Fig. 19-2) or on the homemade one (Fig. 19-3). Since the laying out and the cutting of miter joints involve similar procedures in each case, only one is given here, that of making the miter joint for a picture frame.

To make a miter joint:

1. Make or purchase a molding which will blend with the picture to be framed.

2. Mark the length of the picture to

Fig. 19-34. Cutting a miter joint on molding.

be framed along the rabbeted edge of the molding. There will be two identical pieces for ends and two for the sides.

3. Place the molding in the miter box with the rabbet face down.

4. Hold the molding firmly to the frame of the box, and lower the miter-box saw until it touches the molding on the waste side of the mark.

5. Cut the molding with light, even strokes (Fig. 19-34). Opposite pieces of the picture frame should be exactly the same length.

6. Make a trial assembly to see that all joints fit properly. If necessary, they may be trimmed lightly with a block plane.

Fig. 19-35. Assembling a frame with nails or brads.

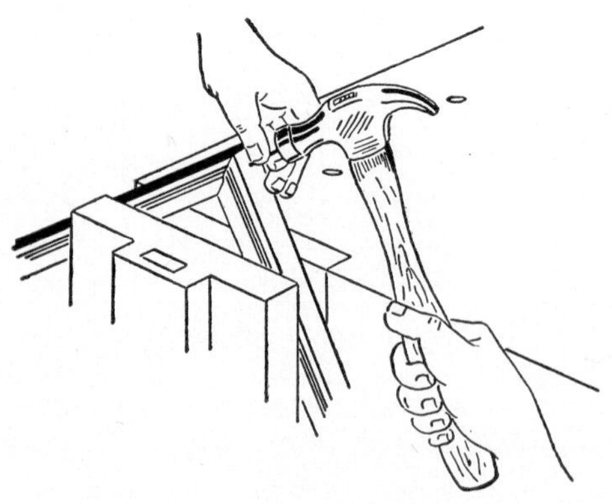

7. Assemble the picture frame by one of the two following methods:

   a. With brads or nails, as shown in Fig. 19-35

   b. With a spline (Fig. 19-1)

In each of the above joint assemblies, glue will help to hold the joints securely.

Discussion Topics

1. List at least two applications or places where you have seen the following types of joints used: butt, dowel, rabbet, dado, cross-lap, mortise-and-tenon, spline, and miter.
2. Give at least two reasons for using a dowel in making an edge joint.
3. What advantage does a grooved dowel pin have over a smooth one?
4. From what kind of wood are most dowels made?
5. What might happen in an edge joint if the dowels were too long for the holes?
6. Why should dowels be pointed or chamfered on the ends?
7. List at least two advantages in using a dowel jig.
8. List at least two advantages which the mortise-and-tenon joint has over the dowel joint in joining rails and legs.
9. Name four types of mortise-and-tenon joints.
10. How should mortise-and-tenon joints be fastened for permanency?

Unit 20. Building Up Plywood and Veneering

Veneering dates back to the Egyptian, Babylonian, and Roman eras when a surface was decorated with beautiful and costly materials, such as woods, ivory, shells, certain metals, and precious stones. It is now possible to veneer plywood construction with very attractive and rich-grained designs in wood. A piece of veneered furniture has certain marked advantages over solid in that it has less tendency to warp, to crack, or to fall apart in steam-heated homes or in climates where humidity is high. A sheet of veneer, such as is used on the outer surfaces in building up plywood, is usually about $\frac{1}{28}$ inch thick.

Veneers are cut commercially by four generally accepted methods: sawing, slicing, rotary cutting, and half-rounding. They are available cut in thin sheets ready for industrial, school, or home use and may be used in construction as described in this unit.

There are numerous glues suitable for plywood and veneer construction. Resin glue is one of the better types of adhesive because it is stain-free on woods and will produce waterproof or highly water-resistant bonds.

Plywood is generally made up of three or more layers consisting of a core, cross bands, and veneers (Fig. 20-1). The construction of plywood involves the building up of the core, cross-banding, and the preparation of the face veneers.

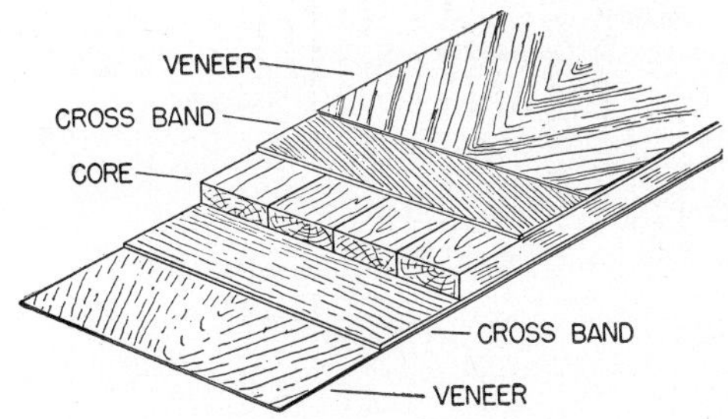

Fig. 20-1. The make-up of plywood.

Building Up the Core

1. Cut enough boards approximately 2 to 3 inches in width, which will be slightly larger than the desired over-all dimensions of the finished panel. These will be edge-glued into a single board to form the core of the plywood.

Place these narrow pieces of wood so that the end grain will form a pattern, as shown in Fig. 20-1. This will reduce warpage in the panel. The thickness of the core stock will depend upon the desired thickness of the finished panel. If the final thickness is to be approximately $\frac{13}{16}$ inch, the core stock can be made from inexpensive lumber $\frac{5}{8}$ to $\frac{3}{4}$ inch thick. The cross-banding is approximately $\frac{1}{8}$ to $\frac{3}{16}$ inch thick; the veneer, $\frac{1}{28}$ inch thick.

2. Plane the edge of the boards until all of them fit and are ready for gluing.

3. Tentatively clamp all of the boards together with bar clamps to make certain that the joints fit properly.

4. Spread glue on the edge of all the boards; place them together in position; and clamp them with bar clamps. Refer to Unit 22, "Gluing and Clamping," pages 81 to 84.

5. Remove the core from the clamps after the glue has been allowed to dry 8 to 10 hours.

6. Plane the core to the required thickness.

Cross-banding

1. Cut the cross-band sheets a little larger than the actual size needed. Cross-band material is available commercially and is cut like veneer except that it is $\frac{1}{8}$ to $\frac{3}{16}$ inch thick and is prepared expressly for this purpose.

2. Spread glue on one of the surfaces of the core but not on the cross-banded veneer.

3. Place the cross-band material, with the grain going at right angles to the grain of the core, on the glued surface of the core, and fasten it in place with four thin, $\frac{1}{2}$-inch brads, one in each corner. These brads or veneer pins hold the cross-banding in place so that it will not slip under pressure. Drive them in approximately $\frac{1}{4}$ inch and cut off the heads with pliers.

4. Place several layers of newspaper over the cross-band surface and then a piece of plywood. Press the plywood until the projection brads go up into it.

5. Turn the panel and plywood upside down.

6. Spread glue on the other surface of the core. Place the opposite cross band in position, and secure it as described in steps 3 and 4.

7. Put this glued assembly in a press or clamp it between boards with handscrew clamps. Allow it to remain in the press until thoroughly dry, the time depending upon the type of glue used.

Fig. 20-2. Side-to-side match.

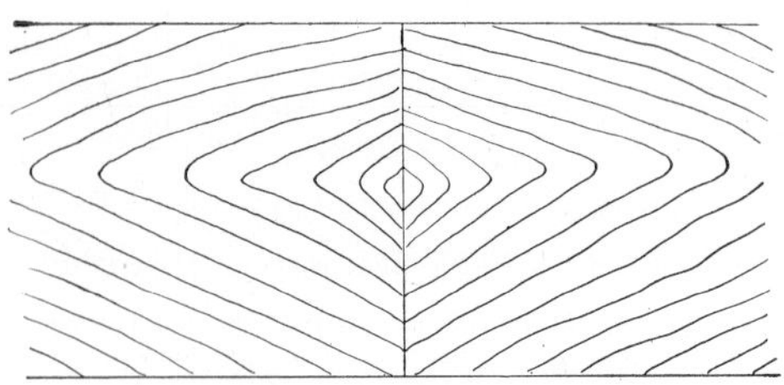

Fig. 20-3. End-to-end match.

Do these operations as quickly as possible, because the cross-band veneer will expand if it is allowed time to absorb the moisture from the glue. This may cause buckling when it is pressed together.

8. Remove the core and cross-band assembly from the press or clamps. Take off press boards and newspaper and pull out the veneer pins or brads.

Preparing Veneer Surfaces

1. Decide on the pattern of matching veneer suggested in Figs. 20-2, 20-3, 20-4, and 20-5. The procedure that follows will be applicable for the side-to-side match.

Fig. 20-4. Four-piece match.

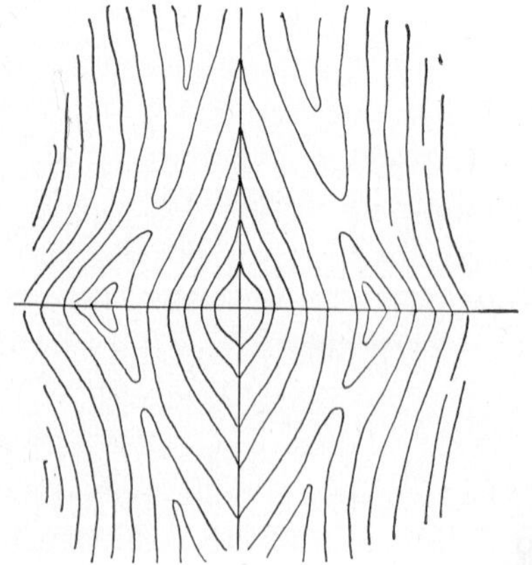

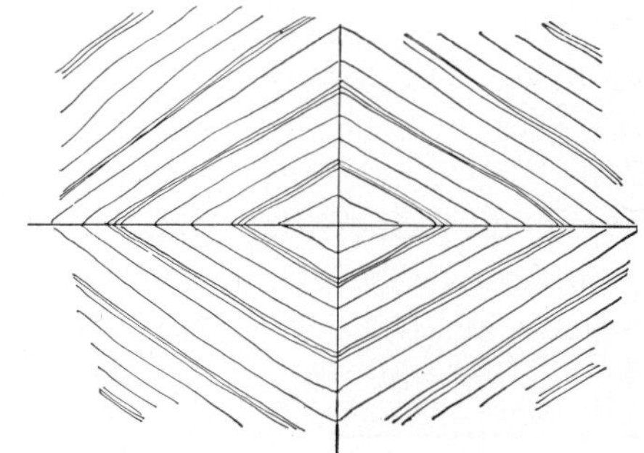

Fig. 20-5. Diamond match.

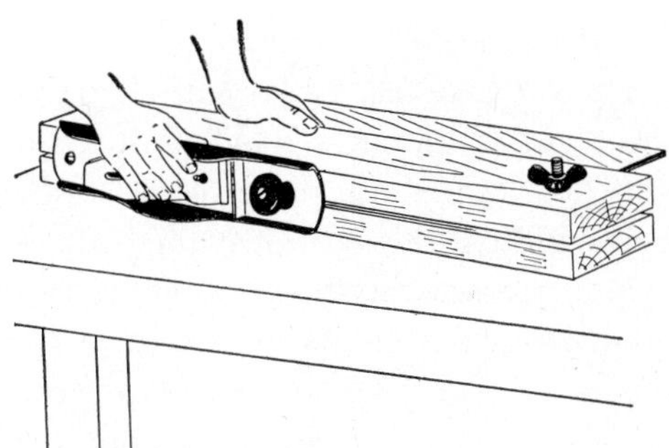

Fig. 20-6. Planing veneer edges for matching.

2. Select two pieces of veneer having the same pattern, and lay them on top of each other so that the figures practically coincide.

3. Place a steel square or metal straightedge along the line of the cut, and cut away the surplus with a sharp knife, plane iron, chisel, or veneer saw.

4. Clamp the two pieces of veneer between two boards with straight edges so that the edges of the veneer barely project beyond the edges of the boards (Fig. 20-6).

5. Plane the edges to form a perfect joint, as shown in Fig. 20-6.

6. Lay the two pieces of veneer on a smooth surface with the jointed edges together. The joint may be kept secure with brads on the extreme ends of the veneer.

7. Cut or tear a piece of gummed paper tape long enough to cover the joint. Gummed tape 1 inch wide, such as is used for securing packages, is satisfactory.

8. Moisten the gummed side of the tape with a sponge and apply the tape along the joint. After it has dried, pull the brads out. The matched veneer is ready to be glued to the cross-band surface.

9. Cut a piece or pieces of veneer for the back side. If the piece of veneer is not wide enough, two or more pieces may need to be taped together. It will not be necessary to match a pattern, because this undersurface will probably not be visible. The veneer on the back or underneath side of the panel is needed to keep it from warping.

Gluing Veneers

1. Smooth the surface of the cross bands by handscraping and sanding. Remove any veneer tape which may have been used to hold the cross-band material in alignment.

2. Spread glue on the surface of the cross band to which the surface veneer is to be glued.

3. Place the veneer on the glued surface so that the grain is running at right angles to the grain of the cross band. Make certain that the taped side of the veneer is out.

4. Press the veneer by hand and fasten it with four brads, one in each corner. Cut them off near the surface.

5. Turn the board over and spread glue on the face side of the cross band.

6. Lay the matched veneer on the glued surface, taped side up. If possible,

see that the general direction of the grain of the veneer is at right angles to the grain of the cross band. Fasten the matched veneer in place with corner brads and cut them off near the surface.

7. Place several sheets of newspaper over each veneered surface, put the plywood panel between two press boards or panels, and apply pressure with a press or hand clamps.

8. Allow the plywood panel to remain in the press or clamps until thoroughly dry; the time required will depend on the glue or adhesive used.

9. Remove from the press or clamps, take off the press boards and newspapers, and pull out the brads or pins.

10. Clean off newspaper, excess glue, and gummed tape from the surface of the veneer. The glue and newspaper will handscrape easily; the gummed tape can be removed by moistening with a sponge.

FIG. 20-7. Wood form for building curved plywood panel for magazine rack. Note that this particular form uses a piece of tin for exerting even pressure.

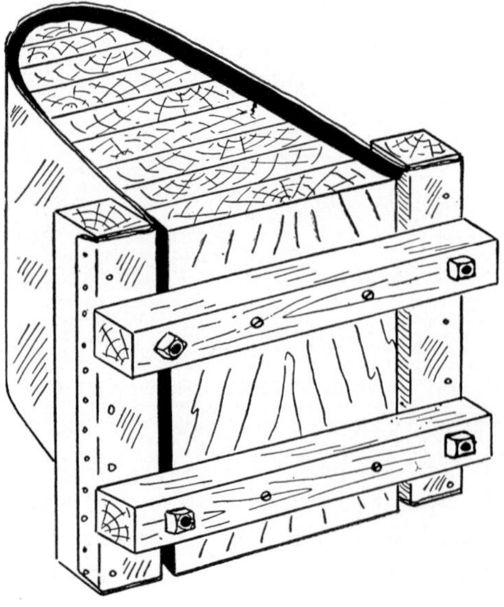

11. Remove glue stains, if necessary, by sponging the stained surface with a solution of oxalic acid. Oxalic acid crystals can be bought at a drugstore. They are mixed for the solution in the proportion of one part oxalic acid crystals to ten parts hot water. The solution should not be used until it has cooled.

12. Sand the surfaces for final finishing with No. 2/0 sandpaper. Sand only in the direction of the grain.

Forming Curved Plywood

1. Make forms for the desired shape of the panels (Fig. 20-7). It will probably be necessary to glue up several thicknesses of stock in making these forms. They can be cut on a band saw to the desired shape.

2. Prepare the stock for making the core. This will usually consist of one, three, or five layers of single-ply poplar veneer $\frac{1}{8}$ to $\frac{3}{16}$ inch thick, the same material as that used for making cross bands in flat panels.

3. Apply glue to the surfaces of the core stock, and place these pieces, one on top of the other, with the grain at right angles. The core piece and surface veneers should have the grain running at right angles when forming large curved pieces, such as chair bottoms and backs and magazine racks, as shown in Fig. 20-7.

4. Spread glue on the outer surfaces of the core stock, and place the thin pieces of veneer in their respective positions.

5. Put several layers of newspapers on each side of the plywood panel, place

it in the form, and clamp it securely in a press with clamps or in a jig (Fig. 20-7).

6. Follow steps 9 through 12 under "Gluing Veneers" for removing the curved plywood from the jig, cleaning it, and sanding.

Discussion Topics

1. What is the difference between "plywood" and "veneer"?
2. What is the true definition of "veneer"?
3. Why do plywood panels have an uneven number of pieces in them, such as three, five, or seven?
4. List five advantages of plywood over solid wood.
5. List three disadvantages of plywood.
6. Describe two common methods of cutting veneer.
7. Explain why cross bands in plywood are at right angles to the core stock and to the veneer.
8. What glue or bonding agent is the most satisfactory for plywood where the humidity is high?

Unit 21. Desk and Table Construction

Building a desk or table presents many problems in construction detail. Fundamental tool-skill processes have been discussed and illustrated in previous units, and many of them are used in the construction of a desk or table. There are, however, a few commercially accepted practices in the fastening of table tops and in making drawers and drawer slides which need clarification. Figure 21-1 illustrates several methods of fastening table tops to side rails.

Fastening a Table Top

1. Determine the method of fastening the table top to the table or desk before making the final assembly of the legs and rails of a table.

2. Saw or plow grooves or bore holes as necessary in the rails; the procedure will depend upon the method of fastening the top as determined from Fig. 21-1.

3. Glue the legs to the rails according to the joint being used, and finish for final assembly to the top.

4. Place the top and the leg-and-rail assembly upside down on a bench (Fig. 21-2).

5. Locate the leg-and-rail assembly in the proper position for fastening to the top and clamp the project to the bench (Fig. 21-2).

6. Fasten the rails to the top by the selected method, as shown in Fig. 21-2.

Making a Drawer

1. Study the working drawing to learn the exact size of the over-all height, width, and length of a drawer.

2. Select the same type of wood for the front of the drawer as that used in the remainder of the project. The grain should be uniform with the grain of the other pieces making up the front rail.

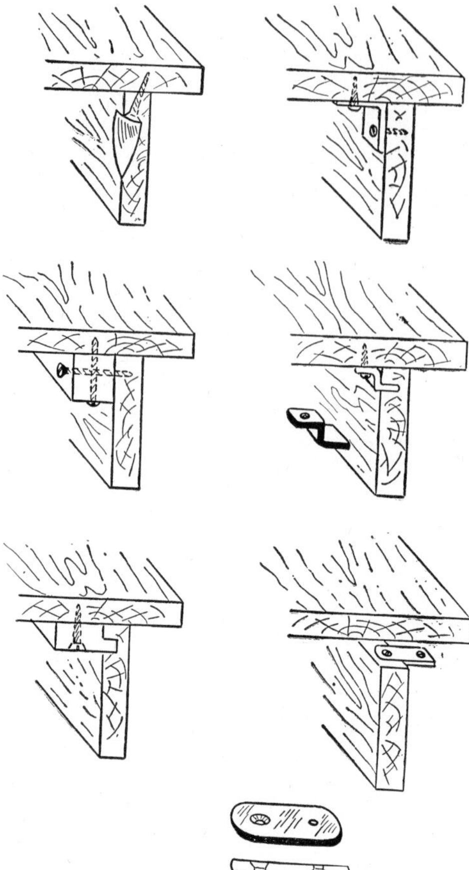

FIG. 21-1. Several methods of fastening table tops.

3. Select a less expensive close-grained wood, such as poplar, basswood, or pine for the sides and backpiece of the drawer.

4. Select material for the bottom, preferably out of three-ply pine or fir $\frac{1}{4}$ inch in thickness or out of Presdwood $\frac{1}{8}$ inch thick. These materials are good for bottoms, because they are not subject to contraction and expansion due to temperature and humidity.

5. Square the pieces of wood for the sides and back according to the dimensions. A suitable thickness for the average sides and back of drawer construction is approximatey $\frac{5}{8}$ inch.

6. Lay out and cut the rabbet joint in the front piece as shown in Fig. 21-3. The combination dado-tongue and rabbet joint, as shown in Fig. 21-3, is a sturdy and well-constructed drawer-front joint.

Note that the front extends barely $\frac{1}{16}$ inch beyond the edge of the sides. This allows the front of the drawers to fit snugly and the sides to have sufficient play in opening and closing.

7. Cut the grooves in the sides into which the bottom panel fits to a depth of one-half the thickness of the side stock. This depth will probably be $\frac{5}{16}$ inch. The cutting of the grooves may be done with the proper width chisel or on the dado head of a power circular saw.

8. Cut a corresponding groove in the back side of the frontpiece to hold the bottom panel.

9. Lay out and mark dado joints on the inside surfaces of the drawer sides, approximately $\frac{1}{2}$ to 1 inch from the back. The width of the dado should be the thickness of the backpiece and should be cut to a depth of one-half the thickness of the sidepieces.

10. Lay out and cut to length the backpiece of the drawer. This piece should fit snugly into the dadoes of the sidepieces.

11. Lay out and cut the piece of wood to be used for the bottom. This should be measured from the insides of the grooves.

12. Make a trial assembly of all parts of the drawer to see that the joints fit snugly and that the drawer is the proper size.

Fig. 21-2. Fastening the top to a table. This illustration shows three types of top fasteners.

13. Fasten the front of the drawer upright in a vise (Fig. 21-4).

14. Drive two or three brads into the drawer sides in preparation for assembly (Fig. 21-4).

15. Apply glue to the joint to be fastened. Place the side on the front and drive two or three brads to hold the joint firmly (Fig. 21-4).

16. Fasten the opposite side to the drawer front in a similar manner.

17. Apply glue to the dado joints at the rear of the drawer, insert the backpiece, and fasten with brads.

18. Remove excess glue from all joints.

19. Slide the drawer bottom in place through the grooves from the rear of the drawer. Do not glue the bottom in place.

Fig. 21-3. Details of drawer construction.

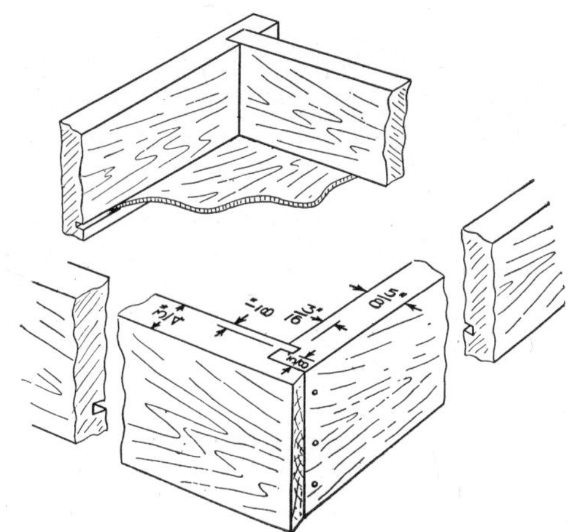

Fig. 21-4. Fastening the side of a drawer to the front piece. This is the first step in drawer assembly.

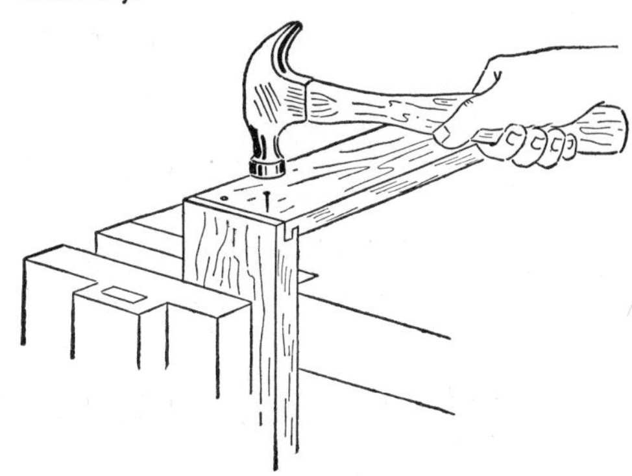

FIG. 21-5. Drawer slides fastened to table rails.

20. Check the alignment of the drawer for squareness.

21. Fasten the bottom to the back-piece of the drawer with one or two brads driven up from the bottom.

22. Dress all joints smooth with sandpaper.

23. Make final test to see that the drawer fits easily into the desk or table opening.

MAKING DRAWER SLIDES

1. Select stock from inexpensive lumber to make the slides according to the working drawing. A convenient method of making drawer slides is shown in Fig. 21-5.

2. Cut the drawer slides as shown in Fig. 21-5.

3. Make pieces to support the slides. These can usually be pieces of wood $\frac{3}{4}$ by 1 inch square. For the length needed to support both drawer slides see Fig. 21-5.

4. Drill or bore the necessary holes for fastening these blocks to the slides as well as to the table or to the desk rails.

5. Fasten the drawer slides to the blocks with glue and screws or brads. The slides should be placed and fastened on the blocks so as to allow ample space for the drawer to slide.

6. Locate the positions on the front and back rails of the table or desk for fastening the slide assembly.

7. Fasten the slide assembly to the desk or to the table rails with screws through the blocks (Fig. 21-5). Do not tighten the screws completely until after you have tested the drawer in position on the slides to see that the front will be in line with the front rails and also that it will work easily.

Discussion Topics

1. Describe six methods of fastening a table top to the rails.
2. Which of these methods will allow the top to expand or contract more easily?
3. Why should the table top not be glued directly to the side rails?
4. Examine the construction of several drawers in commercially built furniture, and study the methods which have been used in their construction.
5. Observe and describe methods for making drawer slides other than those mentioned in this unit.

Unit 22. Gluing and Clamping

Boards are often glued together edge to edge to make larger surfaces or face to face to increase thickness, and the joints may be assembled with glue. When a joint is made properly and the glue is prepared and applied correctly, the glued joint should be as strong as the wood.

Fig. 22-1. Electric gluepot.

Kinds of Glues

There are many kinds of glue for woodworking, and they are generally classified into five types: animal, casein, plastic resin, resorcinal resin, and fish. There are also minor classifications such as blood albumin, starch, all-purpose cements, and adhesives or glues which will bind wood to metals, plastics, and glass. Many variations of the newer glues are being developed in the research laboratories of the great industries. Glues have played a major role in war and in emergency periods when products were needed to facilitate fabrication and to expedite the manufacture of critical items.

Glues, adhesives, and cements are available in all the classifications listed under a great variety of trade names, and for this reason it is advisable to read the descriptions and directions which accompany the packaged product before making a selection of the desired type.

Animal glue remains probably one of the most popular for use by the woodworker. It is made from hides, bones, hoofs, and trimmings of the animal which have been refined and made into the final form of thin sheets, flakes, or powder. Animal glue is also available commercially in a liquid form. It is always wise to study the specifications and directions of the manufacturer before mixing it with water; in this way one can learn the satisfactory mixture and the length of time required for soaking before heating.

In applying hot animal glue, it is necessary that all clamps be adjusted properly in advance, because this type of glue will set very rapidly upon cooling. Figure 22-1 pictures one type of commonly used electric gluepot which has a temperature control to prevent the glue from burning. The commercial cold liquid animal glue does not require heating and, therefore, has a slight advantage in its application.

Casein glue, a product made from the curd of milk, is obtainable in powdered form and may be made into a paste by the addition of cold water. It is particularly useful in furniture construction when humidity is high. It is also used extensively in boat construction. Before mixing with water, read carefully the directions given by the manufacturer.

Plastic-resin glue is a urea formaldehyde powder which must be mixed with

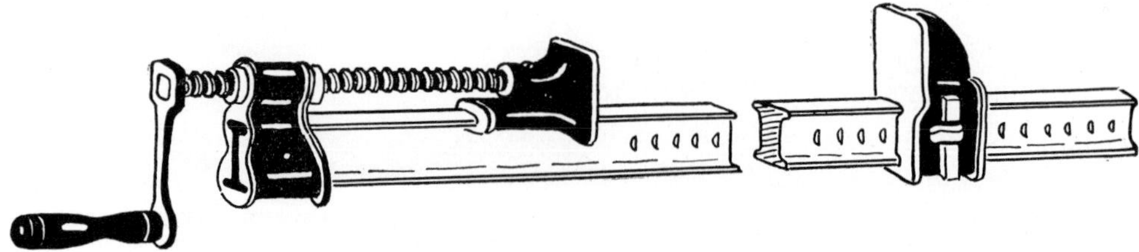

Fig. 22-2. Cabinet or bar clamp.

water to proper consistency for gluing. It has been extensively used in gluing plywood for use on airplanes, boats, and other exterior surfaces. This type of glue is being used more frequently in furniture construction.

Resorcinal resin is one of the glues most recently perfected. It is made by mixing the liquid resin with a catalyst. These two ingredients come packaged in a dual container and must be mixed according to the directions furnished. This is another type of excellent glue for exterior fabrication and for furniture and cabinet work where humidity is high.

Fig. 22-3. Hand-screw clamp.

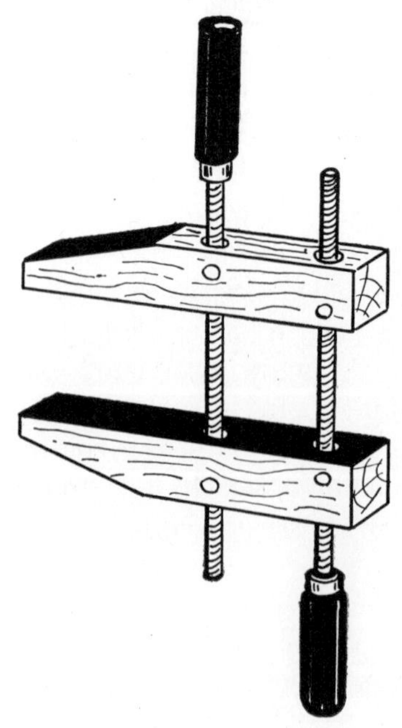

Fish glue is available in a liquid form and is made from fish and the scales of fish. Since the manufacture of this product is slightly more expensive than that of other types, it is primarily used for repair of delicate and valuable wooden objects.

Kinds of Clamps

The kinds of clamps most conveniently used in cabinet and furniture work are the cabinet or bar (Fig. 22-2), the hand screw (Fig. 22-3), and the C clamp (Fig. 22-4). Each type operates with a hand-screw adjustment and has a particular adaptation, as shown in the illustrations cited in the procedure section. It is always advisable to have plenty of clamps available for a job and to have them set so that they may be clamped

Fig. 22-4. C clamp.

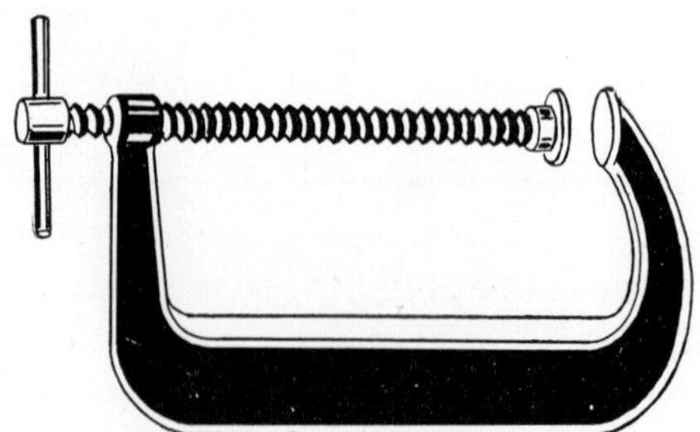

Fig. 22-5. Applying glue on edges.

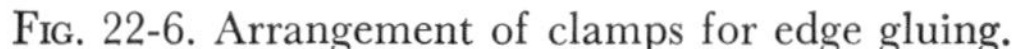

Fig. 22-6. Arrangement of clamps for edge gluing.

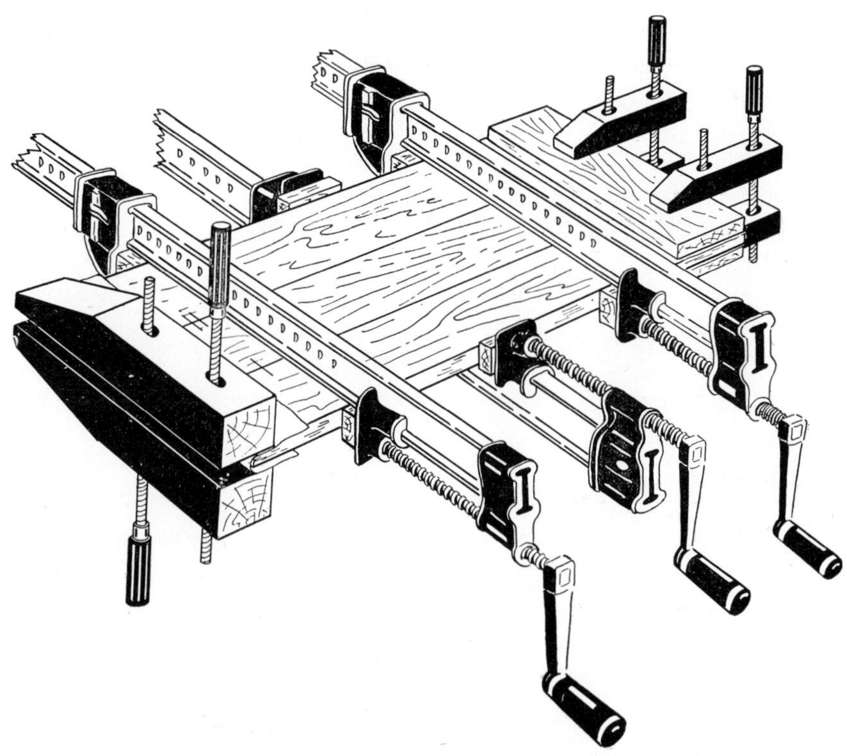

on the project with a minimum of additional adjustment, especially when using hot animal glue.

Gluing and Clamping

1. Mix or prepare cold or hot glue in accordance with the directions furnished by the manufacturer.
2. Set all necessary clamps to approximate distances.
3. Make all necessary protective blocks for the bar clamps and pieces of wood for alignment, and have them available when clamping up the boards. (Fig. 22-6).
4. Make a trial assembly, without glue, of the pieces. This serves as a check to see that all surfaces, edges, or joints fit together properly. Then disassemble for applying the glue.
5. Have available or set up jigs or a clamp donkey for holding bar clamps.
6. Spread glue rapidly and evenly on adjoining pieces (Fig. 22-5). Use a brush for best results.
7. Assemble the parts of the joint properly and fasten the clamps, as shown in Figs. 22-6 and 22-7. In clamping boards, as shown in Fig. 22-6, place bar clamps from 12 to 15 inches apart. Use scrap blocks to protect the edges of the wood and keep the boards in alignment with hand-screw clamps, as shown at the left or right ends in Fig. 22-6. A piece of paper used between the clamps and the boards will keep the clamps from sticking to the glued joints.

In all clamping operations it is highly desirable that you have someone to help you. The unwieldiness of the procedure and the speed necessary for satisfactory glue joints require two persons working together. In gluing and clamping boards to secure additional thickness, make certain that you use plenty of hand-screw clamps, as shown in Fig. 22-7.

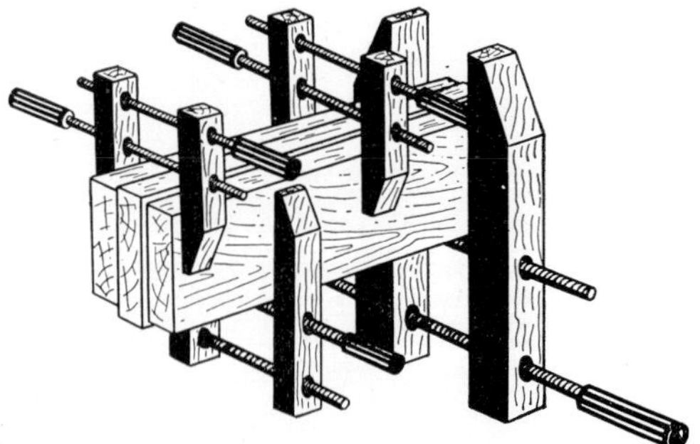

Fig. 22-7. Arrangement of hand-screw clamps for gluing and clamping boards to increase thickness.

8. Remove the surplus glue before it hardens. This may be done with either a scraper blade, wood chisel, old plane iron, piece of wood, or any other specially prepared tool for this purpose.
9. Wipe the joint clean with a damp or wet piece of cloth. It is often possible to remove all traces of glue in this manner and so to save a lot of unnecessary work later.

Discussion Topics

1. Name and give the uses for five types of glue. Which two are most commonly used?
2. Name and describe the three kinds of clamps which are helpful in gluing.
3. Why is it desirable to have the cabinet or bar clamps and the hand-screw clamps arranged to hold from both sides, as shown in Figs. 22-6 and 22-7?
4. Give at least two purposes for which

the hand-screw clamps (Fig. 22-6) may be used.
5. Why should surplus glue be removed from the joint before it hardens?
6. Explain the purpose in using scrap blocks between the wood and the cabinet or bar clamps, as seen in Fig. 22-6.

Unit 23. Fastening Hinges and Other Cabinet Hardware

Hardware is a part of the final trim in making many pieces of furniture or cabinet work and in the interior decoration of a home. The items which could be listed for these purposes would run literally into the hundreds, since ornamentation and variety as well as usefulness play such an important role. Some companies have large catalogues devoted exclusively to hardware items available for the manufacture and trim of furniture and cabinet work. Some of the more common items in hardware for the woodworker are several varieties of hinges, drawer pulls, cabinet catches and hasps, locks, and furniture glides. Figure 23-1 pictures and identifies a few of the better known and more frequently used types of hinges. The ones shown are indicative of only a few of the many kinds. Each of these is also available in different sizes and designs.

Hinges

The *butt hinge* (Fig. 23-1 *A*) is perhaps the most popular; however, it does entail a detailed fitting and gaining (chiseling out) of the cabinet or frame. Some butt hinges are swaged while others are not (Fig. 23-1 *A*). This will determine the depth of the gain. They are available with either loose or stationary pins. If the pins are loose, install the hinges so that the head of the pin is up to prevent its falling out. Figure 23-1 *G* shows an antique-type butt hinge which may be used as a butt or a surface hinge.

The *surface hinge* (Fig. 23-1 *B*) is one of the easiest types to install. It is obtainable, not only in a variety of sizes, but also in patterns varying from a very ornate shape to the crude strap hinge used on barn doors. The name implies the use in that it is fastened to the surface and is entirely visible.

Not shown is the *half-surface hinge,* another popular one, especially in cabinet work. It is installed so that half of it is visible while the other half is gained to the cabinet or into the frame in which it is fitted. The portion to be gained is treated in a manner similar to the fitting of a butt hinge, which will be described in detail.

The *chest hinge* (Fig. 23-1 *C*) supports chest lids, or the newer *combination hinge* (Fig. 23-1 *H*) may be used. The latter pulls the lid away from the wall as it is opened. It serves as both hinge and lid support.

Cabinet hinges are made for use on flush doors (Fig. 23-1 *D*) and on overlapping doors (Fig. 23-1 *E*).

Invisible hinges (Fig. 23-1 *F*) are employed in much fine furniture making, especially radio cabinets and writing

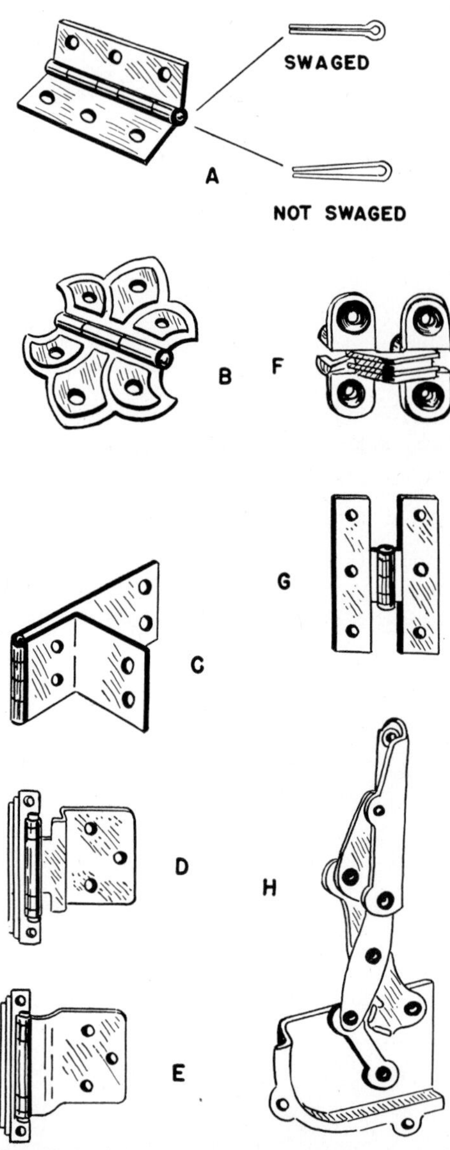

Fig. 23-1. A few commonly used hinges: (*A*) butt, (*B*) embossed-surface, (*C*) chest, (*D*) cabinet-flush, (*E*) cabinet-overlapping, (*F*) invisible, (*G*) antique-butt, and (*H*) combination chest hinge and lid support.

desks. Almost every manufacturer supplies drawings and directions in the packet or on the carton for the installation of his type of hinge.

Fig. 23-2. Four common types of drawer pulls and knobs.

Drawer Pulls and Knobs

Drawer pulls and knobs are obtainable in a great variety of materials, patterns, and sizes. The materials used for these items are wood, plastic, composition, and any of the many metals. The woodworker is limited only by his personal preference, and he may make his own out of wood, if he so desires. Figure 23-2 shows four common types of commercial drawer pulls and knobs.

They are always supplied complete with screws for fastening. The single-post or screw knobs are extremely easy to install; they necessitate merely the marking of the location and the drilling of a hole of the proper size. More elaborate ones with two posts or screws require that the holes be properly centered and aligned for the correct fit.

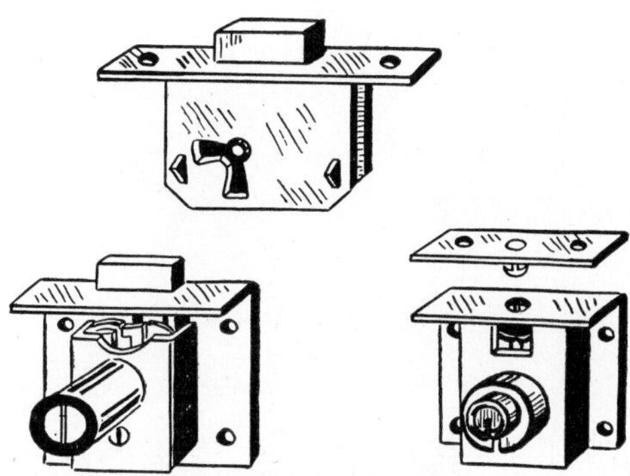

FIG. 23-3. Cabinet and chest locks.

OTHER HARDWARE

Hasps, door and friction catches, and furniture glides are some other types of hardware that are relatively easy to install. For successful installation of the cabinet and chest locks, pictured in Fig. 23-3, carefully study the manufacturer's directions. Here again, there is a variety in size and construction which makes it impractical to outline a uniform procedure for all.

INSTALLING A BUTT HINGE

1. Select the proper size and kind of butt hinge. The size of the hinge is determined by the length.
2. Place the door in the frame or cabinet with wedges under it so located that the clearance above and below the door in the opening is equal.
3. Locate the hinges according to the working drawing. Mark the extremeties of the hinges on both the door and the frame or cabinet.
4. Extend the marks on the edge of the door and frame or cabinet with a sharp pencil and a try square.
5. Mark the width and depth of the grain (a notch or mortise) to be cut out, using a marking gauge (Fig. 23-4).

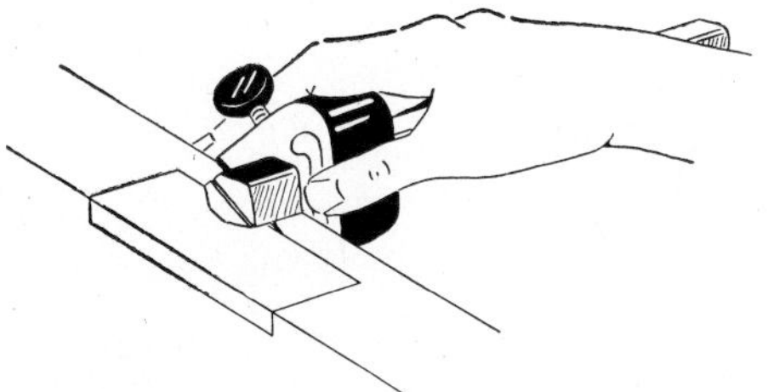

FIG. 23-4. Marking the gain for a hinge.

6. Place a chisel in a vertical position on the pencil line which locates the ends of the hinge, and drive lightly with a mallet (Fig. 23-5).
7. Repeat the chisel cut on the line which goes in the direction of the grain, but be very careful not to split the wood (Fig. 23-5).
8. Make a series of chisel cuts, as shown in Fig. 23-5.
9. Pare the bottom of the gain with a wide wood chisel, as shown in Fig. 23-6.

FIG. 23-5. Chiseling the gain for a hinge.

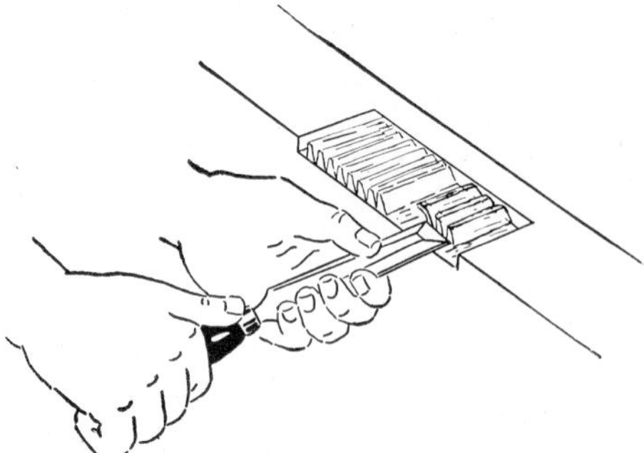

FIG. 23-6. Paring the bottom of a hinge gain.

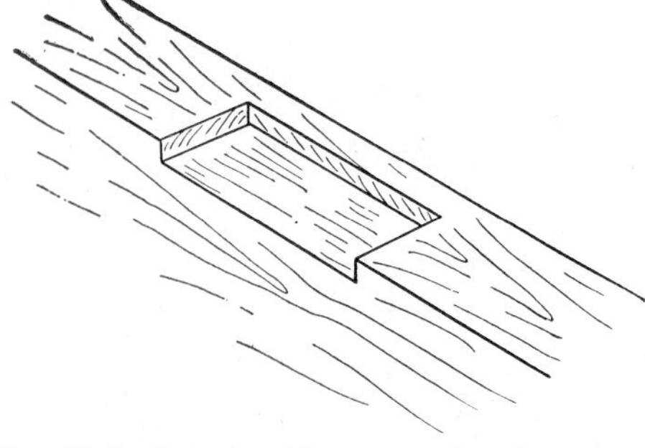

FIG. 23-7. Gain for hinge completed.

10. Make a trial fit of the hinge in the gain. Pare where necessary to make a snug fit.

11. Place the hinge in its proper setting and mark the holes for the screws with a pencil.

12. Drill pilot holes into the wood. Make them smaller than the screws.

13. Drive the screws with a screw driver to fasten the hinge securely. When driving screws into hardwood, soap the screw threads. This tends to prevent the screw from twisting off.

14. Cut the remaining gains for the hinges in the door or frame and cabinet.

15. Fasten the door in its proper position with screws. It is often advisable to fasten only one screw in each hinge leaf to the frame or cabinet to determine whether further alignment is needed in fitting the door.

Discussion Topics

1. Name and describe five common types of hinges.
2. What is a "gain"?
3. What tools are used in making a gain?
4. Describe the many materials from which drawer pulls and knobs may be made.

Unit 24. Preparing for Finishing

Woodworkers sand a project or a piece of furniture thoroughly before applying any finishing materials. A piece of furniture or cabinet work is sometimes sanded after final assembly, or the parts may often be sanded conveniently before the assembly. Proper sanding dresses the planed or scraped surface and edges for final successful finishing.

TOOLS

The abrasive material generally used on wood is called *sandpaper*. Its name is derived from the resemblance of the abrasive material to sand, but it is in reality crushed flint. Garnet paper and emery cloth are also satisfactory tools. The most popular and commonly used *flint paper* can be identified by the grayish-tan color. *Garnet sandpaper* is more durable than flint and is reddish in color. *Emery cloth* or paper is very tough and durable, black in color, and most often used in polishing metal.

Sandpaper which is used by hand is usually sold in sheets 9 by 11 inches in size and comes in grades of coarseness varying from No. $3\frac{1}{2}$ (coarse) to No. 8/0 (fine). The grades most often used on woods begin with a coarseness of No. 1 and graduate to the final sanding with No. 2/0.

Preparing the Surface

1. Inspect all visible surfaces to make sure that all mill marks have been removed with the plane or scraper.
2. Remove all trace of glue on the visible surfaces, especially around joints. It may be necessary to use a combination of both the wood chisel and the hand scraper blade to remove all trace of excess glue.
3. Raise the existing dents by moistening the dented areas with water. Grain cannot be raised if the fiber has been broken.
4. Fill small knots, holes, checks, or other open defects by melting in colored stick shellac (Fig. 24-1), or by pressing in a colored wood plastic or wood dough (Fig. 24-2). Select the color that will match the wood when finished.
5. Dress the hardened shellac or wood plastic smooth to the wood surface with abrasive paper.

Fig. 24-1. Melting stick shellac to fill wood defect.

Fig. 24-2. Pressing in plastic wood or wood dough to fill wood defect.

Preparing Sandpaper

1. Tear a piece of 9- by 11-inch sandpaper into four equal parts. This can be done most conveniently by placing the sheet, abrasive side down, on a flat surface and tearing it along the edge of a framing square (Fig. 24-3).
2. Prepare a block of wood for holding the sandpaper to measure approximately $\frac{3}{4}$ by $2\frac{1}{2}$ by 6 inches.
3. Fold the quarter sheet of sandpaper around this block so that it can be

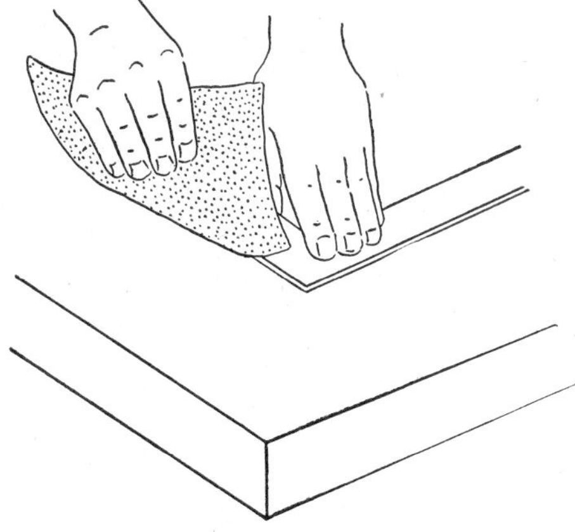

Fig. 24-3. Tearing sandpaper against a steel straightedge.

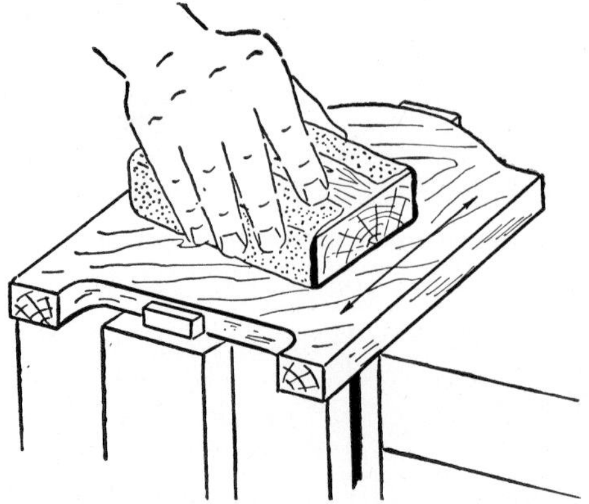

FIG. 24-4. Sanding a surface with the grain.

held securely with the hand (Fig. 24-4). Do not tack the paper on the block because the block may slip and the tacks marr the surface to be sanded.

SANDING

1. Fasten the piece to be sanded securely on the bench, or place the project so that it can be held conveniently while sanding.
2. Sand all flat surfaces and edges with the grain using an even pressure (Fig. 24-4). Avoid sanding across grain or in a circular motion, because this will injure the wood fibers. The first sanding should be done with reasonably coarse sandpaper, possibly No. 1 or No. 1½, the second with No. ½, and the third and final one with No. 2/0.
3. Sand edges and ends in a similar manner (Fig. 24-5).

FIG. 24-5. Sanding an edge.

4. Sand concave, irregular edges and molded or shaped edges by wrapping the sandpaper around a block of wood that is formed to fit the particular outline.
5. Sand rounded edges by cupping the sandpaper in the hand to keep an even pressure on the curvature (Fig. 24-6).

FIG. 24-6. Sanding a rounded edge.

6. Sand all corners and arrises lightly with worn sandpaper. An *arris* is the edge formed by two surfaces meeting at right angles.
7. Inspect all visible surfaces, edges, and ends to make sure that they have been properly sanded in preparation for applying the finish.

Discussion Topics

1. Is sandpaper considered a tool?
2. Name three natural abrasive materials. Which is the more commonly used and why?
3. Sandpaper is often sold by the quire. How many sheets make a quire?
4. Which is the finer grade of sandpaper: No. 2 or No. 2/0?
5. Why is sandpaper held around a block for most sanding?

Unit 25. Finishing

A fine finish on furniture and cabinet work can do much to enhance the final appearance and value. It is important, therefore, to study the different types of finishing materials and to know something about the proper selection of them and how to apply them to best advantage. The prerequisite, or final step before any finishing is done, is to see that all exposed surfaces, edges, and ends of the wood have been smoothly scraped and sandpapered to serve as a proper base for smooth finishes. The following descriptions of finishing materials will provide information pertinent to each type.

Materials for Finishing

Tools and materials used in obtaining the final finish are brushes, sandpaper, linseed oil, turpentine, alcohol, steel wool, pumice stone, rotten stone, rubbing oil, lacquer thinner, synthetic thinning agents, and wax. Finishing materials included here are stains, wood filler, shellac, varnish, lacquer, and paint or enamel.

Brushes. It is advisable to use a good brush in applying the finish if a finish of high quality is desired. For most work a 1- to 2-inch-wide brush with bristles set in rubber will prove best, because it will hold paint or varnish better than other brushes and will not shed bristles.

Linseed oil. This material is a product of flaxseed and is used in bringing out the rich color of walnut, mahogany, and cedar. It is also an ingredient in exterior paints. Boiled linseed oil dries more rapidly than unboiled. When using it to bring out the color of the woods just mentioned, it is advisable to mix two-thirds linseed oil with one-third turpentine and to heat in a double boiler before applying to the wood. It should not be allowed to boil but should be heated to a temperature warmer than your finger can stand. It may be applied with a cloth swab or with a brush. Linseed oil mixed, heated, and applied in this manner will penetrate deep into the wood. If desired, this application may take the place of stain. It is suggested that a sampling be made on scrap lumber to determine whether the desired color tone can be achieved by this means on the above-mentioned woods.

Turpentine. Turpentine is obtained from the sap of the long-leaf pine tree. After considerable processing it is refined to the inflammable liquid used as a thinner in paints, enamels, and varnishes. Since it is a thinner for paints and enamels, it can be the cleaning agent for the brush used in the painting and for wiping up after a painting job.

Alcohol. This is a thinning agent for shellac and is composed of ethyl and wood alcohol. It will also clean brushes used in applying shellac.

Steel wool. Steel wool is available in rolls or in pads. Grades vary from No. 000 (very fine) to No. 3 (coarse). It is sometimes used instead of sandpaper for rubbing down between coats.

Pumice stone. Pumice stone is a light-colored powdered substance made from lava. It can be purchased in many grades, the most suitable for rubbing finishes being No. FF or No. FFF. It is applied by mixing with a rubbing or paraffin oil or with water.

Rotten stone. This dark gray powdered substance is produced from shale. It is a much finer abrasive than pumice and is applied with a rubbing or paraffin oil to produce a smoother final finish.

Rubbing oil. Rubbing oil, used in conjunction with pumice or rotten stone, may be a petroleum or a paraffin oil. The latter type is preferred.

Wax. Wax is available in liquid or paste form, but the latter is the more practical, because it forms a heavier, more durable final coating. Both forms are made from a base of beeswax, carnauba wax, paraffin, and turpentine. A waxed surface must be renewed periodically to be effective.

Stain

Stain is applied on wood to produce the desired effect. Much of the furniture manufactured today commercially is constructed from inexpensive woods with stain applied to make it resemble walnut or mahogany. Certain woods, such as walnut, mahogany, and cedar, have sufficient natural color and, therefore, need only an application of hot linseed oil cut with turpentine to bring out the rich, natural color.

Three widely used stains are oil, water, and spirit. *Oil stain* is the easiest to apply, is obtainable in a wide variety of colors, and produces excellent finishes. Generally it will not raise the grain of the wood. A disadvantage is that colors sometimes tend to fade slightly and are not as clear as in the other types of stains. In applying an oil stain to a project where end grain will show, treat the end grain first with a coat of clear linseed oil. This prevents it from turning many shades darker than the surfaces and edges.

Water stain has the distinction of bringing out the full beauty of the wood. This stain is made by dissolving a powdered aniline dye in hot water when it is to be used. The chief objection to it is that the grain of the wood is raised and must, therefore, be resanded before further finishing can be done. A more uniform finish will result if the wood is first sponged with water, allowed to dry, and then sanded before water stain is applied. This reduces the amount of sanding required after staining.

Spirit stain is obtainable in a wide variety of colors. It is quite expensive, difficult to apply, and has a tendency to fade. It is made by dissolving analine dye in alcohol. Because it better penetrates a surface which has been previously filled, it is often used in refinishing furniture.

To apply *oil stain:*

1. Select the color of stain desired for the final finished effect.

2. Pour some stain into a cup or other open container.

3. Brush the stain on a piece of scrap stock of the same wood as the project to test the color. If the tint is too dark, lighten it by adding turpentine.

4. Apply a coat of linseed oil to all exposed end grain.

5. Apply the stain with a medium-sized brush to the entire project. Brush it on with long, even strokes (Fig. 25-1). It is desirable to stain the underneath parts first.

6. After it has been on approximately 2 minutes wipe off surplus stain from the project with a cloth.

7. Allow the stained project to dry for at least 6 hours. If the wood is open-grained, it will be ready for a filler; if it is close-grained, the filler may be omitted.

To apply *water stain:*

1. Sponge the wood to be stained lightly with water and allow to dry for 2 hours.

2. Sand the dampened area with No. 2/0 sandpaper. Make certain to sandpaper with the grain.

3. Clean the sanded areas with a brush.

4. Mix the water color in a cup or other open container according to the directions given by the manufacturer.

5. Test the color of the stain on a piece of scrap wood. Wait until it dries thoroughly to determine the true color.

6. Apply the stain evenly with a medium-sized brush to the entire project (Fig. 25-1). Brush on with long, even strokes and keep overlapping at a minimum. Surplus water stain is not removed from the surface; therefore, all brush marks will show if the stain is not applied evenly. Allow to dry for at least 6 hours.

7. Sand lightly with No. 2/0 sandpaper to reduce any raised grain.

8. Clean the project thoroughly with a clean brush in preparation for further finishing.

To apply *spirit stain:*

1. Mix the spirit color stain in a cup or other open container according to the directions given by the manufacturer.

2. Test the color of the spirit stain on a scrap piece of wood which is the same as the project. If the stain is too dark, dilute it with denatured alcohol or with the thinner recommended by the manufacturer.

Fig. 25-1. Applying stain to the surface of a clip board.

3. Brush the stain on evenly with a medium-sized brush. Since any surplus will not be wiped off, take care that the brushing is even and that the surface is covered thoroughly. Allow to dry for at least 6 hours.

4. Sand all surfaces lightly with No. 2/0 sandpaper.

5. Clean the project thoroughly with a clean brush in preparation for further finishing.

Wood Filler

Wood filler in liquid or paste form is used to fill the pores of wood so as to form a smooth surface upon which succeeding finishing materials may be applied smoothly. Filler should be applied after the wood has been either oiled or stained; the choice depends upon the desired color effect or the type of wood. Close-grained woods, such as birch, gum, maple, and pine, need to have the tiny pores sealed with a filler or a sealer. Most finishers use a thin coat of white shellac or sanding sealer in place of liquid filler. Open-grained woods, such as ash, mahogany, oak, and walnut, must be filled with a paste filler.

Paste wood filler is made from silex, a ground silicon, mixed with linseed oil, japan drier, and turpentine. The color in filler is obtained by mixing in colors ground in oil. Filler should be colored to the desired tint of the final finish.

Materials needed to apply filler are a stiff-bristle brush of medium width, small pieces of burlap about 10 to 12 inches square, and waste cloth or rags for final rubbing.

To apply wood filler:

1. Mix the filler to a thin paste with turpentine or japan drier. This is assuming that you use the commercial product, which is usually very thick.
2. Add the desired color in oil, and stir the paste until it is thoroughly mixed.
3. Apply the filler on the exposed surfaces of the project with a stubby brush. Rub it into the wood by working the brush across the grain.
4. Continue to rub the paste filler into the pores of the wood thoroughly with the palm of the hand, working across the grain in a circular motion.
5. When the glossy appearance disappears and the filler looks dull, wipe surplus off across the grain with a small piece of burlap. Continue this until the entire project has been covered.
6. Wipe the project lengthwise on the grain with a clean cotton cloth. This removes cross-grain strokes.
7. Clean the filler from corners and grooves with a sharp-pointed stick. Do not use a piece of metal, such as a screw driver or chisel, because it will injure the grain and final finishing surface.
8. Allow the filled project to dry 10 to 12 hours before proceeding with further finishing.

Shellac

Shellac, one of the oldest materials to be used in finishing, has been used for a protective coat on woods since the sixteenth century. It is a product of the lac bug found in the East Indies and Asiatic countries. These insects feed on a resinous material and leave a secretion on the tree. After several generations this secretion forms a coating, which is stripped off by natives and separated from impurities such as twigs and other foreign matter. It is then heated, strained, and processed into sheets, which are later further refined and dissolved in denatured alcohol to form the liquid shellac.

Shellac produces a good finish because it is easy to apply, dries rapidly, is relatively easy to dress smooth, and makes a fairly hard surface. The principal uses of shellac in finishing are as a sealer for close-grained wood and as a base for applying varnish over filled surfaces of open wood.

It is available in two colors: white and orange; the white being the same as the orange except that the flakes of shellac have been bleached. A good mixture for finishing is 4 pounds of shellac to 1 gallon of alcohol. A good quality of shellac is labeled "Four Pound Cut." Since alcohol dissolves shellac, this same agent may be used to thin it further and to clean the brush. A medium-sized brush and No. 00 steel wool are essential when applying shellac.

To apply *shellac:*

1. Check the surface to see that it is free from dust. Also make certain that the stain or filler is thoroughly dry.
2. Pour a small amount of the stock

white shellac into an open container, such as a cup.

3. Thin the shellac with approximately one-half alcohol and stir the mixture.

4. If the project to be shellacked has drawers or other removable parts, take them out so that they can be finished separately.

5. Apply the thinned shellac to the entire project, using a medium-sized brush. In applying shellac to vertical surfaces, start at the top and work down. Finish the lower portions of the project first, leaving the top surface to the last. Apply shellac evenly and quickly because it dries rapidly. Do not overlap more than absolutely necessary.

6. Allow the coat to dry at least 6 hours; then rub it smooth with No. 00 steel wool. Rub with the grain whenever possible. Rub carefully so that you do not rub through the shellac coat at the edges and corners.

7. Wipe the surfaces clean with a cotton cloth and then with the hands.

8. If you desire a shellac finish, apply another coat of a richer mixture of two-thirds shellac and one-third alcohol just as you did the first coat.

9. Allow the second coat to dry 8 to 10 hours; then rub smooth with No. 00 steel wool.

10. Apply a coat of a good grade of furniture paste wax; allow it to dry 15 to 20 minutes; then rub it to a luster with a clean cotton cloth.

Varnish

Varnish is extensively used in preserving wood surfaces. It may be applied either directly to the wood or over a surface that has been filled and sealed with shellac. It is a very durable and lasting finish, and when rubbed down with pumice and rotten stone and oil, it produces a beautiful luster. Originally all good varnishes were made from imported fossil gum; however, during the last few years synthetic resins have replaced the original basic material. Varnish is available commercially as either transparent or colored with any of the many stains. Varnish stains are not suitable for producing finely finished furniture; their virtue is in the ease of application, because wood can be stained and varnished simultaneously.

The spar, quick-drying varnish has become very popular. It is tough, waterproof, and heat-resistant and is used extensively for finishing furniture, floors, boats, and other objects subjected to moisture. It dries to a hard, durable, high-gloss finish which can be rubbed satisfactorily.

The quality of a varnish finish depends upon the grade of varnish, the evenness of its application, and the drying conditions. Varnish should be applied in a room as free of dust as possible with a temperature of about 70°F.

A good grade of fine, long-bristle brush, wet-dry sandpaper, pumice stone, rotten stone, and a paraffin oil are the tools and materials used to secure a satisfactory and pleasing varnish finish on a project.

To apply varnish:

1. Check the surfaces to be varnished to make certain that they are free from dust and that any previous finish is thoroughly dry.

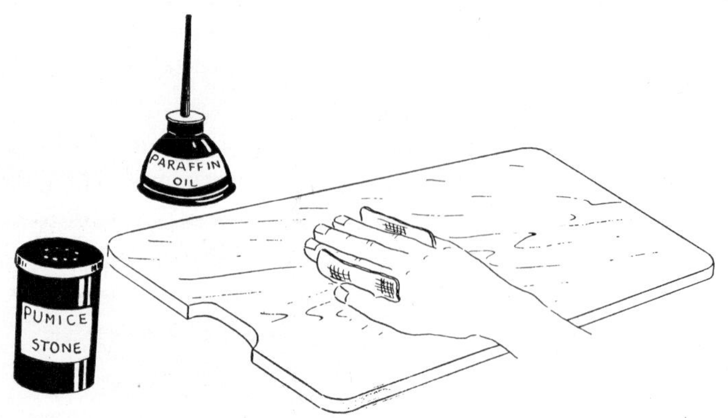

FIG. 25-2. Smoothing varnished surface with pumice stone and paraffin oil.

2. Pour a small amount of varnish directly from the can into a cup or other container of convenient size and shape. It is advisable to follow explicitly any directions on the can regarding thinning the varnish.

3. Thin the first coat of varnish with turpentine if the directions on the can advise it.

4. Apply the first coat with a good grade of fine, long-bristle brush (Fig. 25-1). Flow the varnish on evenly with long strokes. Varnish has a tendency to run; so check your work in a good light from all angles and brush out immediately any runs which develop.

5. Allow the coat to dry at least 24 hours.

6. Rub the varnished surface lightly with No. 6/0 wet-dry sandpaper and water. The rubbed-varnish surface will turn a milky color and remain so until the next coat is put on. This initial rubbing smooths down the high places of the varnish to produce a smooth base for the next coat.

7. Apply two coats of varnish, or more as necessary, without thinning it. All but the last coat should be sanded as described in step 6.

To rub varnished surfaces:

1. Prepare a mixture of No. FFF pumice stone with rubbing, paraffin, or lubricating oil.

2. Rub this on the varnished surface back and forth in the direction of the grain with a soft pad (Fig. 25-2). Rub until all traces of brush marks and other imperfections have been smoothed out.

3. Wipe the surface clean to remove all pumice stone and oil.

4. Prepare a mixture of rotten stone with rubbing, paraffin, or lubricating oil.

5. Rub this on the varnished surface in a manner similar to that described in step 2. Pumice and rotten stone are fine, abrasive powders which smooth the varnished surfaces and remove the gloss. A fine luster and sheen will be the result of hand rubbing. A commercial rubbing compound may be used instead of these mixtures.

6. Apply a coat of high-grade furniture paste wax, allow it to dry 15 to 20 minutes, and then polish it with a clean cotton cloth.

LACQUER

Lacquer is one of the most ideal materials for finishing furniture. It dries quickly, so that several successive coats may be put on in a few hours. When it is properly applied, the surface is very smooth, durable, and attractive. It is obtainable clear or in a vast variety of colors.

The discovery of true lacquer was first made in China about 3000 B.C. Eastern lacquer is the natural sap of the lac tree. The trees are tapped in the summer, and the sap emerges a grayish-white color that darkens and finally turns black when exposed to the air. After being pounded and stirred in wooden tubs, it is heated to evaporate excess moisture and stored in airtight vessels. No other substance, except perhaps a coloring agent, is normally added to the natural juice.

Lacquer is thinned with a commercial lacquer thinner, each manufacturer having a special type for his product. It, like varnish, is obtainable in a high or medium gloss or in a dull tint. Commercially it is applied with a spray gun. It is difficult to apply with a brush because it dries very rapidly; however, small projects can sometimes be coated successfully in this way. It is always advisable to follow the manufacturer's directions which appear on the container.

Applying lacquer with a spray gun or airbrush requires considerable skill. It is always necessary to clean the nozzle and other parts perfectly before and after using the spray gun, the lacquer must be thinned considerably, and it must be free of specks and lumps which might clog the nozzle. The spray gun may be used for applying other finishes, such as varnish, shellac, paint, and enamel, with equal success; however, a special nozzle is sometimes required because these liquids are much thicker.

A special lacquer sealer or sanding sealer should be sprayed on the project before applying lacquer. This seals the pores of the wood just as shellac does for varnish. In fact, shellac may be used as a sealer, particularly over filled surfaces.

A spray gun or airbrush and a compressor comprise the special equipment needed for spraying on a finish.

To apply lacquer with a spray gun:

1. Pour sufficient sealer into the spray-gun container for finishing the project. Dilute the sealer with approximately one-half thinner and stir the mixture.

2. Fasten the container to the spray gun assembly. Make certain that all fittings are secure, and that the gaskets are tight. Consult the manufacturer's chart for the particular spray gun you use to learn its adjustments.

3. Turn on the compressor and regulate the air pressure between 50 and 60 pounds.

4. Pull the trigger of the spray gun and adjust the nozzle so that the liquid will come out in an even mist.

5. Spray the finish by moving the gun from left to right and vice versa in an even pattern. Always try to keep the nozzle of the gun at the same distance from the work. This will require you to follow the path of the gun with your body as it is moved back and forth.

6. Finish the underneath portions of a project first and do the top surface last.

7. Remove the container from the gun and pour the remaining sealer back into its original can. The lid should be kept tight on the can at all times to keep the sealer and lacquer from evaporating.

8. After the sealer has dried approximately 1 hour, sand the sealed surface with No. 6/0 sandpaper.

9. Pour enough lacquer into the spray-gun container to spray the entire project. Never fill the container more than one-third full of lacquer, because thinner must be added.

10. Dilute the lacquer approximately one-third to one-half with thinner and stir the mixture.

11. Fasten the container to the spray gun, checking all connections.

12. Spray a coat of lacquer over the entire project in a manner similar to that employed in spraying on the sealer, step 5.

13. Most projects will require from three to five coats of lacquer. Each coat, except the last, should be sanded lightly with No. 6/0 sandpaper after the lacquer has dried 2 to 3 hours.

14. Remove the container and pour the remaining lacquer mixture into its original can.

15. Clean the spray gun and the container with lacquer thinner. This can be accomplished by spraying some lacquer thinner through it.

16. If desired, rub the final coat with a commercial rubbing compound. This is not necessary in all cases, but sometimes it enhances the final appearance.

17. Apply a coat of good paste wax, allow it to dry 20 minutes, and then polish it with a clean cotton cloth.

Paint or Enamel

Paint or enamel is used as a protective and decorative coating for the less-expensive woods where a transparent finish may not be desirable. Either paint or enamel may be used satisfactorily as a colorful finish on furniture and cabinets and, when properly applied, can produce some beautiful and novel effects.

Paint is generally applied on exterior surfaces or on projects which are exposed to the out of doors. Enamel in gloss or semigloss finish is suitable for interior trim and projects used in the home when transparency is neither desirable nor required. Enamel usually produces a harder finish than paint and differs from it in that, while linseed oil is used in paint, varnish is used in the enamel to produce the harder, smoother finish. Both are available in commercial colors of all types or can be obtained in white and then tinted with colors ground in oil.

To mix and apply paint or enamel:

1. Prepare the surfaces for painting or enameling. It is assumed that the project has been properly planed, scraped, and sanded, but perhaps a final touching up with No. 2/0 sandpaper will be necessary.

2. Read the directions on the can or container before it is opened. Each manufacturer prescribes the correct mixture and technique for the application of his particular brand of paint or enamel. The drying time is also specified.

3. Note whether the directions specify

the use of a primer coat. If so, this should be applied before proceeding.

4. Shake the can thoroughly, remove the lid, and pour off some of the top liquid into a temporary container.

5. Stir the base mixture with a wooden paddle, and mix the liquid back into it a little at a time until it is thoroughly blended.

6. Add turpentine, linseed oil, or the recommended thinner in accordance with the instructions on the can.

7. Select a suitable brush of high quality with the bristles set in rubber.

8. Dip the brush into the paint so that about three-fourths the length of the bristles absorbs paint. Press surplus paint or enamel off on the edge of the can as the brush is removed.

9. Apply the paint or enamel to the project with long, even strokes. A little practice will determine the proper amount to apply to the surface. It should cover smoothly and evenly but not be allowed to run.

10. Allow the coat to dry thoroughly according to the time given in the directions, and then sand smooth with No. 2/0 sandpaper. Wipe the surface off with a clean cloth before applying the next coat.

11. Apply a second and third coat, if needed, according to these instructions, omitting sanding the final coat.

Care of Brushes

The selection and care of the brush determines to a great extent the final result of a finish. Since better brushes made from Chinese or Russian boar bristles set in rubber are expensive, they must be cared for properly to get full value from the expenditure. Some finishers keep a separate brush for each type of finish, so that there is no chance of using a poorly cleaned shellac brush for applying varnish.

When brushes are not in use, they should be kept in the solvent which serves as a thinner for the particular finish being applied, such as alcohol solvent for shellac, turpentine for enamel or varnish, linseed oil for exterior paint, and lacquer thinner for lacquer. One way to keep the bristles of a brush from bending while they are in a container with solvent is to drill a hole through the handle and then to suspend the brush by means of a wire passed through this hole and across the top of the can.

If a brush is not to be used for an indefinite period of time, it should be thoroughly cleaned in several changes of the solvent or in a suitable thinning agent and wiped clean and dry with rags. Benzine, lacquer thinner, or varnish remover will be helpful in the thorough cleaning of a brush. All rags and waste materials used in finishing and cleaning brushes should be disposed of as soon as possible as a precaution against spontaneous combustion.

Discussion Topics

1. List three reasons for applying finishes on wood.
2. What are the principal ingredients of shellac, lacquer, varnish, and paint?
3. What is the essential difference between white and orange shellac besides its color?
4. Why does shellac dry rapidly?

5. What is the purpose of stain?
6. Mention at least three woods on which stain is not necessary.
7. What type of stain is used most frequently? Why?
8. What is the purpose of wood filler?
9. List five kinds of wood which do not need filler.
10. Which should be applied first on open grain wood, stain or filler? Why?
11. Why is varnish stain not desirable for high-quality finishes?
12. What is the purpose of pumice stone in rubbing down a varnish finish?
13. From what source are the bristles of a good brush obtained?
14. From what materials are furniture waxes made?

Unit 26. Upholstering

The art of simple upholstering can be mastered by the amateur if he will study the materials, tools, and procedures given in this unit. There are also numerous excellent books available which supply detailed information on materials, the more elaborate tools, and intricate techniques which are often practiced in the upholstery trade.

Types of simple upholstery described in this unit are the removable slip seat with a webbing base and the coil-spring seat built in a wooden frame. Some furniture manufacturers use no-sag springs (Fig. 26-18) instead of the coil type (Fig. 26-13). This unit gives the very elementary application of no-sag and coil-spring seats. The slip seat with a webbing base is especially popular on foot stools and dining-room chairs where it is desirable to remove the slip seat and to tack on a new cover frequently.

Materials

Basic materials used in the structure of upholstering are webbing; burlap; various types of stuffings, such as horse, cattle, and hog hair, moss or tow; cotton; muslin; cambric; sewing twine; spring twine; tacks; steel upholstery springs; and the final covering of upholstering fabrics.

Upholstering webbing is made from coarsely woven jute fiber. It is obtainable in various widths and grades. The $3\frac{1}{2}$-inch width is most satisfactory for general classes of upholstering. Webbing is stretched and tacked across both directions of a slip seat or back to form a flexible base. It is also often stretched across the bottom of a frame for fastening coil springs.

Burlap is a cloth woven from jute yarn. It can be obtained in many widths and weights. The 40-inch width in an 8- to $10\frac{1}{2}$-ounce weight is especially satisfactory for use over springs to form the base for the stuffing.

Stuffing materials made of curled hair from horses, cattle, and hogs make an ideal substance for stuffing. They are purchased by the pound and must be thoroughly separated before using in order that all lumps and foreign inclusions are removed. They then form the base over webbing or springs on top of the burlap.

Rubberized hair has become very popular and is available in sheets of different thicknesses, widths, and lengths. Owing to the rubberizing process, these sheets are easily cut and formed to maintain an excellent resilience.

Moss is considered an excellent stuffing material, second to curled hair.

Tow, a fiber of the flax class, is deemed a general-purpose stuffing. It will produce a firm, durable pad and is relatively inexpensive.

Cotton used for upholstering is spun into sheets about $\frac{1}{4}$ inch thick and generally 27 inches wide. It comes by the roll and is used as padding over the stuffings and between temporary and final covering.

Muslin of the unbleached kind is ideal for basic covering and as a general-utility fabric. The standard widths are 36 to 40 inches.

Cambric is a glazed cotton fabric which is tacked under the bottoms of upholstered seats to serve as a dust cover as well as to hide upholstery ravelings.

Sewing twine, a thin twine made from flax fiber, is used for the many sewing operations preparatory to the final covering.

Spring twine is used for tying the tops of springs in place. Since all spring work is dependent upon the strength of the twine, it is important that this material be of the best grade. Six-ply Italian hemp should be used for tying furniture coil springs.

Tacks used in upholstering vary according to their purpose. The upholsterer's tack has a smooth, flat head and serves for general-utility purposes. The 12- to 14-ounce tack is desirable for fastening webbing, while the 8- to 10-ounce may be used for tacking spring twine. The 4- to 6-ounce is used for general fastening down of burlap and muslin and for the final covering; and 2- to 3-ounce is suitable for fastening the cambric underneath the seat.

The tack designed for fastening webbing is known as the webbing tack. It is very similar to the upholsterer's tack except that little points project from the shank.

Gimp tacks have small, round heads and are ideal where tack heads may be visible. It is interesting to know, however, that many upholsterers prefer to fasten gimp to the final covering with hot animal glue used sparingly. This gives a very neat appearance, is easily applied, and eliminates the use of gimp tacks.

Steel upholstery springs are made in a variety of styles and sizes. The coil spring with both ends open is most commonly used for seat work. Each size is available with a wide or narrow center, the wide centers being softer than the narrow twisted type. The standard sizes, varies from No. 00 (4 inches high) to No. 6 (14 inches high), are generally sold by the pound.

Final covering for the upholstered project offers a wide selection for many varieties and colors of fabrics. Mohairs, velours, and tapestries have been standard for many years and are not too difficult to work with. Leathers, leather-

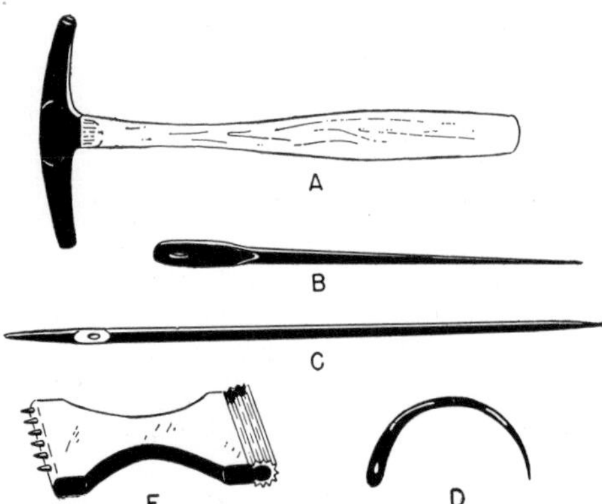

FIG. 26-1. Some basic upholstery tools: (*A*) magnetic tack hammer, (*B*) regulator, (*C*) double-pointed straight needle, (*D*) curved needle, and (*E*) webbing stretcher.

ettes, and the more recently developed plastic fabrics are also very colorful and serviceable, but they are a little more difficult to manipulate. Other choices are offered in a wealth of modern textures and patterns.

Tools and Equipment

The person who upholsters does not need elaborate tools and equipment for doing many of the fundamental types of upholstering. The more common tools are the magnetic tack hammer, regulator, double-pointed straight needle, curved needle, and a webbing stretcher (Fig. 26-1). Ordinary shears for cutting materials are also essential.

The *tack hammer* is possibly the most important tool. The double-faced type is the most convenient, and it is advisable that one face be magnetic.

The *regulator* comes in sizes ranging from 6 to 12 inches. It is used to smooth out irregularities in the stuffing and to assist in shaping edges.

The *straight needle,* pointed at both ends, is very convenient for sewing back and forth without turning. One about 8 inches long is suitable for this work.

Curved needles are pointed at one end and may be obtained from $1\frac{1}{2}$ to 10 inches in circumference. The 3-inch curved needle is satisfactory for most general purposes. It is used in sewing through flat surfaces where all sewing must be done from one side.

The *webbing stretcher,* measuring approximately 4 by 6 inches, may be made in the shop. It is best to pad the end which does not have the teeth.

Shears should be sturdy and serviceable enough to cut twine and coarse fabrics.

If much upholstery work is done, it will be best to have a few trestles (sawhorses) on which to set projects while upholstering. A trestle should have padded edges to protect the wooden portions of the project.

Upholstering Slip Seat

1. Make a wooden frame which will fit the footstool, bench, or chair. This frame may be made from stock $\frac{3}{4}$ inch thick. The length of the various pieces will depend upon the size seat to be made. A good joint construction is the butt joint with two dowels. See Unit 19, "Joining," pages 63 and 64.

2. Round the edge of the top side of the frame to prevent the upholstery materials from wearing through easily.

3. Tack one end of the webbing to the frame with No. 12 upholstery tacks (Fig. 26-2). Space the distance between webbing at $\frac{1}{2}$ to 2 inches. Drive three tacks through the first layer, fold back $\frac{3}{4}$ inch of webbing, and then anchor down with two more tacks (Fig. 26-3).

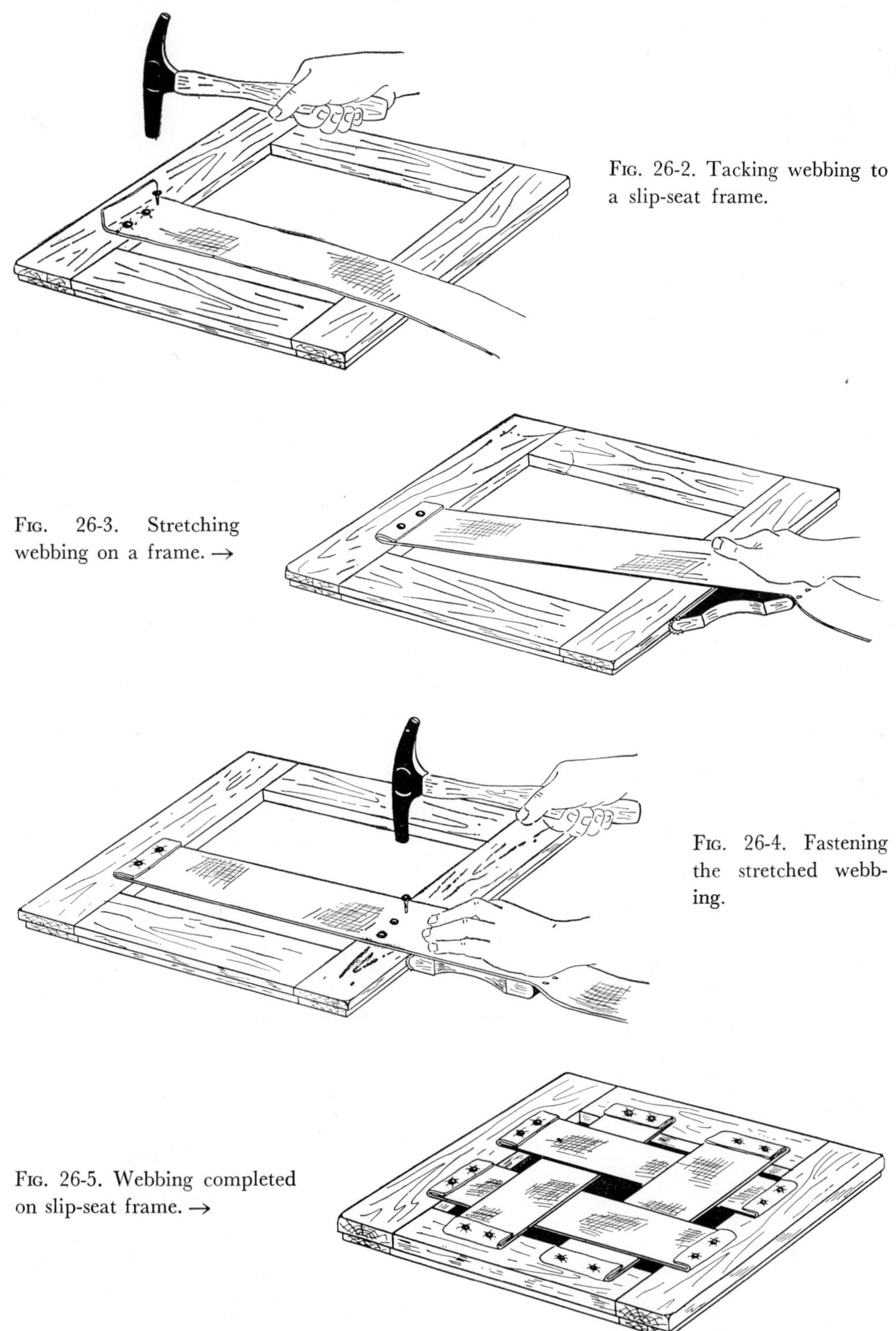

Fig. 26-2. Tacking webbing to a slip-seat frame.

Fig. 26-3. Stretching webbing on a frame. →

Fig. 26-4. Fastening the stretched webbing.

Fig. 26-5. Webbing completed on slip-seat frame. →

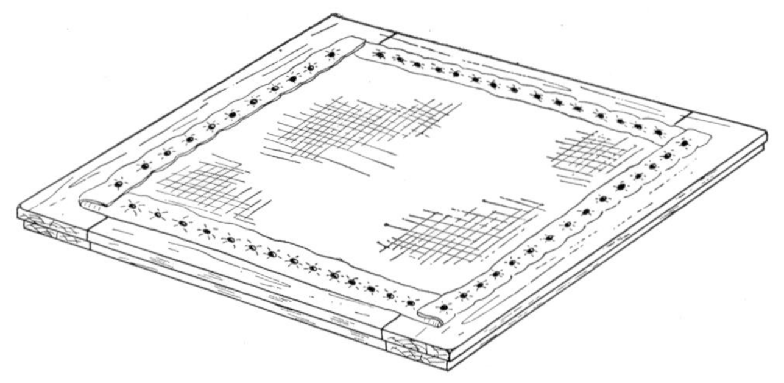

Fig. 26-6. Burlap fastened over webbing.

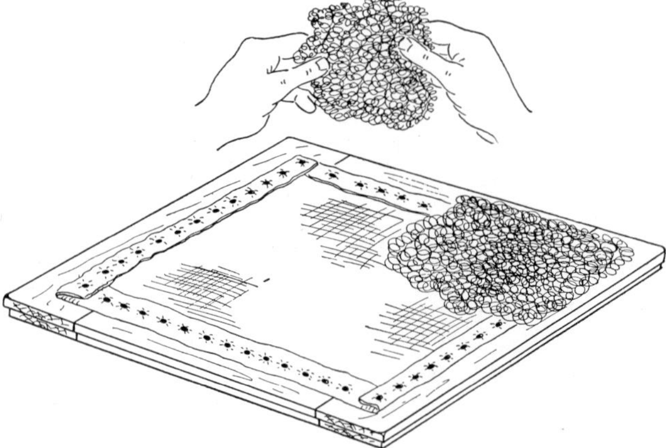

Fig. 26-7. Spreading curled hair on slip-seat frame. →

Fig. 26-8. Adjusting stuffing with the regulator for smoothness.

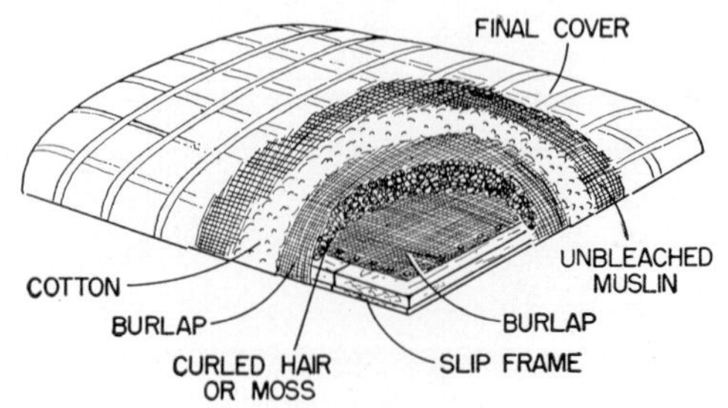

Fig. 26-9. Cross section of upholstered slip-seat frame. →

4. Stretch the webbing with a webbing stretcher until it is tight (Fig. 26-3).

5. Secure the end of the webbing by driving three tacks, as shown in Fig. 26-4.

6. Cut the webbing with the shears about $\frac{3}{4}$ inch beyond the tacks, fold back, and drive in two more tacks.

7. Fasten the remaining strips of webbing as shown in Fig. 26-5. The strips should form an interwoven pattern.

8. Cover the webbed section of the frame with a single thickness of close-grained burlap, and fasten in place with No. 8 tacks (Fig. 26-6).

9. Pull apart a quantity of curled hair, moss, or tow, and spread it evenly over the burlap on the slip frame to a depth of approximately 2 inches (Fig. 26-7). Remove all sticks and other foreign matter. A rubberized hair pad 1 inch thick may be used instead of the stuffing.

10. Cover the stuffing with a thickness of close-grained burlap and tack it under the frame. Drive the tacks only about halfway in so that they may be withdrawn, if necessary, to tighten the burlap further. It should be pulled down tight when finished (Fig. 26-8).

11. Adjust loose stuffing with the regulator for uniform smoothness (Fig. 26-8). Cut away surplus burlap on the corners to eliminate bulkiness.

12. Cover the tightly tacked burlap with a layer of cotton padding or batting (Fig. 26-9).

13. Cover the cotton with a piece of unbleached muslin and tack it tightly under the frame.

14. Arrange the final covering fabric in place and tack it under the frame. The corner shown in Fig. 26-10 makes a satisfactory finish.

15. Cover the underneath of the seat with a piece of black glazed cambric or with some other closely woven material.

16. Fasten the slip-seat frame in place with screws from underneath (Fig. 26-11).

Upholstering Coil Springs

1. Make, or have ready for the upholstering process, a chair frame, ottoman, or other suitable piece of furniture that is to be upholstered with the use of coil springs. This might also be a reupholstering project in which the frame might need to be reglued.

2. Decide whether to use webbing or wood strips as a base for fastening the springs.

3. Fasten the solid wood or strips of wood in place, or stretch webbing to serve as a foundation for the springs. Put in as large tacks as the frame will stand when using webbing.

4. Determine the height of the springs and the number to be placed. This depends entirely upon how high the seat is to be built and how hard or soft it is to be. The best way for an inexperienced person to decide this is to place several springs of various sizes in different positions until a decision is reached. Whenever possible, the springs should be placed at points where the webbing crosses.

5. Place the selected springs in rows to be fastened to the wood or web base. Figure 26-12 shows a neat spacing.

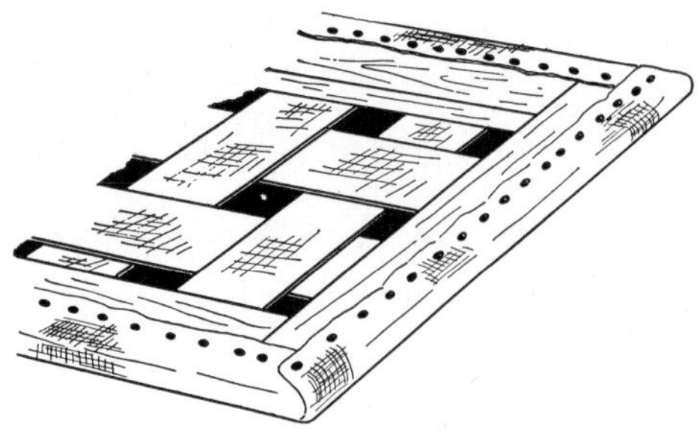

Fig. 26-10. Underneath of slip-seat frame showing the finished corner.

Fig. 26-11. Fastening slip-seat frame to stool through corner brace. →

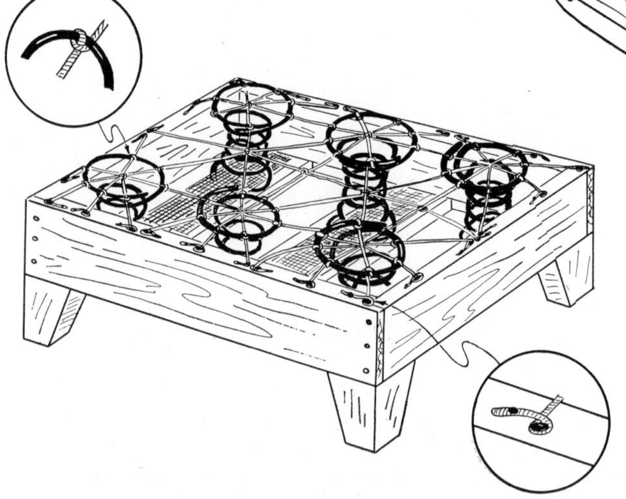

Fig. 26-12. Springs properly tied in an ottoman.

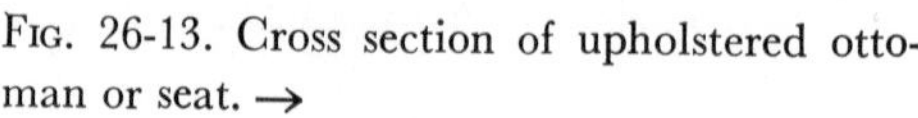

Fig. 26-13. Cross section of upholstered ottoman or seat. →

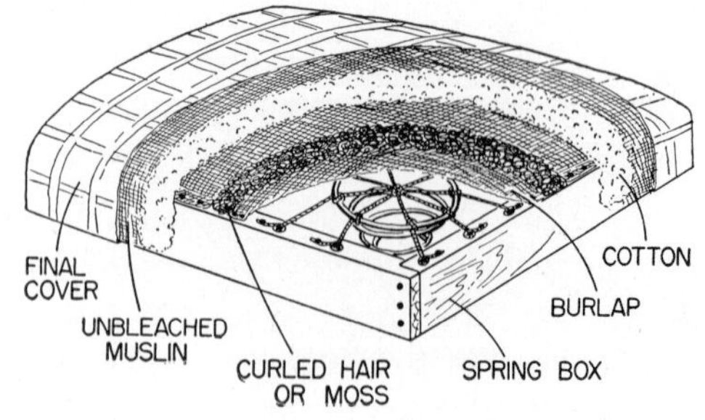

6. Fasten the coil springs to the wood or web base. If they are secured to a web base, they should be sewed with sewing twine and a needle. If they are fastened to a wood base, anchor them with staples, which, in turn, are covered with a piece of burlap to serve as a silencer so that the spring will not be noisy when it hits the base (Fig. 26-12).

7. Drive a No. 10 upholstery tack part way into the edges of the wood frame for each outer spring, as shown in Fig. 26-12.

8. Cut several pieces of spring-tying twine to length. This will be about double the length or width of the frame.

9. Knot one end of the twine around a tack on the edge and drive it down. This begins the tying of a row of springs. Leave a $\frac{3}{4}$-inch surplus to serve as an anchor for the twine and the first tack (Fig. 26-12, detail).

10. Hold the first spring in position and pull the twine over the top, form the spring-tying knot, and proceed across the row of springs (Fig. 26-12, detail).

11. Fasten the end of the tying twine in the same way that it was secured when starting.

12. Finish the tying procedure for all the rows of springs until the pattern resembles that shown in Fig. 26-12. As each spring is tied, it must be pressed to a uniform height so that symmetry and firmness of contour are achieved.

13. Tie all springs diagonally, as shown in Fig. 26-12. A cross section of the springs and the frame will resemble Fig. 26-13.

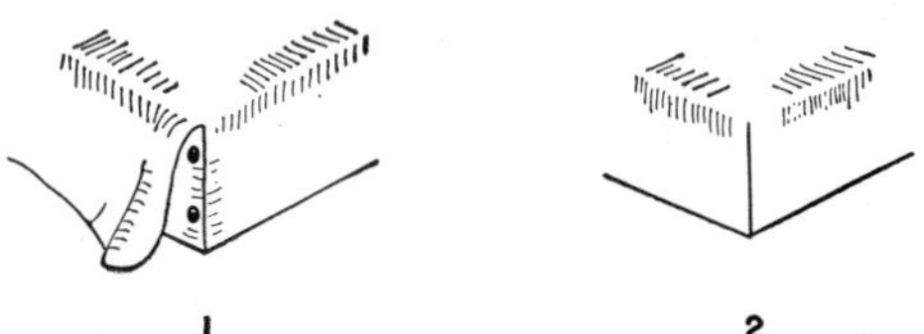

FIG. 26-14. Final steps in forming corner.

14. Cover the springs with a single layer of close-grained burlap, fold the edges, and tack to the edges of the frame (Fig. 26-13).

15. Pull apart a quantity of curled hair, moss, or tow, and spread evenly over the burlap on the springs to a depth of approximately 2 inches. Remove all sticks and other foreign matter. A sheet of rubberized curled hair 1 inch thick may be used instead of the loose stuffing (Fig. 26-13).

FIG. 26-15. Essential steps in tying spring-steel wire edge to coil springs.

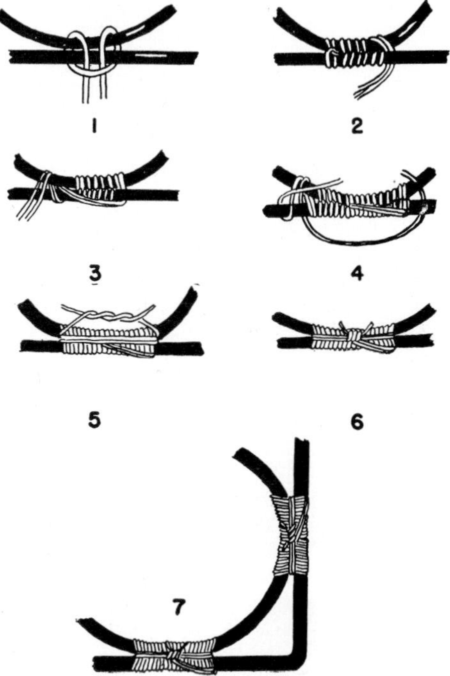

Fig. 26-16. Wire edge fastened to springs and two rows of springs properly tied.

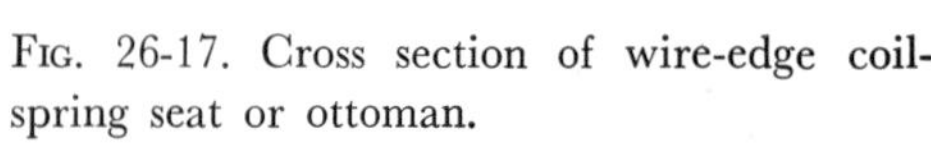

Fig. 26-17. Cross section of wire-edge coil-spring seat or ottoman.

Fig. 26-18. An ottoman frame with no-sag springs fastened in place ready for further upholstery.

16. Cover the stuffing with a thickness of close-grained burlap and proceed with the processes completing the upholstering as described, beginning with step 10 in the preceding section, "Upholstering Slip Seat."

17. Form the corners of the final covering as illustrated in Fig. 26-14.

Upholstering Wire-edge Coil Spring

1. Follow steps 1 through 5 of the preceding section, "Upholstering Coil Springs."

2. Bend a spring-steel upholstery wire to the contour of the wooden frame.

3. Tie this spring-steel wire to the coil springs as indicated in Fig. 26-16. Follow the steps shown in Fig. 26-15 for tying.

4. Follow steps 6 and 7 in the preceding section, "Upholstering Coil Springs."

5. Knot one end of the twine around one end of the tack on the edge, leaving a surplus of 5 inches. Drive the tack to hold the twine securely.

6. Start another tack about $\frac{1}{2}$ inch from the first one, wrap the surplus end of the cord around it, and fasten the tack (Fig. 26-16).

7. Tie the surplus end of the twine to the wire edge to the desired height (Fig. 26-16).

8. Follow steps 9 through 13 of the preceding section, "Upholstering Coil Springs."

9. Sew a hard-edge roll to the burlap, following the contour of the wire frame (Fig. 26-17).

10. Complete the upholstering job by following steps 15 through 17 in the preceding section, "Upholstering Coil Springs."

Upholstering No-sag Springs

No-sag springs are often used to replace coil springs. The spring stock may be cut to length and fastened in place as shown in Fig. 26-18. The procedure for upholstering over a no-sag spring base is practically identical with that followed in the preceding section.

Discussion Topics

1. List six of the essential tools used in upholstering.
2. What is the meaning of "slip seat"?
3. What is the advantage in using webbing for the foundation of a slip-frame seat instead of a solid board?
4. What size tacks should be used for fastening (*a*) webbing, (*b*) spring-tying twine, (*c*) burlap, (*d*) final covering, and (*e*) cambric?
5. Inspect several pieces of factory-built furniture to see how the coil or no-sag springs have been fastened to the frame and how they have been tied into place.
6. List and describe six types of cover fabrics which may be satisfactorily used for the final covering of upholstered projects.

Unit 27. Sharpening Tools

Excellent workmanship in woodworking depends, to a high degree, upon sharp tools. The expert craftsman does not think of building anything unless every tool to be used has the sharpest possible edge. Sharpening tools requires exactness and skill. The beginner who pays proper attention to basic techniques can develop this skill to a satisfactory degree. He may not wish to begin by sharpening such tools as auger bits and saws, but it is a relatively easy matter to sharpen plane irons, chisels, pocketknives, spokeshave blades, and scraper blades. Whenever a plane iron or chisel does not cut properly or leaves slight ridges in the work, it is an indication that the cutting edges need to be sharpened on the grinder, oilstone, or perhaps on both.

Tools

The essential pieces of equipment necessary for sharpening edge tools, such as plane irons, spokeshave blades, chisels, drawknives, pocketknives, and sloyd (or wood-carving) knives, are the

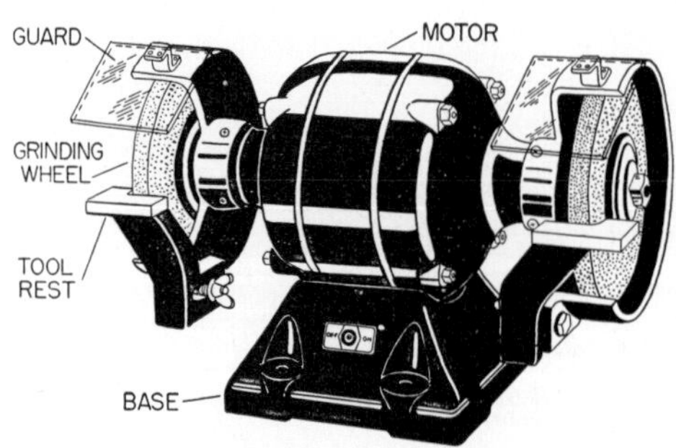

Fig. 27-1. Grinder.

grinder (Fig. 27-1), or the more elaborate slow-speed *oil grinder* built especially for grinding edge tools in woodworking, and the *oilstone* (Fig. 27-2).

Sharpening scraper-blade edges requires a *smooth-mill file,* the *oilstone,* and the *burnisher* for turning edges (Fig. 27-3).

The setting and sharpening of handsaw teeth require a special *clamp* (Fig. 27-4), a *saw set* (Fig. 27-5), a *mill file,* and *triangular, slim, tapered files* (Fig. 27-6).

Auger bits can be sharpened effectively with *triangular, slim, tapered* files, or with *special flat files* for this purpose.

Fig. 27-4. Saw clamp.

Sharpening Plane Iron, Chisel, and Spokeshave Blade

1. Remove the plane iron from the plane, or the spokeshave blade from the spokeshave frame. For the assembly or disassembly of these tools refer to Unit 8 "Assembling and Adjusting Planes," page 23 and to Unit 11, "Assembling and Adjusting a Spokeshave," page 32.

2. Fasten the plane iron in the holder assembly on the grinder (Fig. 27-7). The procedure which follows will per-

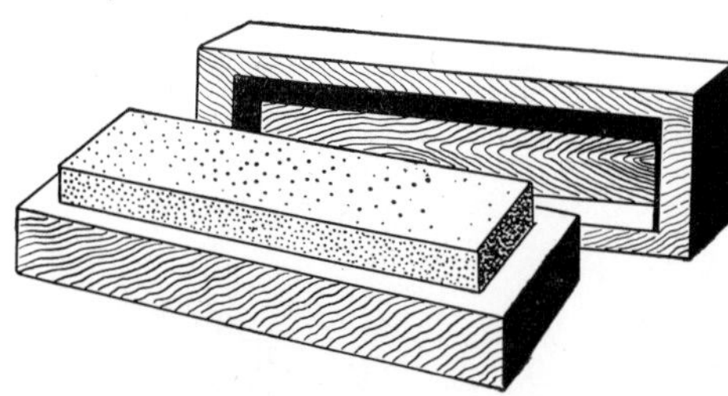

Fig. 27-2. Oilstone.

Fig. 27-3. Burnisher.

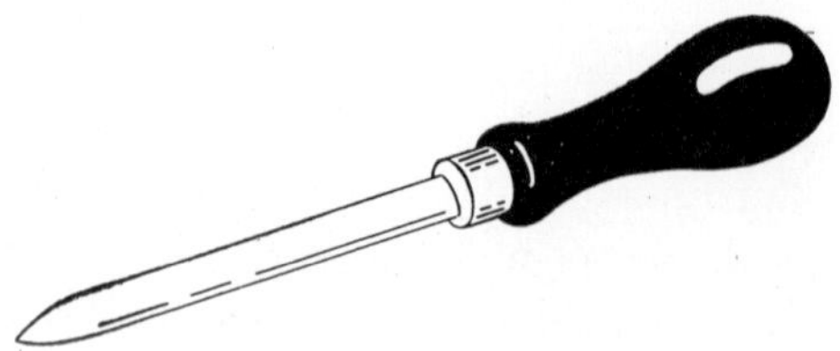

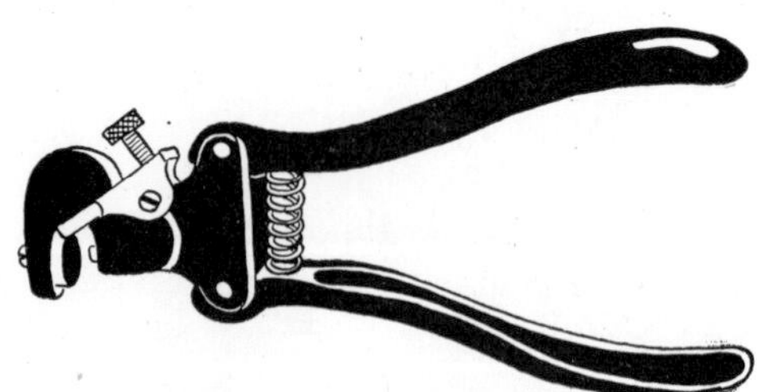

Fig. 27-5. Saw set.

Fig. 27-6. Triangular slim-tapered file.

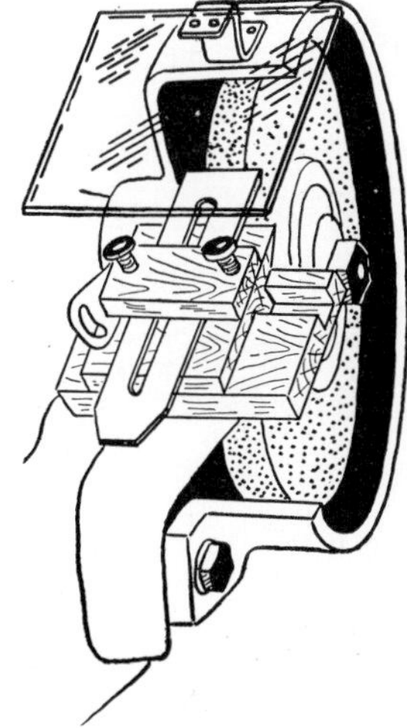

FIG. 27-7. Plane iron held in grinder assembly.

tain equally well to the grinding of a spokeshave blade and chisels. It will only be necessary to grind the plane iron, chisel, or blade if the cutting edge is nicked or if it has been incorrectly ground. The blade may also be held with the hands, as shown in Fig. 27-8, but with less accuracy.

3. Turn on the grinder and move the blade or chisel from side to side while the grinding wheel is in motion (Figs. 27-7 and 27-8).

FIG. 27-8. Plane iron held on grinder with hands.

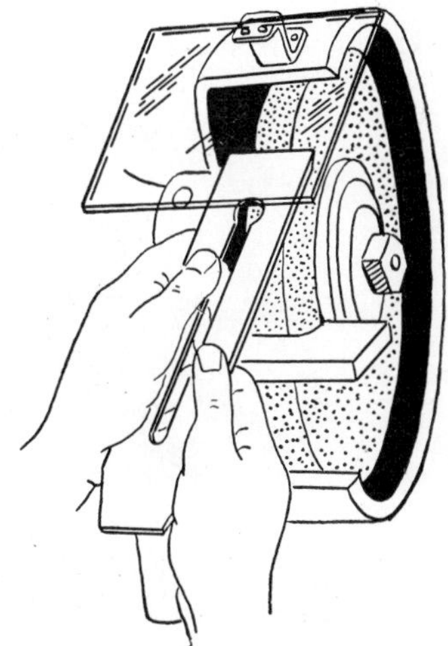

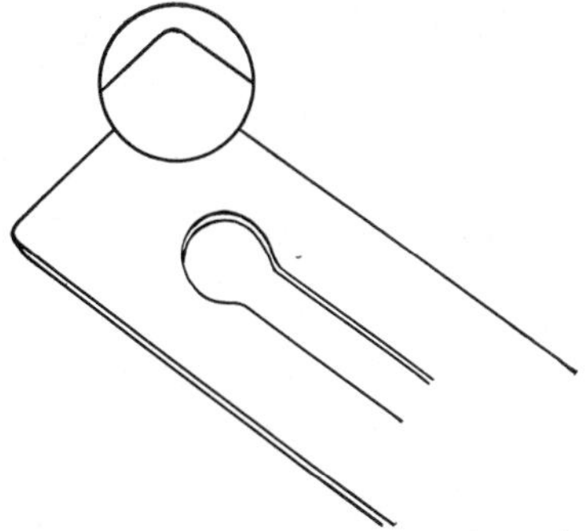

FIG. 27-9. Proper way to round edges of plane iron.

4. Continue grinding until all nicks are removed. At all times use a cooling lubricant on the wheel to carry away metal particles and to protect the abrasive wheel.

Figure 27-9 illustrates how the edges of a plane iron may be rounded so that the iron will not leave ridges in planing. This method does not apply to the chisel or the spokeshave blade.

5. Test the cutting edge for the correct grinding angle (Figs. 27-10 and 27-11). A jig for testing the correct angle is often available from tool manufacturers, or one may be made easily in the shop from metal.

6. Test the plane iron for squareness (Fig. 27-12).

7. Whet or hone the plane iron,

FIG. 27-10. Angle for grinding plane iron.

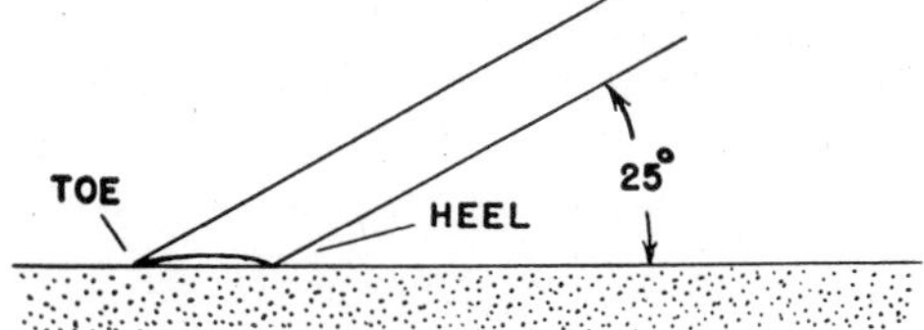

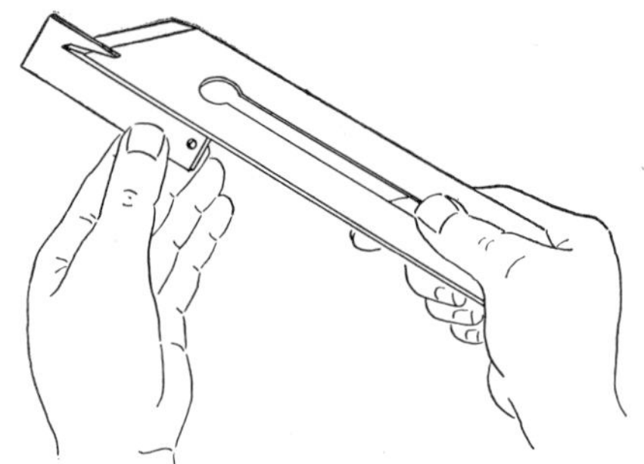

Fig. 27-11. Testing proper angle of plane iron.

Fig. 27-12. Testing cutting edge of plane iron for squareness.

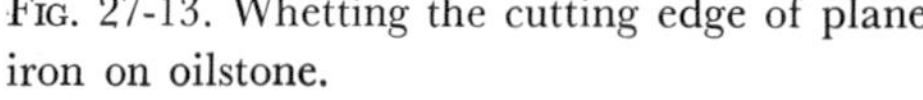

Fig. 27-13. Whetting the cutting edge of plane iron on oilstone.

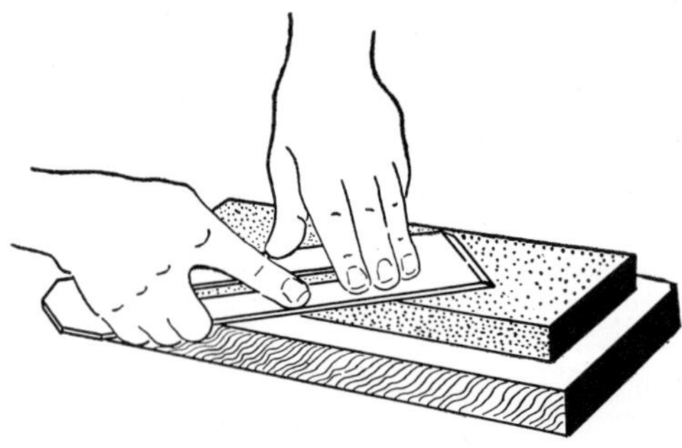

Fig. 27-14. Whetting back side of plane iron.

chisel, or spokeshave blade with the bevel side down, on an oilstone (Fig. 27-13). Hold the plane iron so that the toe and heel both ride on the oilstone as it is moved in a circular motion. Keep oil on the stone to remove steel particles.

8. Turn the plane iron over on its back or flat side on the oilstone and move it back and forth gently (Fig. 27-14).

9. Remove the burr or wiry edge by pulling the plane iron lightly across a piece of wood (Fig. 27-15).

10. If an extremely fine edge is desired, finish whetting with a few pulling strokes on a piece of oily leather.

11. Sharpening a drawknife is a procedure similar to that for sharpening the

Fig. 27-15. Removing burr edge from plane iron.

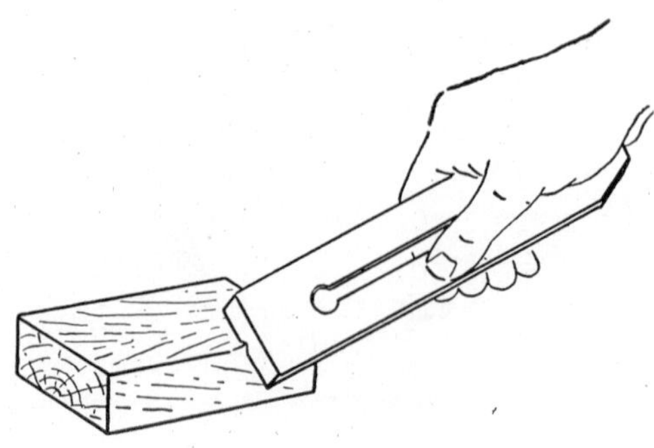

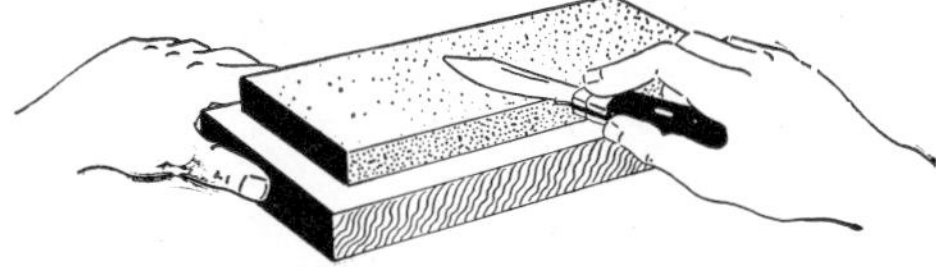

Fig. 27-16. Whetting a knife on an oilstone.

plane iron and other edge tools. The drawknife will have to be held against the grinding wheel with both hands.

12. The sharpening of the blade of a sloyd or of a pocketknife is similar to the above steps except that these knives are held against the grinding wheel with one or both hands. Figure 27-16 shows how to whet a keen edge on a knife when using the oilstone.

Sharpening Hand Scraper

1. Fasten the hand-scraper blade securely in a vise, preferably a metal one.

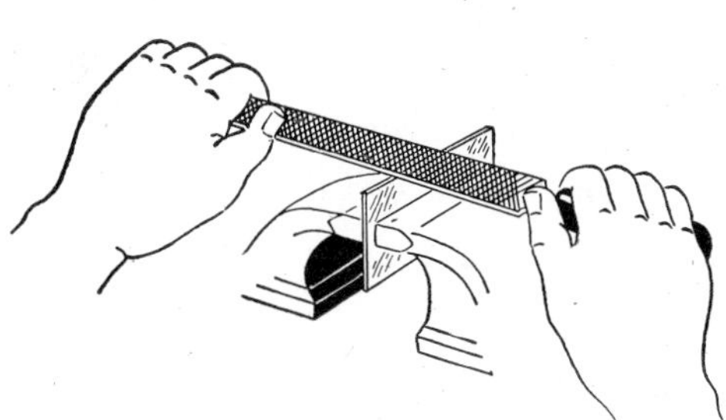

Fig. 27-17. Drawfiling the edge of a scraper blade.

Fig. 27-19. Removing filed burr with an oilstone.

2. Drawfile the edge at a 90-degree angle with a mill file (Fig. 27-17).

3. Whet the filed edge by moving the scraper blade back and forth on an oilstone (Fig. 27-18). Make certain that the blade is moved at right angles to the stone.

4. Place the scraper blade flat on an oilstone and move it back and forth to remove the burr (Fig. 27-19). Turn the blade over and remove the filed burr from the opposite side.

5. Place the scraper blade in a vise and turn the edge slightly with the burnisher (Fig. 27-20). The edge should be turned on both sides. This will make an edge which will produce shavings when handled as described in

Fig. 27-18. Whetting a scraper blade on an oilstone.

Fig. 27-20. Burnishing a scraper-blade edge.

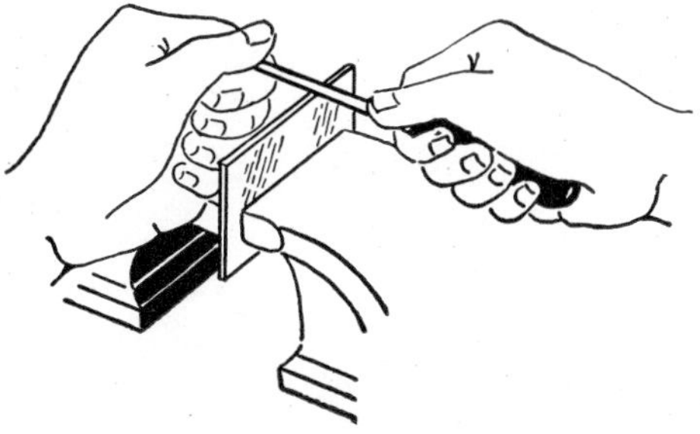

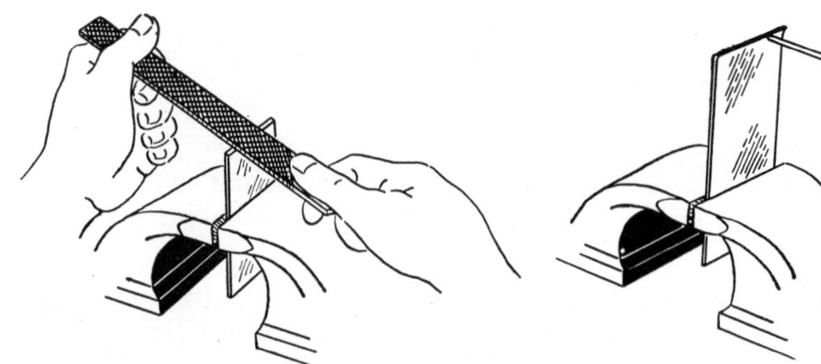

FIG. 27-21. Filing edge for cabinet scraper blade.

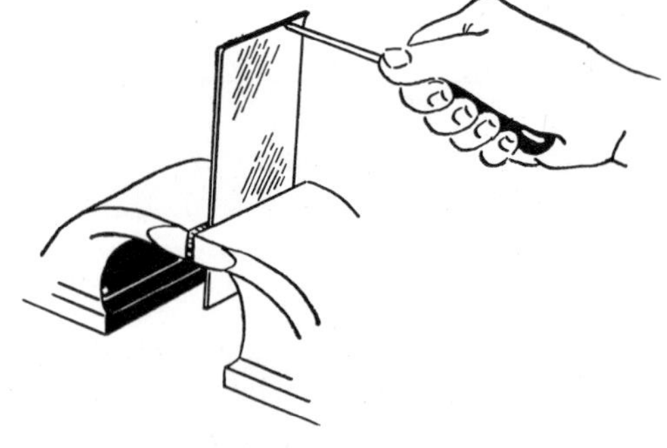

FIG. 27-23. Pulling burnished edge clean.

Unit 15, "Smoothing a Surface by Scraping," pages 47 to 48.

SHARPENING SCRAPER BLADE

1. Remove blade from scraper frame.
2. Remove the old burr from the flat side of the blade with a flat mill file.
3. Place the blade in a vise, preferably a metal one.
4. File a bevel at 45 degrees with a flat mill file (Fig. 27-21). Push the file forward and to the side to produce a shearing cut.
5. Whet the beveled edge on the oilstone. This will be similar to whetting the plane iron (Fig. 27-13).
6. Whet the back side of the blade flat on an oilstone. This also resembles the procedure for whetting the back side of the plane iron (Fig. 27-14).

FIG. 27-22. Burnishing an edge of cabinet scraper blade.

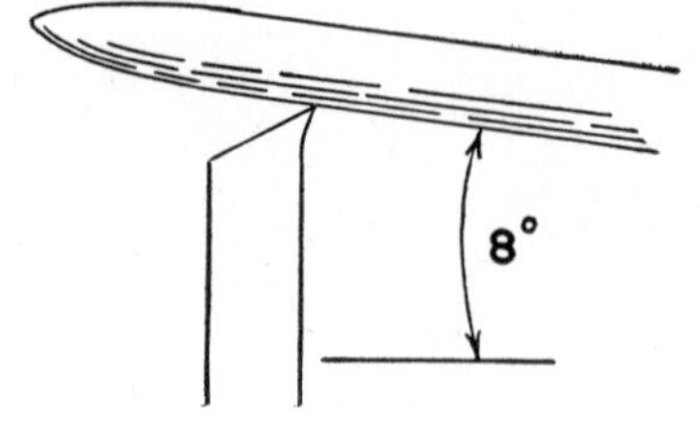

7. Fasten the blade in a vise and turn the edge with a burnisher as illustrated in Figs. 27-20 and 27-22.
8. Pull the burnished edge back slightly with the point of the burnisher (Fig. 27-23).

SETTING HANDSAW TEETH

1. Carefully inspect the teeth of the ripsaw or crosscut saw to see if they have been previously set and filed uniformly. This can be done by sighting down the blade from the handle end.
2. If the teeth are uneven in length, *joint* them by pushing a flat mill file the full length of the saw blade until all teeth have been touched (Fig. 27-24). The saw may be held between two pieces of wood in a wood or metal vise or in a saw clamp.
3. Adjust the saw set so that it will set the teeth of the handsaw properly. Each manufacturer of a saw set provides instructions for adjusting his product.
4. Set the teeth, starting from the heel of the saw, by bending the points of alternate teeth in the direction in which they were originally bent (Fig. 27-25).

Fig. 27-24. Jointing teeth of handsaw with a file.

5. Reverse the saw in the clamp and set the remaining alternate teeth in the opposite direction.

SHARPENING SAW TEETH

1. Fasten the saw clamp to the bench top.

2. Fasten the saw in the saw clamp with the teeth pointing up.

3. File the teeth with a triangular, slim, tapered file by starting at the heel

Fig. 27-25. Setting saw teeth.

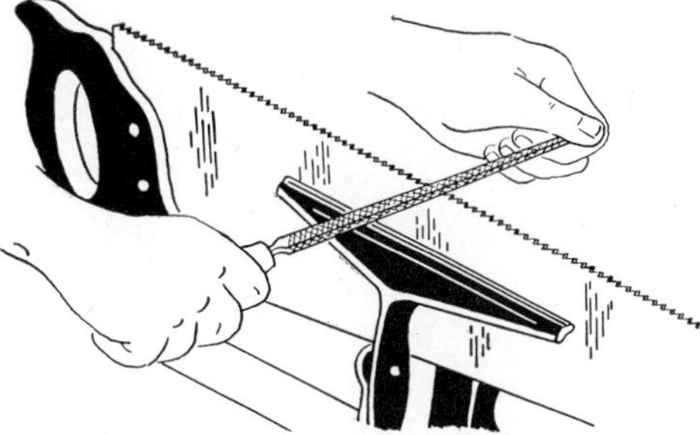

Fig. 27-26. Filing saw teeth.

of the saw. The angle at which you file will be determined by whether the teeth are crosscut or rip. Refer to Unit 7, "Sawing Across or with the Grain of the Wood," page 18. When filing, even pressure should be exerted on the forward stroke; the file should be raised on the backward stroke.

4. File all teeth at the proper angle until the points are sharp (Fig. 27-26). There should be no trace left of saw jointing, which produced flat points as mentioned in step 2 under the preceding heading, "Setting Handsaw Teeth."

SHARPENING AUGER BITS

1. Rest the auger bit on a piece of wood, as shown in Fig. 27-27.

2. File the upper side of the auger bit *lips* until a sharp cutting edge is made (Fig. 27-27). A triangular, slim, ta-

Fig. 27-27. Filing upper side of lips of an auger bit.

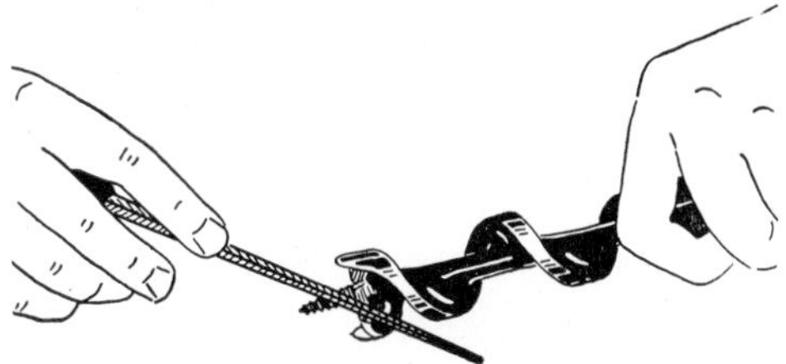

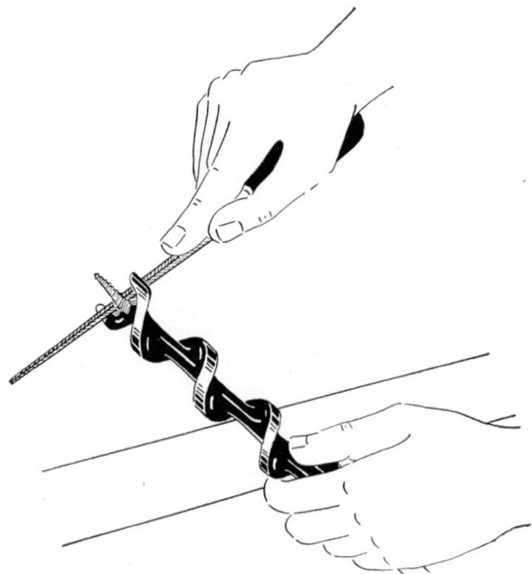

FIG. 27-28. Filing inside surfaces of the nibs of an auger bit.

pered file or a small, flat auger-bit file is most suitable for this purpose.

3. File the inside surface of the *nibs* of the auger bit until a sharp cutting edge is produced (Fig. 27-28). Hold the auger bit against a bench top as shown.

Discussion Topics

1. Explain the purposes of the grinder and the oilstone in sharpening tools.
2. Why do plane irons and wood chisels have a bevel on one side only?
3. Describe the steps for sharpening the plane iron, wood chisel, or spokeshave blade.
4. At what angle should the plane iron be ground for ordinary cutting?
5. List three reasons why edge-cutting tools should be kept sharp.
6. Why are scraper blades sharpened differently from plane irons?
7. How does the metal of a plane iron, wood chisel, or spokeshave blade become damaged if the cutting edge is allowed to turn blue while it is being ground?
8. What is the essential purpose of a lubricant on a grinder or oilstone?
9. What is the name of the tool used to turn the edges of scraper blades?
10. What is meant by "jointing" the teeth of a saw blade?
11. Illustrate the difference between crosscut and rip teeth. Explain the purpose of each.
12. Why do the teeth of the saw need to be "set"?
13. What two essential parts of an auger bit may be sharpened readily?

Section III. MACHINE TOOL PROCESSES

Unit 28. Sawing on the Circular or Table Saw

The circular or table saw is one of the oldest kinds of power machines for woodworking. The modern circular saw (Fig. 28-1) can perform a wide variety of processes and is, therefore, one of the most useful woodworking machines for the school, industry, or home workshop. Basically, the numerous circular saws produced by different manufacturers perform in a similar manner.

The lighter weight or home-workshop circular or table saw is manufactured as a tilting-arbor saw or as a tilting-table saw. The most popular and con-

Fig. 28-1. A 12-inch circular or table saw with vernier-fence adjustment and safety guard.

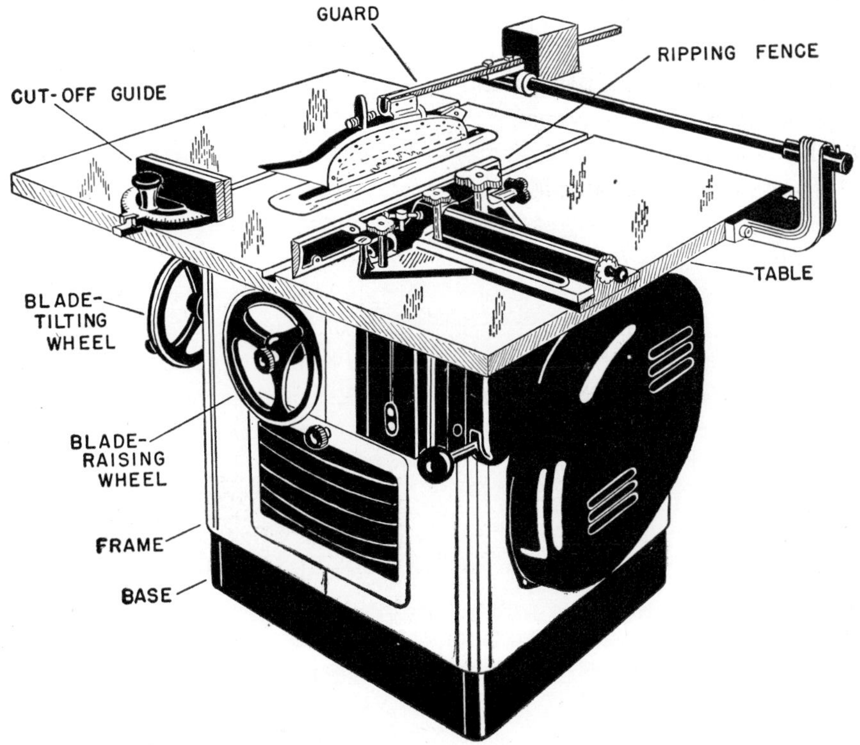

venient type is the tilting-arbor saw. Its essential parts consist of an arbor, on which the saw blade is fastened, a frame, a table, a ripping fence, and a safety guard.

Machine sawing requires special types of blades for ripping and cross-cutting just as hand sawing does. A combination blade, such as that shown in Fig. 28-1, is satisfactory for most general work, especially for the home workshop.

Wide cuts or dadoes may be made most effectively by the use of a dado, or grooving, head. This consists of two outer dado blades with cutters (Fig. 28-8), which can be placed between them to provide the proper width of cut, varying from $\frac{1}{8}$ to 2 inches, and which may be used in cutting with or across grain. Each of the outer or single dado blades will cut a kerf $\frac{1}{8}$ inch. Combined, the two outer blades will cut a $\frac{1}{4}$-inch groove which is ideal for building in or installing three-ply panels $\frac{1}{4}$ inch thick.

Safety

The circular saw is an efficient and effective piece of equipment if it is treated properly, that is, if the blade is always kept very sharp and if it is operated with the proper use of guards and with other precautionary measures.

Safety factors to be observed are:

1. Keep the saw blade sharp at all times.
2. Make certain that the safety guard is in place and properly adjusted.
3. Set the saw blade so that it will protrude above the stock being sawed only $\frac{1}{4}$ to $\frac{1}{2}$ inch.
4. Stand to one side of the saw so that if the board does kick back from binding it will not hit you.
5. Use a push stick when necessary.
6. Do not reach over the saw to hold a board which is being cut.
7. Always use the fence of the cut-off guide.
8. Do not try to cut without the use of the cut-off guide or the ripping fence.

Ripping

1. Adjust the ripsaw, or the combination-saw blade, to cut $\frac{1}{4}$ to $\frac{1}{2}$ inch higher than the thickness of the stock to be cut.
2. Set the ripping fence the desired distance from the saw blade (Fig. 28-2).
3. Fasten the ripping fence in place with the adjusting screws and remeasure the width for ripping.
4. Make a trial cut on a piece of scrap wood to see if the width has been accurately set. It is advisable to allow approximately $\frac{1}{8}$ inch for further dressing of the edge on the jointer or with the hand plane.
5. Place the piece of wood to be ripped on the table top with the edge pressed firmly against the ripping fence, and push it with a steady pressure into the saw (Fig. 28-3). Make certain that the guard is in place and that you do not stand directly behind the piece which is being cut.
6. In ripping narrow stock, be sure to use a push stick for safety. Sometimes

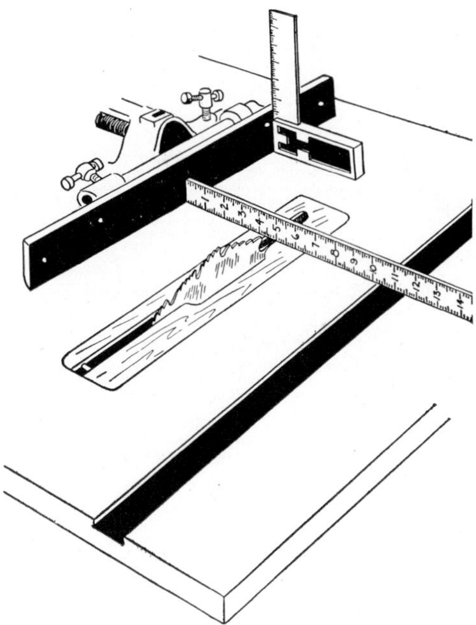

Fig. 28-2. Adjusting the ripping fence to the desired distance. The ripping fence should be at right angles to the table top.

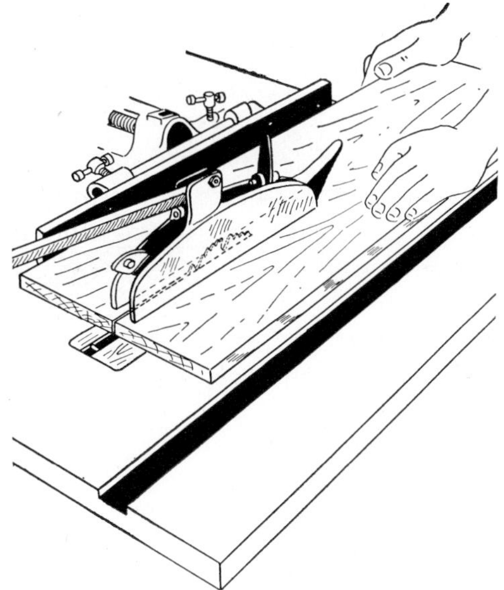

Fig. 28-3. Ripping a board.

in ripping through very thick material, it is wise to set the saw so that it will cut only a portion of the thickness the first time; then re-set it for a deeper cut; and if necessary, re-set for a third and final one.

Crosscutting

1. Place the cut-off guide in the slot, or groove, on the table top. The left groove is the most convenient for crosscutting.

2. Check the guide to see that it is set at the correct angle, 90 degrees for a right angle. This may be checked by holding a try square or framing square against the guide and saw blade.

3. Mark the board where it is to be cut off.

4. Place the board on the table top firmly against the cut-off guide so that the saw cut will be on the salvage side of the marked line.

5. Start the saw and allow it to come to full speed.

6. Push the guide and the piece of wood forward while it is being held firmly against the cut-off guide (Fig. 28-4).

7. At the end of the cut pull back both the board and the cut-off guide. Allow the waste stock to remain on the saw table.

8. When several short pieces are being cut to the same length, a block may be clamped to the ripping fence, as shown in Fig. 28-4. This allows sufficient clearance between the saw blade and the ripping fence.

9. Mark and cut remaining pieces in a similar manner. Miters, bevels, and

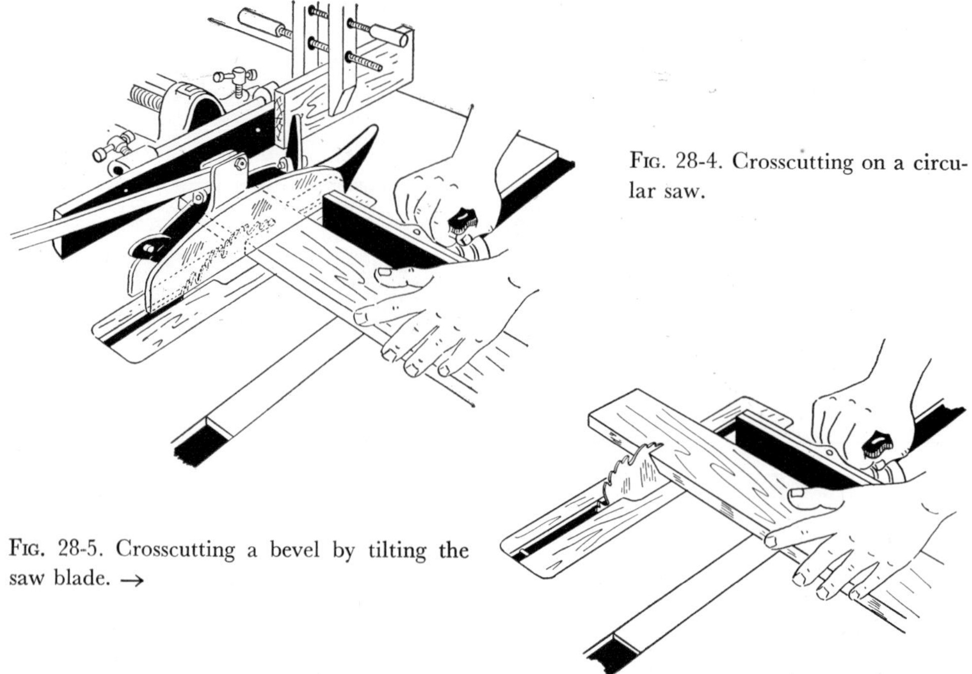

Fig. 28-4. Crosscutting on a circular saw.

Fig. 28-5. Crosscutting a bevel by tilting the saw blade. →

chamfers can be successfully made by adjusting the saw arbor or table to produce the cut, as shown in Fig. 28-5.

Rabbeting

1. Square the stock to the given dimensions. This involves making the boards the required thickness, width, and length.

2. Lay out the size for the rabbet on the end of the piece which is to come in contact with the saw.

3. Set the width of the rabbet by adjusting and moving the ripping fence (Fig. 28-6).

4. Adjust the saw blade for the depth of the rabbet cut (Fig. 28-6).

5. Make a trial cut on a piece of scrap wood.

6. Make the first cut for the rabbet (Fig. 28-6). If several pieces are to have the same rabbet, cut them all with the same saw setting before readjusting it.

7. Turn off the saw and readjust the cutting width with the ripping fence and the cutting height of the blade for making the final cut (Fig. 28-7).

8. Make a trial cut with the same piece of scrape wood used in step 5.

9. Make the second and final cut on the one or several pieces (Fig. 28-7). This completes the procedure for making the rabbet.

The procedure described in this unit may be used for cutting across grain.

Grooving

1. Assemble a dado, or grooving, head, with the blades and cutters, as shown in Fig. 28-8. The number of cutters to use will depend upon the

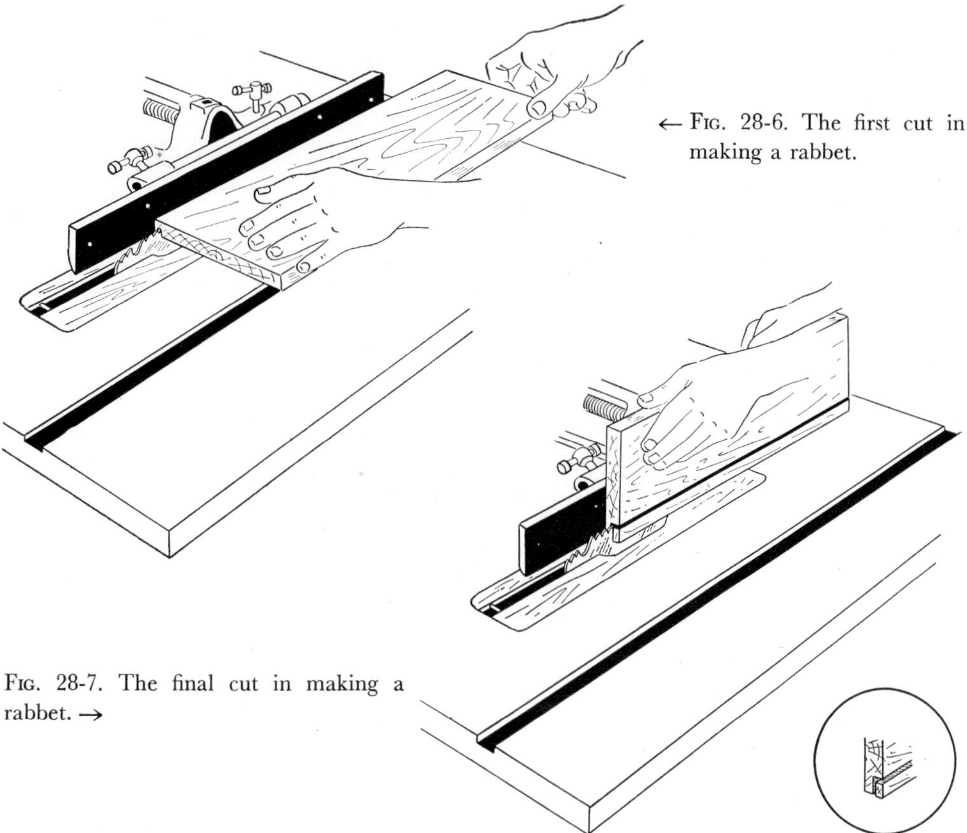

← Fig. 28-6. The first cut in making a rabbet.

Fig. 28-7. The final cut in making a rabbet. →

width of the desired groove, or dado (Fig. 28-8).

2. Remove the plate from the table top and replace the regular blade with the dado-head assembly.

3. Replace the plate on the table saw with one which has a wider opening to accommodate the dado head.

4. Inspect the dado-head assembly to make certain that the teeth are pointed in the proper direction and that the cutters are spaced evenly.

5. Lay out and mark the groove, or dado, on the end of the stock to be cut.

6. Adjust the ripping fence to the distance the groove is to be cut from the edge of the stock.

7. Adjust the cutting height of the dado, or grooving, head to the desired cut.

8. Turn on the saw and make a trial cut on a piece of scrap wood. Caution should be exercised in making a cut with the dado, or grooving, head, because there are several blades and cutters exerting force in the cut.

9. Place the board to be grooved, or dadoed, on the table top, and hold it firmly against the fence while pushing it with even pressure until the cut has been completed (Fig. 28-9). It is permissible, when practicable, to lift the guard out of place when cutting a dado, or groove, because the blades are not ex-

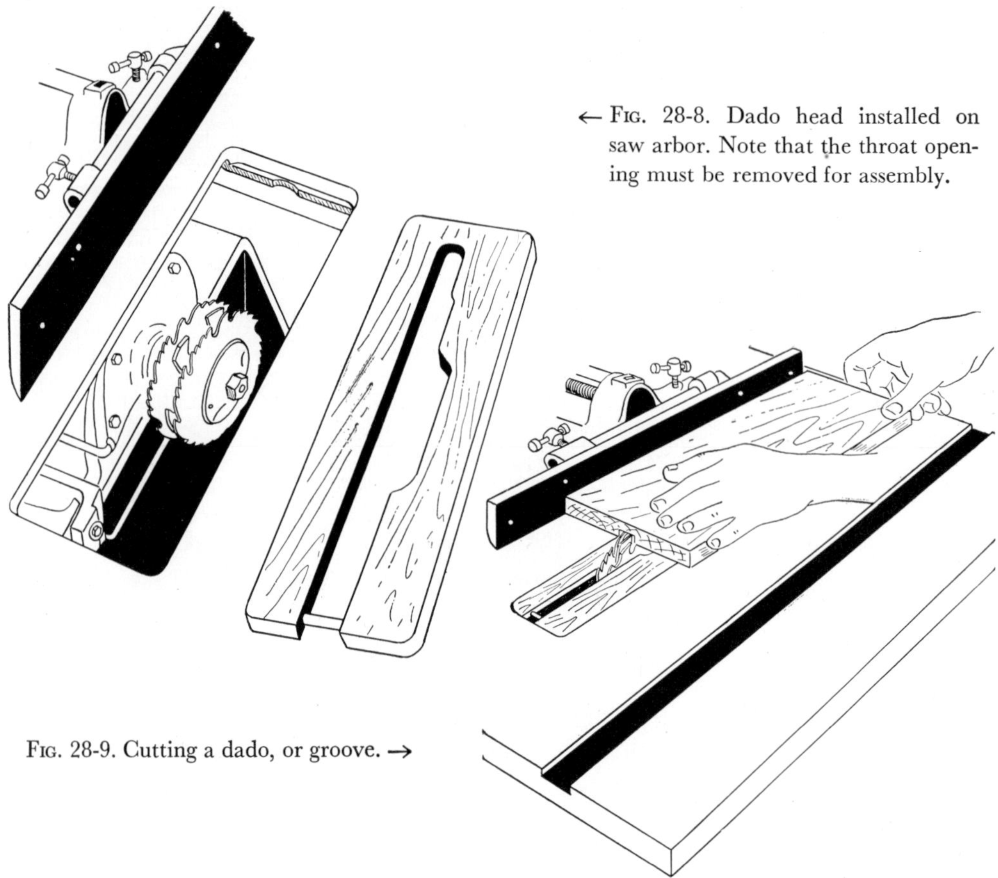

← Fig. 28-8. Dado head installed on saw arbor. Note that the throat opening must be removed for assembly.

Fig. 28-9. Cutting a dado, or groove. →

posed in the cutting process. A groove, or dado, can be made across grain as easily as with grain.

Making Tenons

1. Lay out the tenon on the rail, apron, or any other piece of wood needing a tenon. See Unit 19, "Joining," page 69.
2. Adjust the saw blade so that it will cut the length of the tenon. Use a crosscut or combination saw blade.
3. Adjust the ripping fence so that the saw will cut on the outer edge of the tenon layout.
4. Check the ripping fence for squareness with the saw table top (Fig. 28-2).
5. Remove the saw guard, because it will interfere with cutting the tenon.
6. Turn on the saw and make a trial cut on a piece of scrap wood. Adjust the height of the saw or make any necessary adjustments on the fence.
7. Hold the tenon piece with the working face firmly against the ripping fence, push it slowly into the saw blade, and proceed with the cut (Fig. 28-10).
8. Repeat this process on the opposite end and on other pieces if there are several identical tenons to be cut.
9. Stop the machine, and adjust the

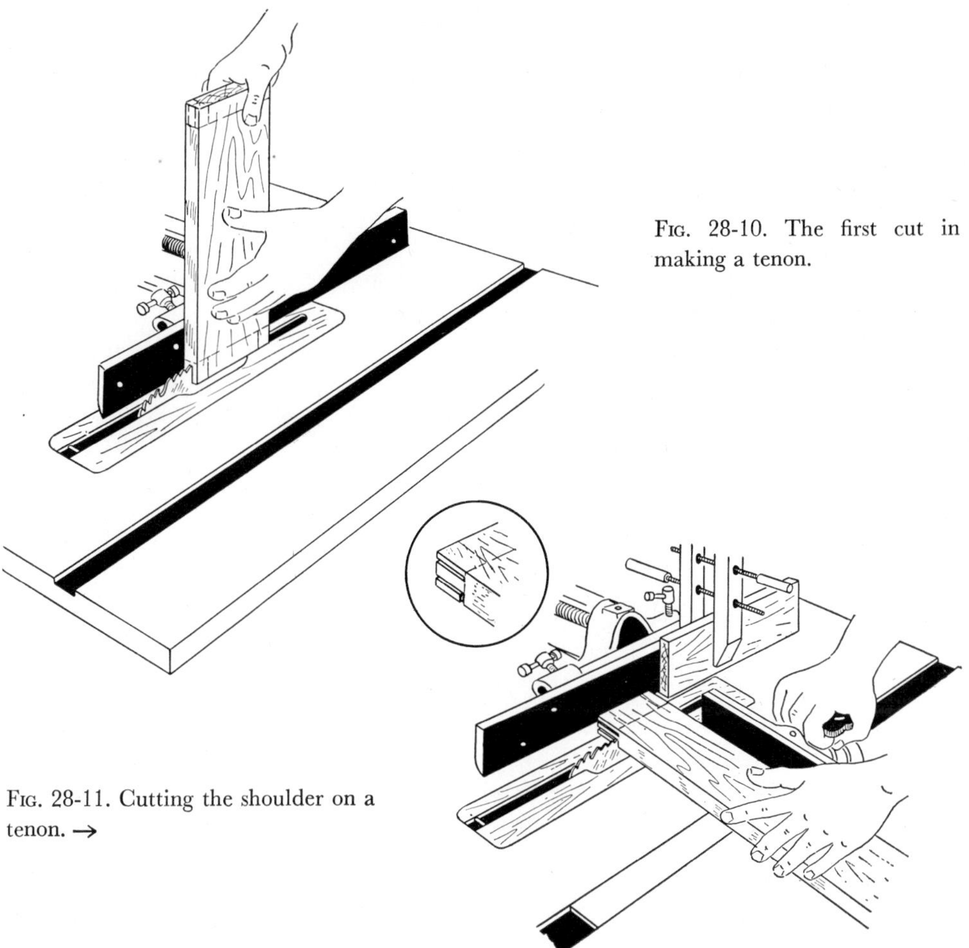

Fig. 28-10. The first cut in making a tenon.

Fig. 28-11. Cutting the shoulder on a tenon. →

ripping fence to the distance necessary to make the other side of the tenon cut.

10. Turn the machine on, and make another trial cut on the original scrap piece to check whether the tenon is being cut to the desired thickness. Adjust the fence if necessary.

11. Again place the tenon piece with the face side against the ripping fence, and proceed to cut as in step 7.

12. Adjust the ripping fence, and make the remaining two small cuts across the ends of the tenons if necessary.

13. Place the cut-off guide in the left groove of the table top, and adjust it for squareness with the saw blade. This is in preparation for cutting the shoulders of the tenons.

14. Clamp a block on the ripping fence as shown for cutting short pieces to equal lengths (Fig. 28-11).

15. Adjust the ripping fence so that the surface of the clamped-on block will be set to the length of the tenon from the far side of the saw blade.

16. Lower the saw blade until it pro-

trudes above the table surface only the distance to the surface of the tenon.

17. Turn on the saw and make a trial cut on the original scrap tenon piece. Adjust the ripping fence or the height of the cutting edge if necessary.

18. Place the tenon piece with the tenon end against the wood block on the ripping fence, and hold it firmly in the cut-off guide while pushing it slowly over the saw blade (Fig. 28-11).

19. Repeat the previous process for forming the shoulders on the other side of the tenon and for fixing the shoulders on all tenons.

Discussion Topics

1. Name the essential parts of a circular saw.
2. List at least six safety rules to be observed in using the circular saw.
3. How far should the saw blade extend above the work for safe operation?
4. When is it desirable to use a push stick?
5. Why is it desirable to fasten a block on the ripping fence when crosscutting several pieces to the same length, as shown in Fig. 28-4?
6. What is the purpose of the dado head?

Unit 29. Sawing on the Band Saw

The band saw is a piece of machinery essential to the cabinetmaker. It can be used for straight sawing as well as for cutting curved pieces. If a circular or table saw is available, however, the use of the band saw is generally confined to curved sawing.

The essential parts are the frame with two wheels mounted on it, an adjustable table, two adjustable saw guides located above and below the table, wheels and levers for making the various adjustments, a band-saw blade, and necessary guards (Fig. 29-1). A ripping fence and cut-off guide are available for doing straight cutting on some of the large types.

The size of the band saw is indicated by the diameter of the wheels. The 18- to 30-inch band saw is conveniently used in school shops, while the home workshop enthusiast will probably use a smaller size saw. A 12- to 14-inch one is a popular size. Wheels of smaller diameters tend to crystallize band-saw blades in a relatively short time causing them to break more easily. This cuts down their length of service.

Safety

1. Keep a sharp blade in use at all times.

2. Examine the blade in use frequently to make sure that breaks owing to crystallization have not developed.

3. Braze the band-saw blade or have it brazed whenever checks do occur.

4. Check tension on the blade frequently in accordance with the specifications of the manufacturer.

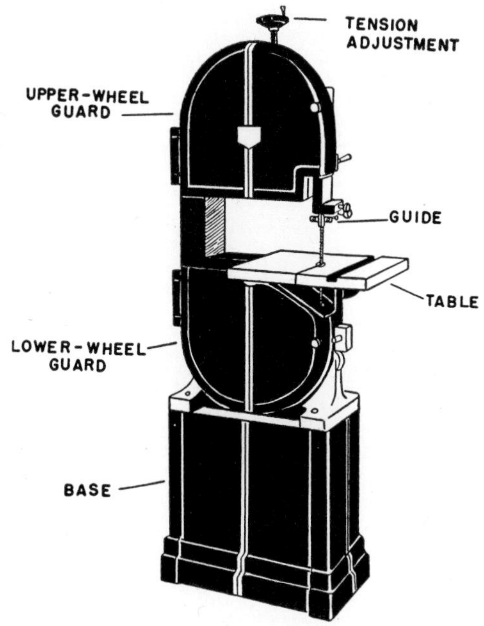

FIG. 29-1. An 18-inch band saw.

5. Keep the machine well lubricated at all times.

6. Keep safety guards fastened firmly.

7. Feed work into the band-saw blade firmly but without pushing it too fast.

8. Maintain a well-balanced stance on both feet while working at the band saw.

FIG. 29-2. Sawing a curve on the band saw.

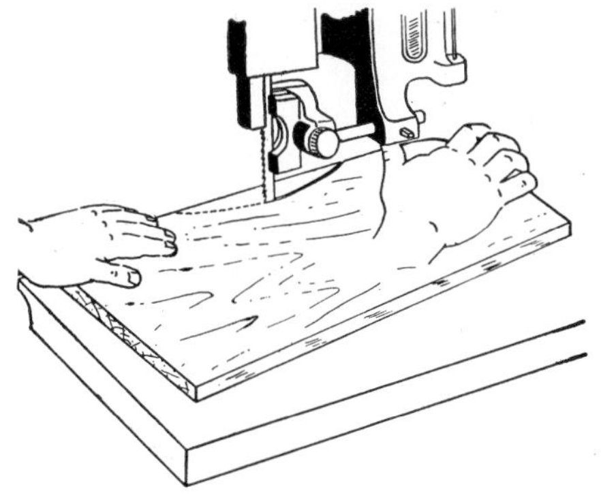

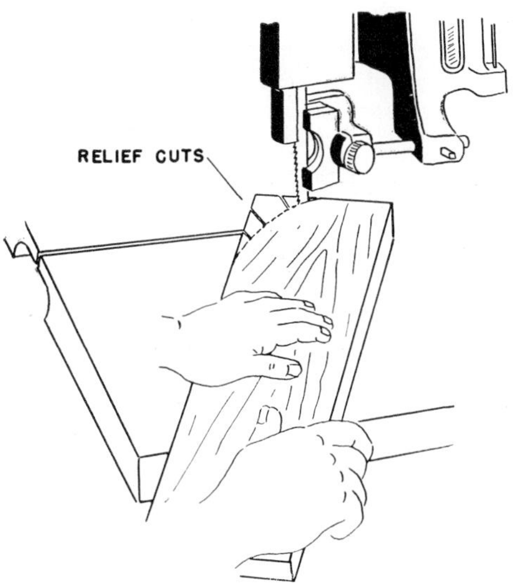

FIG. 29-3. Relief cuts are desirable when sawing sharp curves.

SAWING

1. Surface or plane the stock to the required thickness.

2. Mark the board, make a layout, or transfer the pattern to the board.

3. Adjust the upper guide on the band saw to clear the thickness of the stock approximately $\frac{1}{4}$ inch (Fig. 29-2). This height may be obtained by placing the edge of the board against the band saw and then adjusting the upper guide.

4. Start the saw, and make certain that it is running full speed before attempting to cut.

5. Move the board gently against the saw blade and start the cut on the waste side of the line (Fig. 29-2). Allow approximately $\frac{1}{8}$ inch of surplus for final smoothing.

6. If there are sharp curves to be sawed, there should be several relief cuts made before attempting to cut the board (Fig. 29-3). This will depend

somewhat upon the type of material being cut and the width of the saw blade. A $\frac{1}{8}$-inch blade will cut to a radius of approximately 1 inch, while a $\frac{3}{8}$-inch blade will cut to a radius of $1\frac{1}{2}$ inches.

Discussion Topics

1. Name the essential parts of the band saw.
2. Name at least six safety precautions to be observed when cutting on the band saw.
3. How does one determine the size of a band saw?
4. What is the purpose in making relief cuts?
5. What other types of sawing besides curved cutting can be done on the band saw?

Unit 30. Sawing on the Jig Saw

The jig saw, or scroll saw (as it is often called), is used for cutting either internal or external curves of designs. The essential parts are the base, frame, table, upper and lower chucks, tension sleeve, and guide (Fig. 30-1). Many jig saws also have hold-down devices.

The size of a jig saw is determined by the horizontal distance between the saw blade and the arm of the frame; this gives clearance in cutting. Often jig saws are referred to in size by the clearance measurement, which varies from 12 to 24 inches. The most popular and practical sizes are 18 to 24 inches.

Fig. 30-1. A 24-inch jig saw.

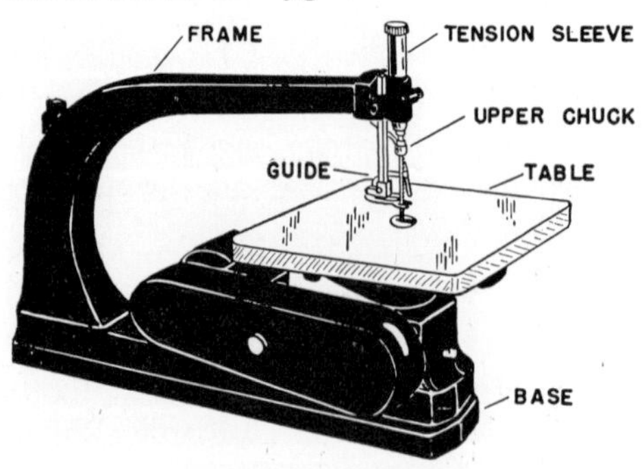

Blades used in jig saws are often manufactured expressly for that purpose; however, jeweler's and coping-saw blades may be used with equal success. Each machine will have certain specifications for blade tension and adjustments, which are recommended by the manufacturer. These should be followed in operating the jig saw

Safety

1. Make certain that all adjustments are set as prescribed by the manufacturer's specifications.

2. Fasten the blade in the chucks with the teeth pointing downward.

3. Maintain the proper tension on the blade.

4. Always adjust the hold-down device so that it will barely clear the work.

5. Use both hands to handle the board being cut.

Sawing

1. Mark, lay out, or transfer the design to the stock.

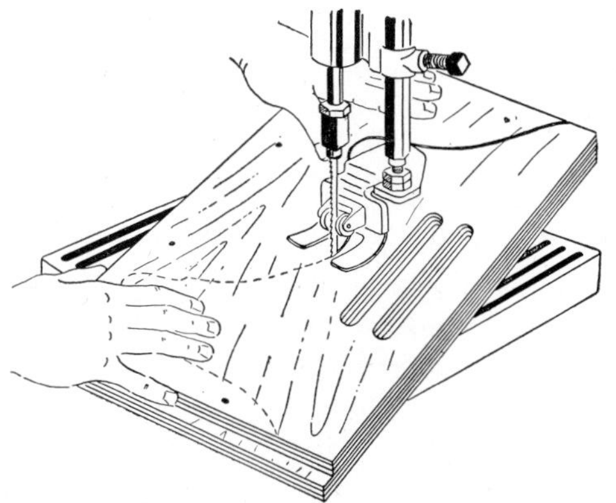

FIG. 30-2. Cutting a curve on a jig saw.

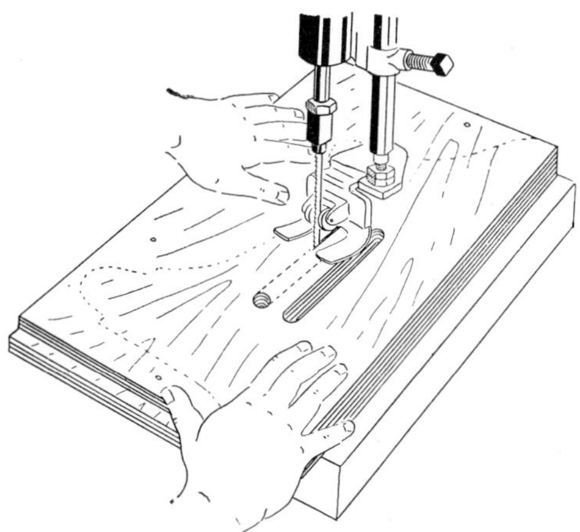

FIG. 30-3. Sawing an internal pattern on a jig saw.

2. Insert the saw blade through the hole or slot in the table, and drop it to fit the lower chuck.

3. Fasten the lower end of the blade by securing it in the lower chuck.

4. Release the tension for the top chuck and fasten the top end of the blade in it.

5. Adjust the tension of the blade according to instructions from the teacher or those in the accompanying saw manual.

6. Place the stock to be cut on the table top and against the saw blade. Lower the top guide and adjust it so that it will barely clear the stock. Frequently the hold-down device is fastened to the top-guide assembly so that this entire adjustment can be made at the same time (Fig. 30-2).

7. Turn on the saw, gently move the stock against the saw blade, and start the cut just barely outside of the mark or pattern line (Fig. 30-2). This will allow for a minimum of edge dressing.

8. When cutting internal designs (Fig. 30-3), either drill or bore a hole in a waste portion of the design; then insert the blade through this hole as outlined in steps 2, 3, and 4.

9. Cut the internal design in a manner similar to that explained in step 7.

10. Continue sawing by moving the stock with both hands so that the cutting follows the design lines.

11. In sawing duplicate parts on thin stock, fasten them together with brads so that all parts will be identical (Figs. 30-2 and 30-3).

Discussion Topics

1. What are the essential parts of the jig saw?
2. Name at least five safety precautions to be observed when using the jig saw?
3. How is the size of a jig saw determined?
4. What is another name for the jig saw?
5. What is the procedure for internal sawing?
6. How may duplicate parts be sawed identically?

Unit 31. Planing on the Jointer

The jointer is a piece of power-driven machinery which does the work of a hand plane. It is capable of performing a great variety of processes in addition to straight planing. The more experienced workman will often cut rabbets, tapers, bevels, chamfers, stop chamfers, and molding on it. However, this variety of process should not be attempted by the beginner.

The essential parts of a jointer are the base, front and rear tables, cutter head with blades, fence, and safety guard (Fig. 31-1). The cutter head contains three and sometimes four blades. The size of a jointer is determined by the width of cut it can make. Six- or eight-inch jointers are adequate for small-shop and home-workshop activities, but frequently a 10- or 12-inch one is used in the larger school shops and in industry. The rear table is adjustable for alignment with the cutting edge. The front table, which is nearest the operator, has a hand-wheel adjustment for depth of cut.

Fig. 31-1. An 8-inch jointer.

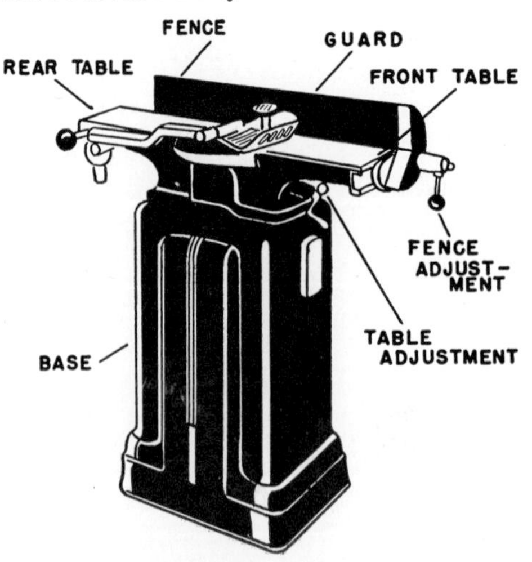

Safety

1. Keep the safety guard in place at all times.

2. Plane only boards longer than 12 inches on the jointer. Stock shorter than 12 inches is unsafe, because your hands get too close to the blades. Dress this short stock with a hand plane.

3. Use the push block in surfacing boards on the jointer.

4. Always hold the board firmly against the fence or on the table in jointing.

5. Surface the concave side of a warped board first.

6. Make certain the jointer blades are sharp at all times.

7. Assume a firm stance to the left of the machine and never at the end of the front table, because a board may accidentally kick back.

Planing on the Jointer

1. Adjust the front table so that the cut will be approximately $\frac{1}{32}$ inch for surface planing and $\frac{1}{16}$ inch for edge planing. Many jointers have measurement indexes on them.

Fig. 31-2. Testing the squareness of a fence with the table on a jointer.

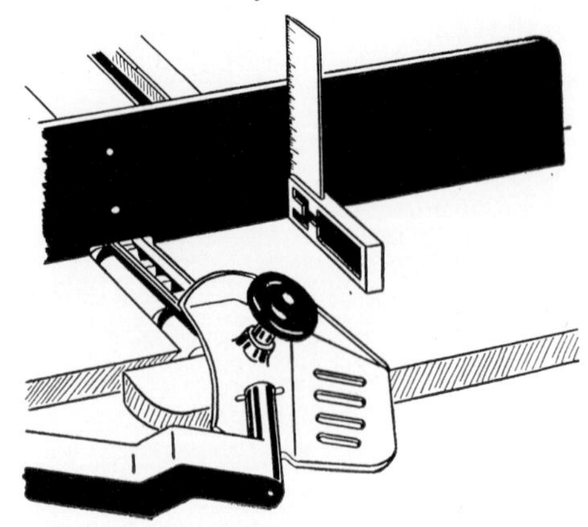

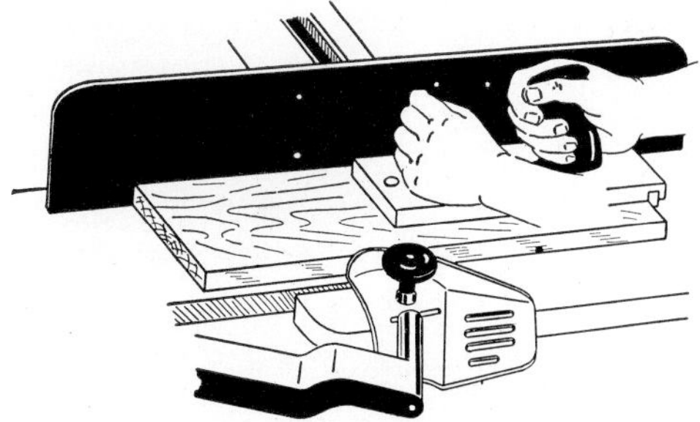

FIG. 31-3. Planing the surface of a board on a jointer.

2. Test the fence for squareness with the table surface by the use of a try square (Fig. 31-2). Make necessary adjustments on the fence to obtain the 90-degree angle.

3. Place the safety guard in position over the cutter head and see that the guard is working properly. Some guards go up as material is fed through, and others spring out.

4. Turn on the jointer and make a trial cut on a piece of clean scrap stock. Make any adjustment needed for depth.

5. For planing the surface, place the board flat on the front table top. If the board is warped, the concave face should be placed down.

6. Feed the board slowly but firmly over the rotating cutter head, and continue pushing it through until the entire face has been planed. It is advisable to use the push block in the final follow-through, especially on shorter boards (Fig. 31-3).

FIG. 31-4. Planing an edge of a board on a jointer.

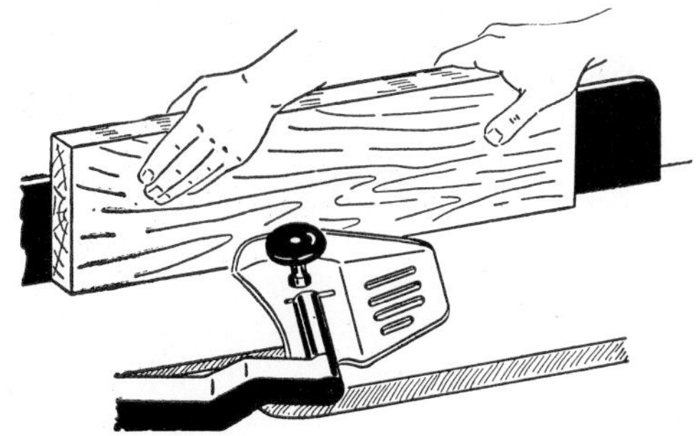

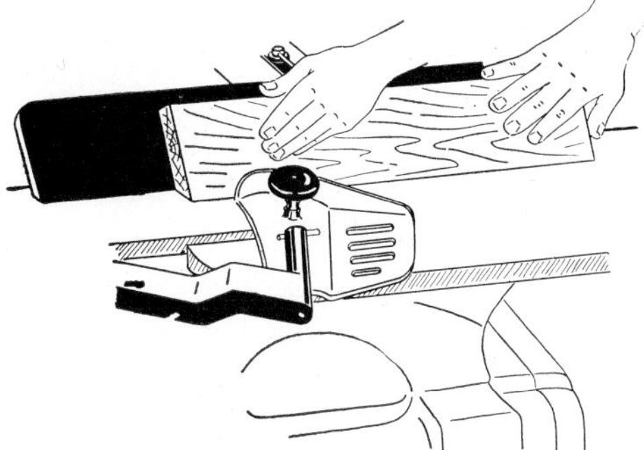

FIG. 31-5. Planing a bevel on the edge of a board on a jointer.

7. In planing an edge, place the board on its edge on the front table firmly against the fence and feed it slowly over the rotating cutter head (Fig. 31-4).

8. Chamfers and bevels may be cut easily by adjusting the fence to the angle desired with the front table (Fig. 31-5) and then following the process described in step 7.

Discussion Topics

1. What are the essential parts of a jointer?
2. List at least six safety precautions to be observed in using the jointer.
3. How is the size of a jointer determined?
4. Which table should be adjusted to determine the depth of a cut?
5. Enumerate four additional uses of the jointer for the experienced craftsman.
6. What adjustment must be made for cutting a chamfer or a bevel?

Unit 32. Boring and Drilling Holes with the Drill Press

The drill press is a machine often thought of in connection with metalworking; however, it is also very well adapted to, and suitable for, woodworking. It is one of the less expensive pieces of equipment and can perform many operations besides the basic ones considered here of boring and drilling holes. The additional operations are mortising, shaping, routing, and sanding. The essential parts are the base, table, vertical column, housing and motor support, spindle, chuck, motor, V belt, and adjusting devices (Fig. 32-1).

To perform the various operations listed in the previous paragraph, drill presses are available with arrangements of pulleys to obtain speeds varying from approximately 350 to 6,000 revolutions per minute (rpm). Charts and tables of speeds dependent upon the several pulley-and-belt arrangements are furnished for all the machines by their manufacturers. The lower speeds are suitable for drilling and boring; the higher ones are for mortising, shaping, routing, and sanding. This unit, however, will discuss only the more simple processes of boring and drilling holes, since it is concerned essentially with the basic and beginning processes in woodworking.

Fig. 32-1. A bench-model drill press.

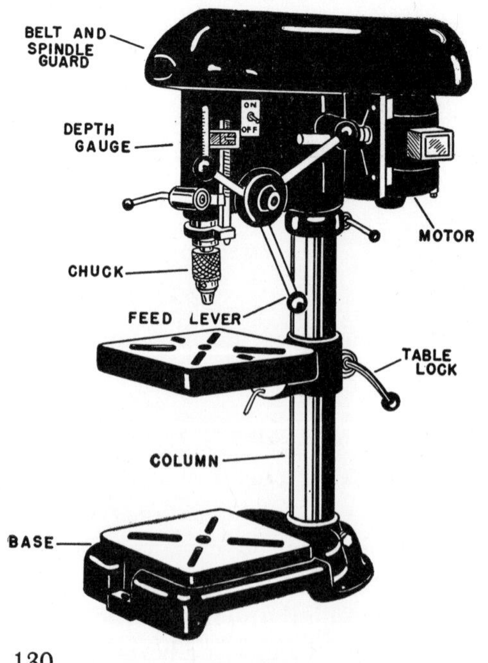

To bore holes with an auger bit fastened in the chuck of a drill press, cut off the tang with a hack saw to permit the round shank to fit in the chuck jaws, and file off the thread of the feed screw so that the point will not screw into the wood (Fig. 32-4, left view).

The average-size chuck for the small-bench or floor-model drill press will accommodate drill bits up to $\frac{1}{2}$ inch in diameter. The usual drill bits used in metalwork are sufficiently serviceable for wood. For holes larger than $\frac{1}{2}$ inch in diameter, it is advisable to prepare some old auger bits as shown in Fig. 32-4, left view.

Safety

1. If the chuck uses a key, be sure that it is removed before starting the drill press.
2. Always check the pulley combinations to see if the proper speed is set up.
3. Keep loose clothing, such as necktie and sleeves, well protected.
4. Use goggles or face shield when using the drill press at high speed.
5. Cover the pulleys with a guard to keep clothing and hair out of them.

6. Hold the work firmly so that it will not fly off the table and injure someone.

Boring and Drilling

1. Lay out and mark the center for drilling or boring a hole. The center should be definitely marked with an awl (Fig. 32-2).

2. Select a drill or auger bit of the correct size and fasten it in the chuck.

3. Place the board on the table of the drill press and adjust the table to the correct height. If the hole is to be bored or drilled through, allow approximately one extra inch for a scrap piece of wood to be used underneath the board.

4. Turn on the drill press, and observe the action of the bit to see that it is properly fastened in the jaws of the chuck and that it does not wobble.

Fig. 32-2. Marking the center with an awl for drilling or boring a hole.

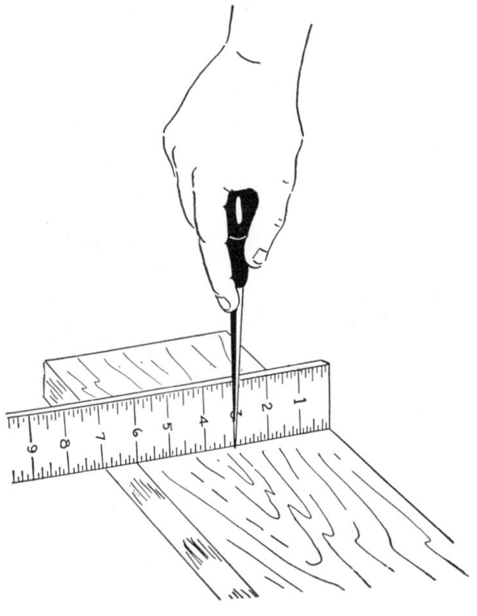

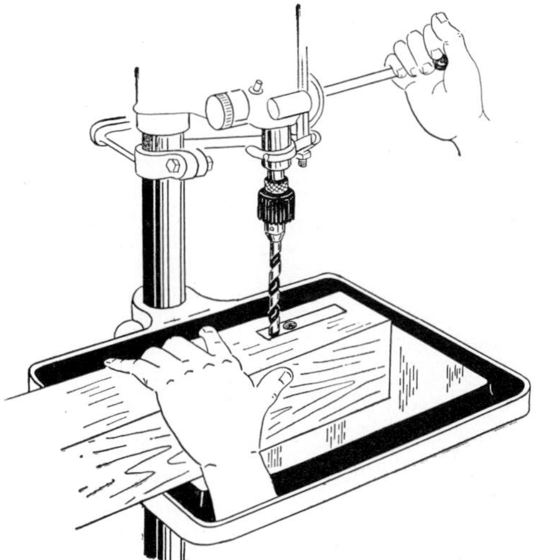

Fig. 32-3. Drilling a series of holes for making a mortise.

5. Hold the board securely and apply even pressure in feeding the bit into the wood slowly. If the wood smokes, the speed should be reduced. Figures 32-3 and 32-4 illustrate the use of the drill and the auger bits on wood.

Fig. 32-4. Boring a hole with a specially prepared auger bit.

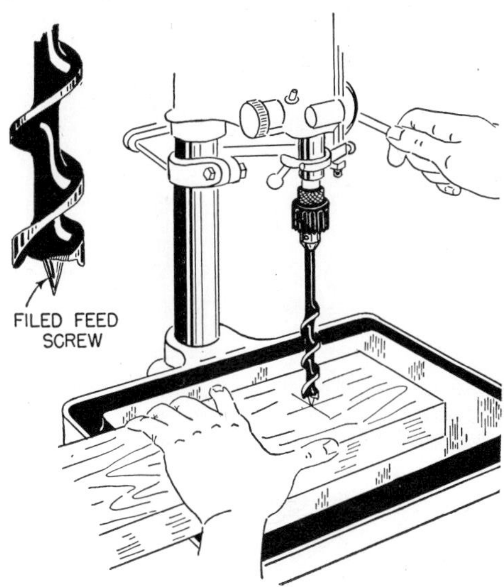

Discussion Topics

1. Name the essential parts of the drill press.
2. List at least five safety precautions to be observed in using the drill press.
3. How is the speed of the drill press changed?
4. What must be done to an auger bit to make it adaptable for use on the drill press?
5. What will happen if the lead screw of the auger bit is not filed smooth?
6. Name at least three other operations which may be performed on the drill press in addition to drilling and boring holes.

Unit 33. Shaping on the Shaper

The power shaper used in woodworking is designed primarily for making molding, paneling, and grooving on straight or curved edges. It may be used for fluting legs on elaborate furniture. This, like other woodworking machines, is available in light-weight equipment for the home workshop, heavier or sturdy machinery for the school, or heavy-duty machines used in industrial mass production. The vertical spindle rotates at a speed of from 7,000 to 10,000 revolutions per minute (rpm).

Fig. 33-1. A shaper.

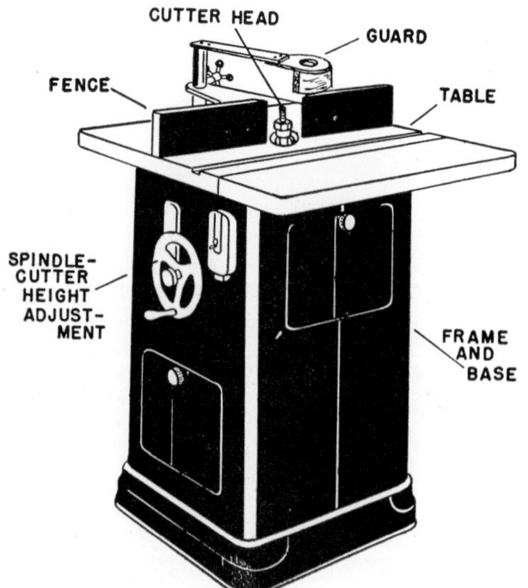

The essential parts of the shaper shown in Fig. 33-1 are the frame, vertical spindle cutter head, table, adjustable fence, adjustable guard, various collars and cutters, and the motor. On some shapers the table is adjustable, while others have the spindle adjustable to allow for adaptation to the shaping needs. Cutters are obtainable as separate knives which fit between grooved collars or in the three-cutter type, which is generally used on home-workshop and lighter weight machinery. The latter type is the safer.

Safety

1. Always keep the cutters sharp.
2. Make certain that the cutter or cutter knives are fastened securely before using the shaper.
3. Keep all moving parts well lubricated.
4. Keep the safety guard in place when using the machine.
5. Maintain a well-balanced stance on both feet when operating the shaper.

Fig. 33-2. Shaping a straight edge.

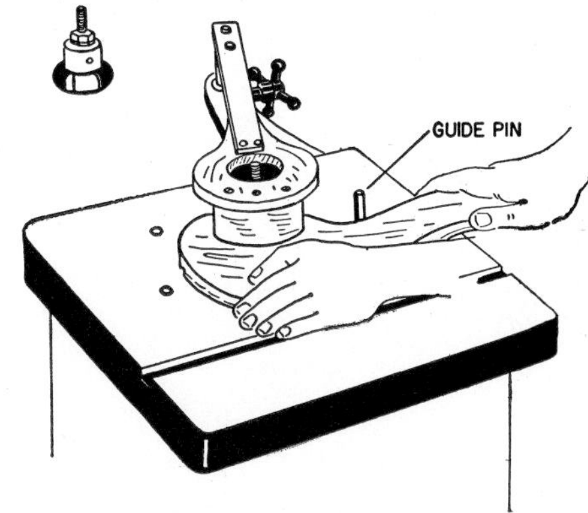

Fig. 33-3. Shaping an irregular edge.

6. Have plenty of shadow-free illumination on the work.

7. Hold the stock firmly against the fence for straight work or directly against the spindle for curved work, and feed it slowly into the cutter.

Shaping

1. Select a cutter or cutters for edge shaping. The solid three-cutter kind is suggested for the inexperienced person. There are many shapes available in this type.

2. Place the cutter (or cutters) on the spindle and tighten the nut, which holds the cutter, with a wrench. Practically every shaper has some means of locking the spindle while tightening the assembly.

3. For straight cutting, place the adjustable fence on the table and fasten it in the position desired. This will be determined by the depth and width of cut which is to be made on the edge of the board. (Fig. 33-2).

4. When shaping curved or irregular edges on a board, leave the fence off. However, a guide pin should aid the operator in holding the work against the shaper blades (Fig. 33-3).

5. Start the machine.

6. Test the cut on a piece of scrap wood of the same thickness. Examine the edge pattern and make any necessary adjustments.

7. Shape the edge of the board by holding it firmly against the fence or pin and pushing it slowly into the cutter (Figs. 33-2 and 33-3).

Discussion Topics

1. Name the essential parts of a shaper.
2. What are the approximate revolutions per minute at which the spindle operates satisfactorily?
3. Why is such a fast speed necessary?
4. How may the depth and height of a cut be controlled?
5. Mention five uses for the shaper in woodworking.
6. List at least six safety precautions.

Unit 34. Turning on the Wood Lathe

The wood lathe is one of the oldest types of power equipment known to mankind for fashioning wooden objects. The primitive machine was driven with an endless-rope belt hand-propelled by a helper. Modern lathes enable inexperienced workers to produce beautifully turned pieces with much less effort. The basic operations performed on the lathe are turning between live and dead centers and turning on a face plate.

The size of a lathe is usually determined by the maximum length of piece which can be accommodated between centers and by the swing of the face plate, which indicates the diameter to be turned on it.

The essential parts of a lathe (Fig. 34-1) are the headstock, which frequently has the motor attached to it, the live center, the face plate, the tailstock, the dead center, the tool rest and holder, the frame which supports the ways on which the tailstock and tool holder move, and the several necessary hand wheels and adjusting levers.

On the more elaborate machines the speed is controlled by a variable-speed motor built in the headstock; on the less expensive ones, by a combination of step-down pulleys and an individual motor. A general rule to remember is that the larger the stock to be turned, the slower the speed required.

Special types of chisels or wood turner's tools are used in conjunction with the lathe. Some of the more commonly used ones, shown in Fig. 34-2, are the gouge, the skew, the parting tool, the round nose, and the diamond point. The latter three are used principally for scraping.

The *gouge* (*A*) is generally used for rough turning, particularly in reducing stock between centers. It is available in sizes varying from $\frac{1}{8}$ to 2 inches, which are suitable for producing small and large coves and circular grooves.

Fig. 34-1. Wood-turning lathe.

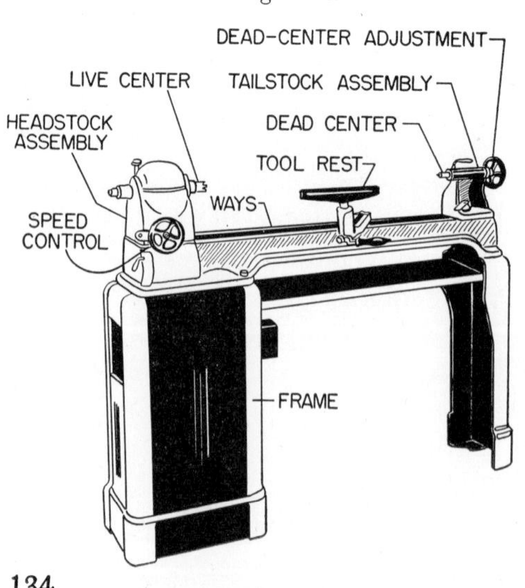

Fig. 34-2. Five of the more common wood-turning tools: (*A*) gouge, (*B*) skew chisel, (*C*) parting tool, (*D*) round nose, and (*E*) diamond point.

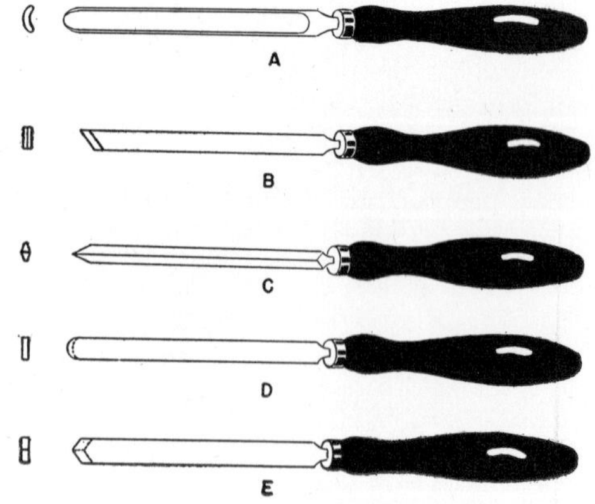

The common one to use for roughing is the 1 inch.

The *skew chisel* (*B*) is so-called because the cutting edge is skewed at an angle to the side. It is used in producing a shearing cut and for making smooth cuts after the stock has been reduced to the approximate diameter. Skew chisels are available in varying sizes, the common one being the $\frac{3}{4}$ inch.

The *parting tool* (*C*) is used for cutting grooves with straight sides and a square bottom. This tools cuts by a scraping action. The parting tool with a cross section of $\frac{3}{16}$ inch is very satisfactory for this work.

The *round nose* (*D*) is a scraping tool used principally in rough turning and for forming grooves and coves. A convenient size is the $\frac{1}{2}$-inch width.

The *diamond point* (*E*) is a scraping tool used mainly as a substitute for skew chisels. It is obtainable in a variety of sizes, of which the $\frac{1}{2}$-inch width is the most sturdy and serviceable.

Additional tools used in wood turning are the caliper and the slip stone. The *outside caliper* (Fig. 34-3) is commonly used to check the proper diameters in turning. The *slip stone* (Fig. 34-4) with the rounded edge is extensively used for whetting turning tools.

Fig. 34-3. Outside, spring caliper.

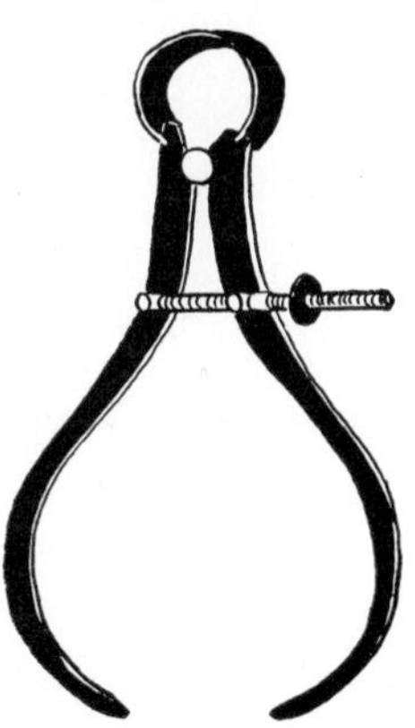

Safety

1. Make certain that the live and dead centers on straight turning stock are properly located and fixed so the piece will not fly out while it is being turned.

2. Check frequently to see that the locking adjustment on the tailstock assembly does not become loose. If it is not secure, the turning stock will work loose and will be thrown from the lathe.

3. Loose clothing worn by the operator should be well protected. If possible, roll sleeves up out of the way and fasten necktie to the shirt.

4. Wear clear-glass goggles or a face shield as good insurance against small particles of wood which may hit the eyes.

5. Keep the turning chisels extra sharp. Dull tools are the cause of many minor accidents and produce inferior work.

6. If possible, have plenty of natural light while turning.

7. Maintain a firm, well-balanced stance on both feet.

8. Adjust the lathe for its slowest speed for all beginning rough turning.

Fig. 34-4. Slip stone.

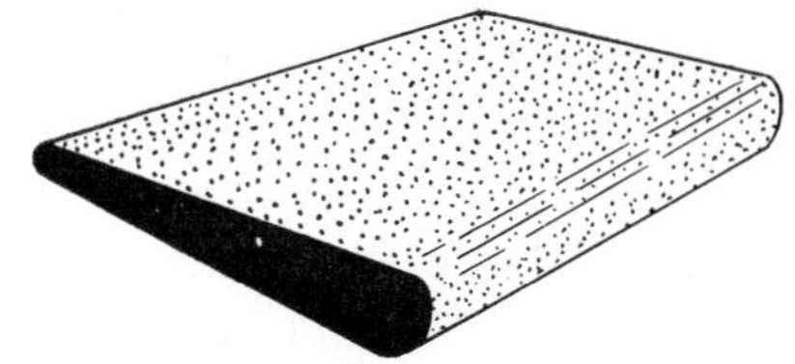

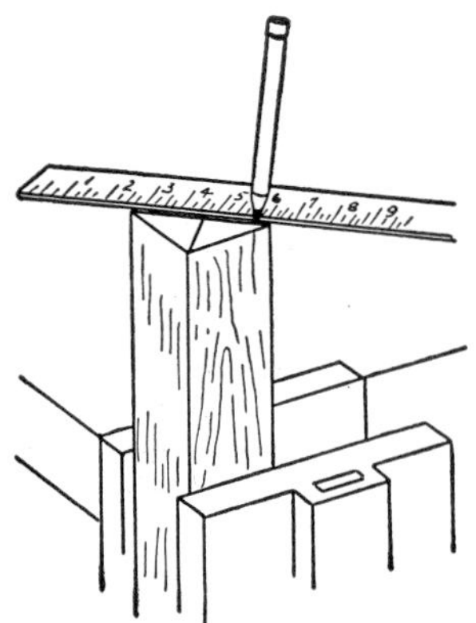

Fig. 34-5. Drawing diagonal lines to locate centers.

The speed may be advanced as the work smooths out.

Straight or Spindle Turning

Stock for turning between centers must be well centered for balance and even turning.

Preparing stock for turning. 1. Select a piece of wood approximately 1 inch longer than the finished size and approximately square in cross section, allowing at least $\frac{1}{4}$ inch for turning down to the finished size.

2. Draw lines diagonally across both

Fig. 34-6. Sawing on diagonal lines for locating live center.

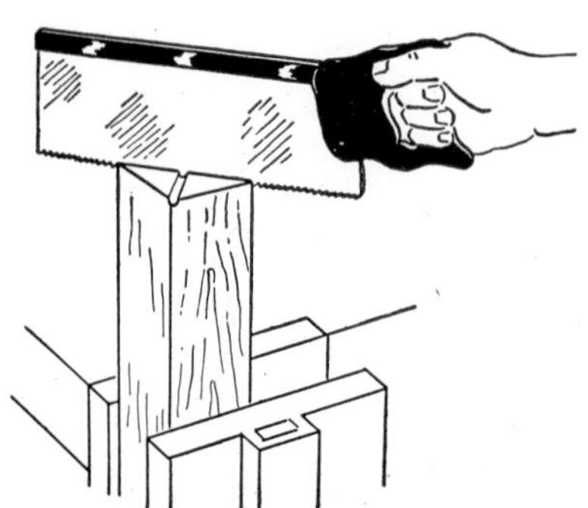

ends of the stock (Fig. 34-5). The point of intersection will serve as the center.

3. Cut a saw kerf on the diagonal lines on one end about $\frac{1}{8}$ inch deep (Fig. 34-6).

4. Place the stock to be turned on a solid surface or hold it securely in a bench vise.

5. Remove the live center from the headstock of the lathe, using the pin or rod provided for that purpose.

6. Place the live center in the saw grooves or kerfs, and tap a couple of times with a mallet to drive it in firmly, seating the prongs in the kerf and the spur point at the point of intersection (Fig. 34-7).

7. Remove the live center, using the hand, and place it back in the headstock on the lathe.

8. Make a small hole with an awl at the point of intersection marked on the opposite end of the stock.

Fig. 34-7. Locating the spur point, or live center.

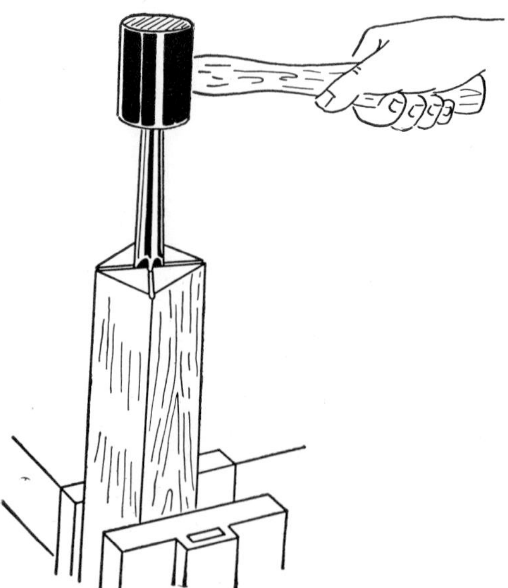

FIG. 34-8. Turning stock fastened between centers.

9. Put two or three drops of lubricating oil on this hole.

10. Place the wood with the grooved end against the live center; hold the stock in position with the left hand.

Release the tailstock and draw it up to within about one inch of the stock, and clamp the tailstock against the bed of the lathe frame.

Turn the handwheel on the tailstock so that the spindle will guide the point of the dead center into the hole made with the awl.

11. Tighten the stock with the handwheel on the tailstock until it feels secure, then lock the handwheel with the adjusting lever. Figure 34-8 shows the stock between centers.

Turning stock between centers. 1. Adjust the tool rest slightly above the center of the piece to be turned. Allow at least $\frac{1}{8}$-inch clearance between the outer edges of the piece to be turned and the tool rest.

FIG. 34-9. Starting the rough cut with a gouge.

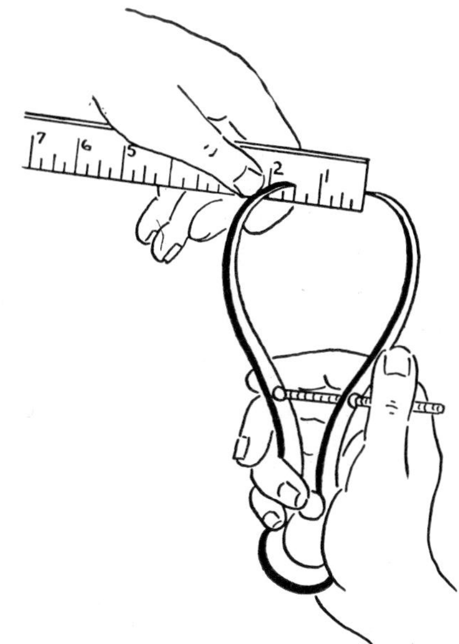

FIG. 34-10. Setting the caliper to the desired diameter.

2. Revolve the work by hand or with the handwheel to make certain that there is sufficient clearance.

3. Adjust the lathe to run at a slow speed; then start the motor.

4. Place the gouge (Fig. 34-2 *A*) on the tool rest, holding it in a position similar to that shown in Fig. 34-9.

5. Start the rough cut by moving the gouge from right to left on the tool rest, pushing it with the right hand and guiding it with the left (Fig. 34-9).

If the operator wishes to cut from left to right, the positions of the hands on the gouge will be reversed.

6. Continue the rough cutting until the piece of wood is reduced to a cylindrical form. As the piece is cut down, the amount of vibration will lessen and turning will become easier.

7. Set the caliper to the maximum diameter desired (Fig. 34-10).

8. Cut the stock with the gouge at one place until the caliper will barely slip over the work (Fig. 34-11).

9. Dress down the entire length to the diameter established in step 8.

10. Turn off the motor and mark locations for the shoulders on the stock with a pencil and a rule (Fig. 34-12).

11. Revolve the stock by hand or with the handwheel, and finish marking around the cylinder with a pencil, as shown in Fig. 34-12.

12. Trim the ends with a skew (Fig. 34-13).

13. Set the caliper (or calipers) to the sizes of the various shoulders indicated in the design or drawing (Fig. 34-10).

14. Set the tool rest about $\frac{3}{16}$ inch below the center of the work and out about $\frac{1}{2}$ inch.

15. Turn on the motor. Place the parting or cutoff tool on the tool rest at a place marked for any one of the shoulders.

16. Hold the parting tool firmly on the tool rest, and push it into the wood steadily until the caliper will barely slip over (Fig. 34-14).

17. Cut to the remaining shoulders with the parting tool in a similar manner.

18. Set the caliper to the smallest diameter needed in a concave cut (Fig. 34-11).

19. Cut the stock to form the concave design shown in a working draw-

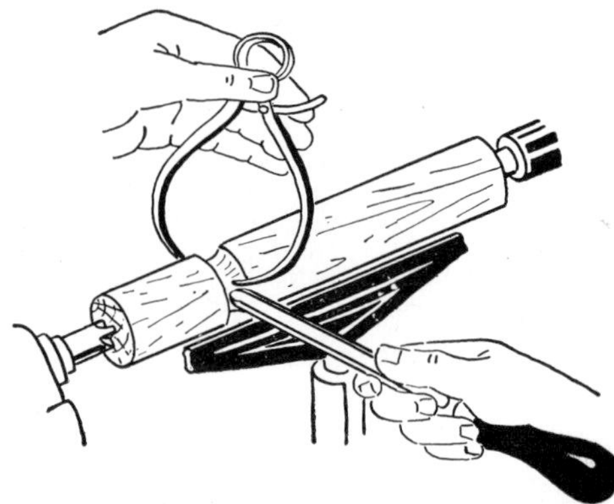

Fig. 34-11. Reducing the turned stock to the required diameter.

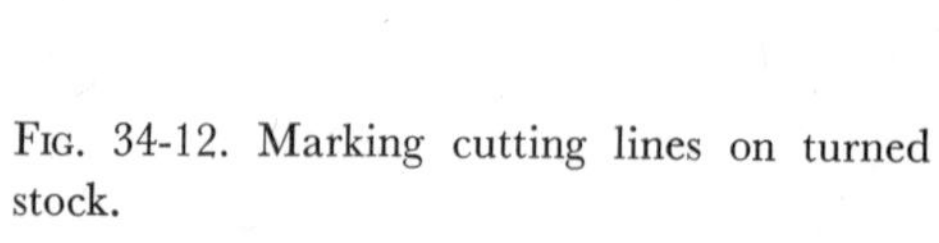

Fig. 34-12. Marking cutting lines on turned stock.

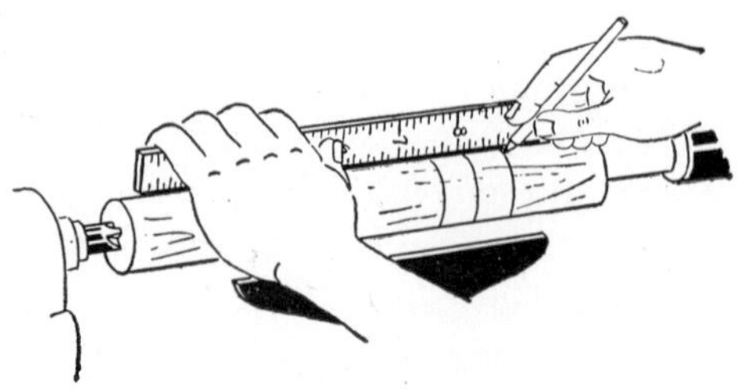

Fig. 34-13. Trimming the ends with a skew chisel.

Fig. 34-14. Cutting shoulders with parting tool to required diameters.

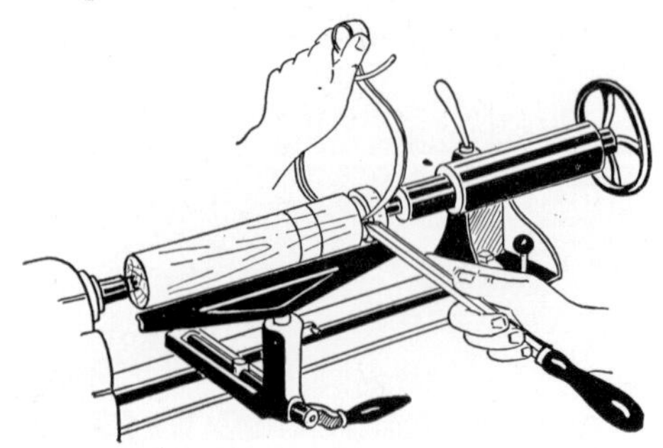

ing. A gouge is most satisfactory for this purpose and it may be handled so that it will produce a cutting action.

Continue cutting the concave portions until the minimum diameter is reached, as indicated by use of the caliper (Fig. 34-11).

20. Cut convex parts and beads with a gouge or scraping chisel.

21. Many designs, such as desk and end-table legs, require the turning of only certain parts of the object or leg while other parts remain square. In this case, the stock should be marked and a shoulder cut first, as shown in Fig. 34-15. The part to be turned can be roughed down, as shown in Fig. 34-9. The remainder of the turning process will be similar to what has been previously described and illustrated.

Sanding. 1. Tear off a narrow strip of No. $\frac{1}{2}$ or No. 1 sandpaper.

2. Start the lathe at a medium speed.

3. Sand all shoulders first with the sandpaper folded. Make certain that the paper is held so that the shoulders are not rounded.

4. Tear off a piece of sandpaper, approximately one sixth of a sheet, for sanding the other parts of the turning.

5. Fold the sandpaper as shown in upper left of Fig. 34-16 so that it forms the curvature of the cove, and hold it to the wood with a finger to fit the cove.

6. Sand the remainder of the turning, as shown in Fig. 34-16.

7. Use finer sandpaper, such as No. 2/0, and repeat the sanding processes as described in steps 2 through 6.

8. Stop the lathe, and sand the turning lengthwise, or with the grain, to remove conical scratches which may have been made while the work was turning.

Face-plate Turning

Turning on the face plate involves the careful location of stock on the face plate.

Preparing stock for turning. 1. Select and cut the stock for turning on the face plate for thickness, width, length, and the type of wood desired. When rough-cut, it will resemble the piece in Fig. 37-17. Allow approximately $\frac{1}{2}$ inch

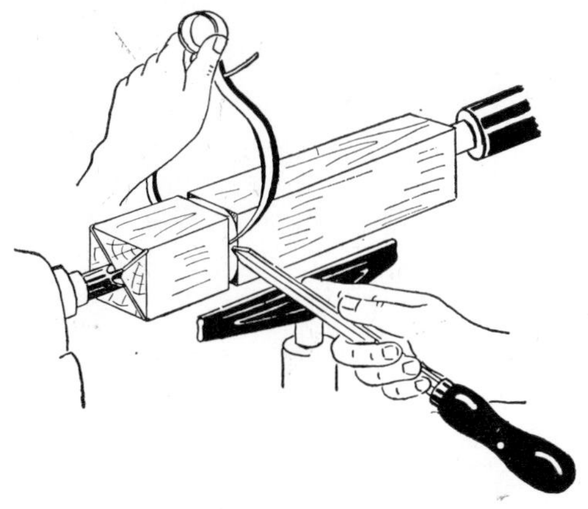

Fig. 34-15. The first cut in turning a leg (or any other piece) of which sections are to remain square.

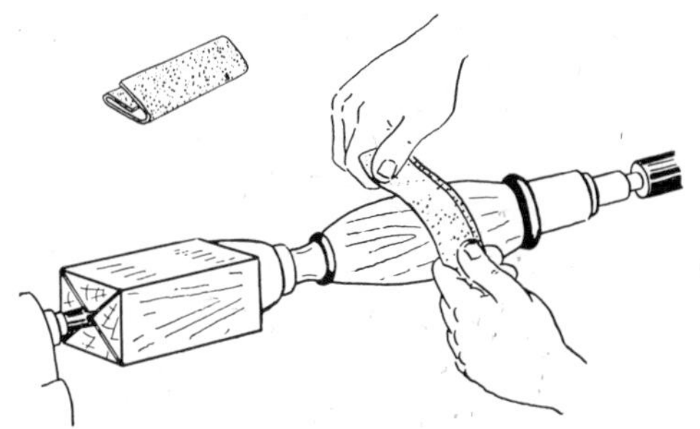

Fig. 34-16. Sanding a turning on the lathe.

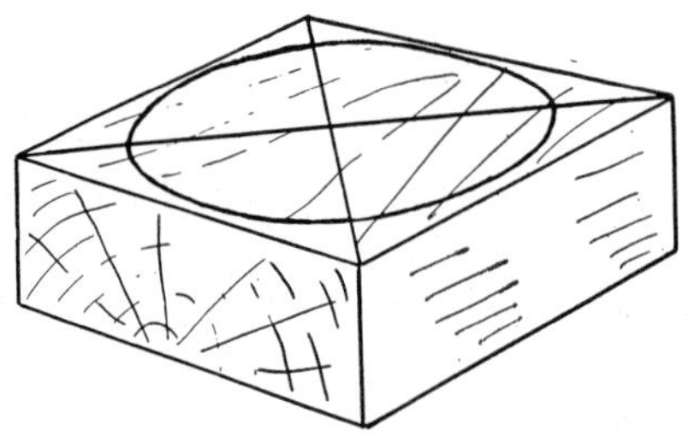

Fig. 34-17. Square stock cut and marked for face-plate turning.

in width and length and $\frac{1}{8}$ inch in thickness for surplus.

2. Plane one face smooth.

3. Set dividers or a compass to the radius of the finished object shown in your working drawing. Add at least $\frac{3}{16}$-inch surplus allowance for turning (Fig. 37-17).

4. Lay out the circle by drawing diagonals on the block to locate the center (Fig. 37-17).

5. Cut off the corners, as shown in Fig. 34-18, or cut off waste stock on the band saw so that it will be round, as pictured in Fig. 34-21.

6. Select a face plate of the appropriate size.

7. Measure and lay out the diameter of the face plate on the block of wood. This will give the location of the face plate.

8. Fasten the face plate to the block of wood with screws (Fig. 34-19). It may be necessary to drill small holes in the wood to serve for fastening the screws. Make sure that the screws are not too long or they may show through when the piece has been turned down.

Fig. 34-18. Corners cut for face-plate turning.

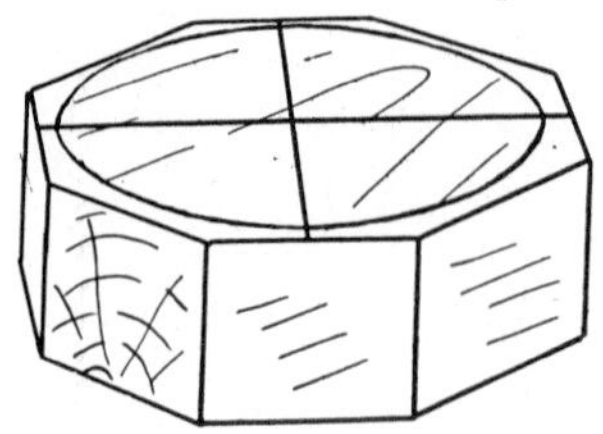

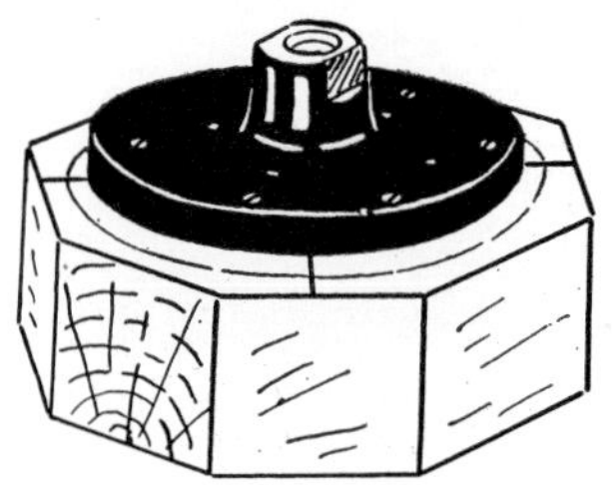

Fig. 34-19. Face plate fastened to wood.

Face-plate turning. 1. Screw the face-plate assembly on the lathe spindle.

2. Fasten the tool rest for dressing down the face of the block. The tool rest should be parallel to the face of the block, about $\frac{1}{4}$ inch from the outer edge of the stock, and down about $\frac{1}{8}$ inch from the center.

3. Turn the lathe on to run at a slow speed.

Fig. 34-20. Smoothing the face with a gouge.

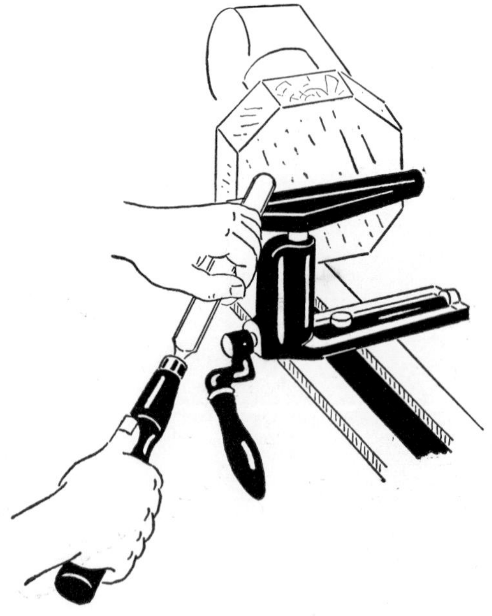

4. Smooth the face with a gouge (Fig. 34-20).

5. Reset the tool rest so that it will be parallel with the ways of the lathe bed about $\frac{1}{4}$ inch from the outer edge and down $\frac{1}{8}$ inch from the center.

6. Revolve the wooden block by hand to see that it does not hit the tool rest.

7. True the edge with a gouge, as depicted in Fig. 34-21.

8. The remainder of the turning on the face plate will involve the use of any of the turning chisels which fit the particular design curvature. Scraping tools are often used in much face-plate turning (Fig. 34-22).

9. Sand the face-plate turning. This process is very similar to that employed in sanding spindle turning (steps 1 to 8 under the heading "Sanding," page 139).

Finishing on the Lathe

Sometimes it is expedient to apply a finish to a lathe project as a final step before removing it from the lathe. Such a finish is referred to as a shellac-oil treatment. It is not difficult to put on, and with some care and practice an inexperienced person can learn to apply this unique finish with success. If you desire to stain the project first, it should be done 24 hours before observing the following procedure:

1. Remove all circular sandpaper scratches by sanding with the grain.

2. Remove all dust from the project, and also from the lathe, so that dust will not be stirred into the air while applying the finish.

3. Make a pad by folding a piece of clean, soft cotton cloth five or six times to give it body, as shown in Fig. 34-23.

4. Lay the pad on a flat surface and moisten the center with thin white shellac; then add a few drops of linseed oil (Fig. 34-23).

Fig. 34-21. Truing the edge in face-plate turning with a gouge.

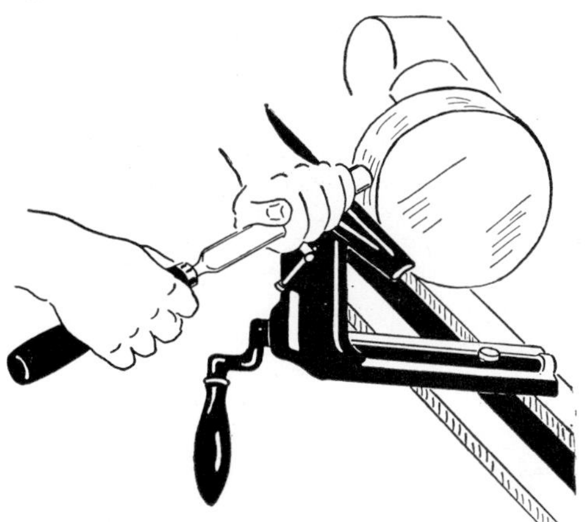

Fig. 34-22. Forming a bowl in face-plate turning.

Fig. 34-23. Preparing a pad for finishing. Center of pad moistened with thin white shellac and a few drops of linseed oil.

5. Start the lathe to the speed used in turning the project.

6. Hold the pad against the revolving surface with an even pressure, as shown in Fig. 34-24. A pad held under the turning will enable you to see how smoothly the finish is going on.

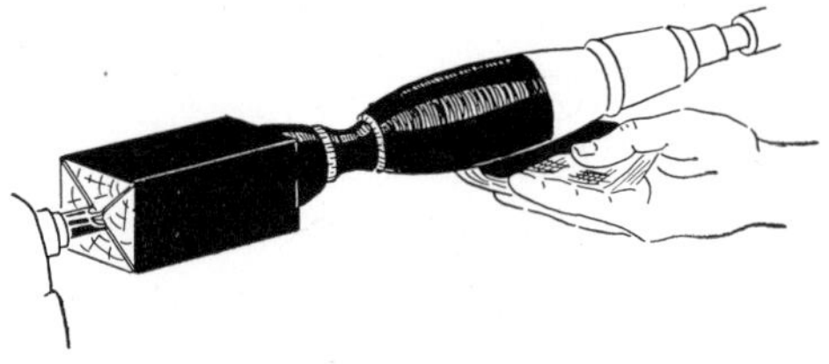

Fig. 34-24. Applying a shellac and oil finish to a revolving turning.

7. Add more shellac and linseed-oil mixture, and continue to apply it to the turning until the desired effect is obtained. This will take several coats, and they can be applied successively until a satin sheen results.

Discussion Topics

1. What are the essential parts of a wood lathe?
2. How is the size of a lathe determined?
3. List at least six safety precautions in turning on a lathe.
4. Name and describe at least five of the basic turning chisels.
5. What lubricant is used on the dead center? What is its purpose?
6. What are the two general types of turnings which may be produced on the lathe?
7. Mention two methods of dressing the corners of face-plate work for turning.
8. What are the ingredients for applying a finish on turned stock?

Section IV. RELATED INFORMATION

Unit 35. Trees and Forests

Trees provide the raw material for many thousands of wood-fabricating industries and their hundreds of thousands of products. They are also the basic material for the novice or hobbyist in fashioning articles of wood. One should, therefore, have an understanding of the parts of a tree, its growth, and its structure and some notion of how it is cut.

The Tree

A study of the explanatory notes in Fig. 35-1 will reveal much interesting information about the structure of a tree. The tree consists of three main parts: crown, trunk, and roots. The buds, root tips, and cambium layer are the growing parts of a tree.

The leaves of the tree contain a green pigment called *chlorophyll,* which can utilize the energy of light to combine the gas carbon dioxide (coming from the air) with water (absorbed by the roots and carried up through the sap wood to the leaves) into a simple food known as *carbohydrate.* This food is carried by the inner bark to all parts of the tree, even to the root tips. Some of the water evaporates from the internal part of the leaves and passes out through the leaf pores in the process of *transpiration.*

Figure 35-2 portrays a microscopic view of a cross section of softwood. This clearly shows the relatively porous formation of wood. The complete cross

Fig. 35-1. How a tree grows. (*American Forestry Association.*)

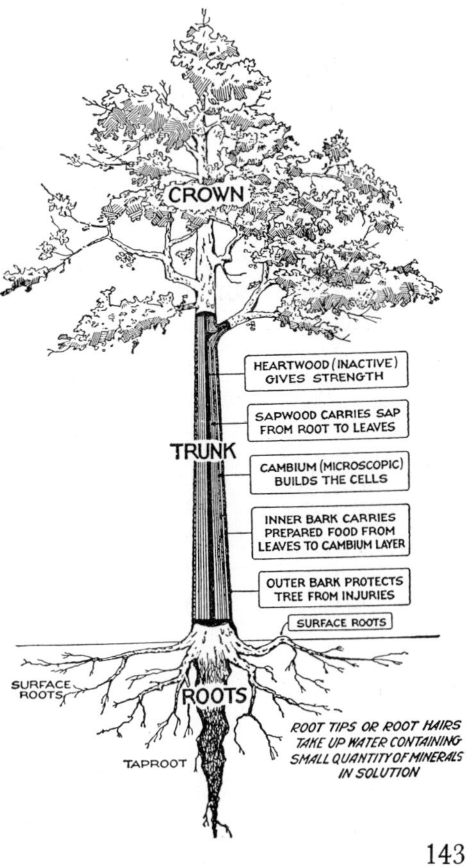

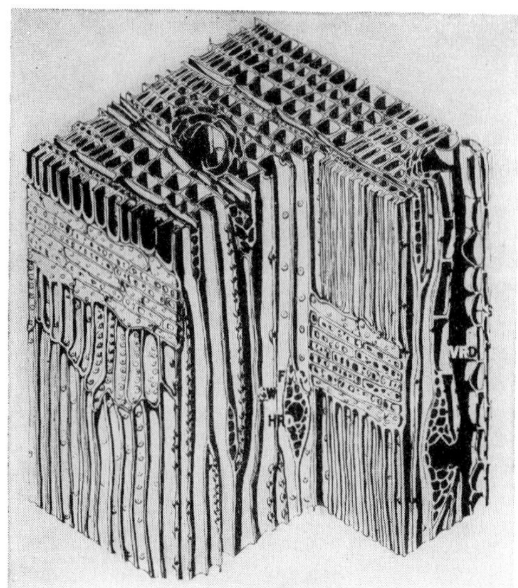

FIG. 35-2. Microscopic view of wood cross section. (*American Forest Products Industries.*)

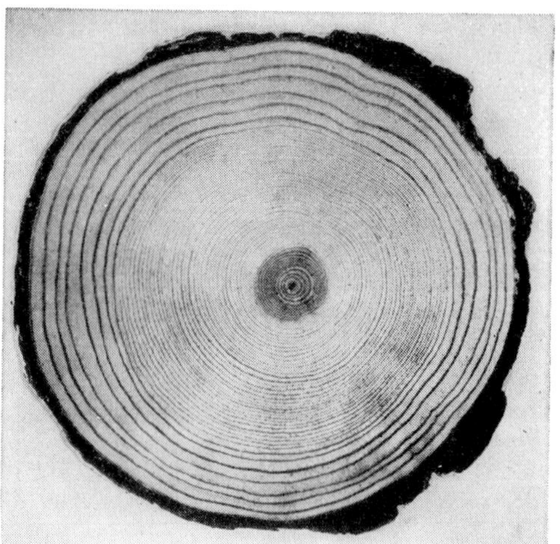

FIG. 35-4. Annular rings of a shortleaf pine. (*American Forest Products Industries.*)

section of a log is shown in Fig. 35-3, which gives a description and the location of the vital growing parts of a tree. The heartwood is surrounded by the newer growth of sapwood, generally lighter in color. The circular, or annular, rings denote the growth of a tree during the year. Figure 35-4 shows the annular rings of a shortleaf pine. The outer rings in this figure represent the most recent growth and are farther apart, indicating that a thinning of the forest, completed eight years before the picture was taken, had allowed the tree to grow more rapidly.

The log of a tree may be cut by two methods, as shown in Fig. 35-5. The left half of the cross section illustrates the cutting for plain-sawed lumber; the

FIG. 35-3. Cross section of a log.

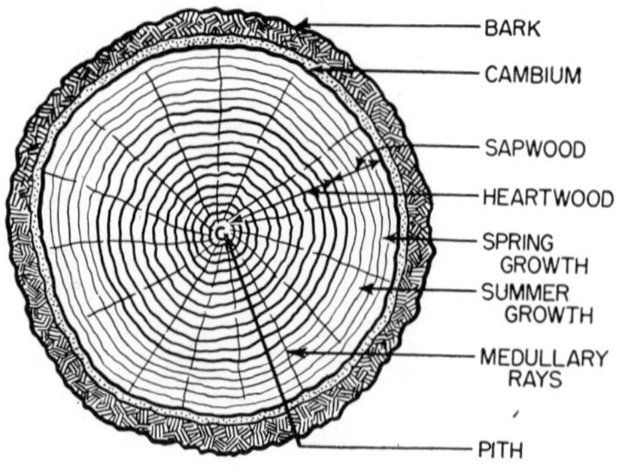

FIG. 35-5. Two methods of sawing lumber: *left*, plain sawing; *right*, quarter sawing.

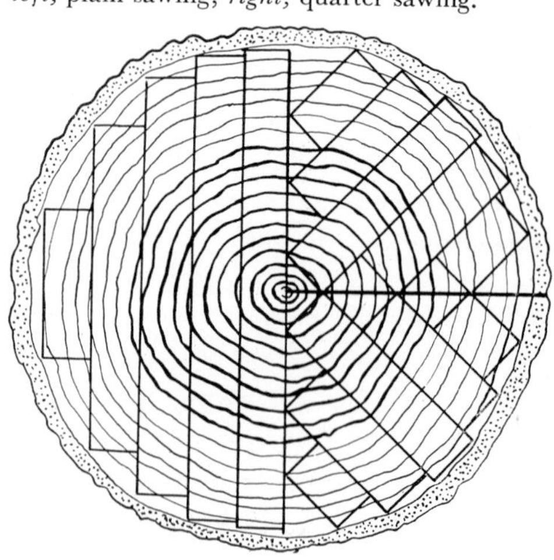

other, how the log must be cut to produce quarter-sawed lumber.

Trees differ from other natural resources, such as oil, coal, and sulfur, in that they can continually produce a crop through their seedings. New crops may be produced also by intelligent reforestation.

Forests

There are five commercial forests in the United States from which our timber crops are harvested.

The *Northern Forest* contains white pine, red spruce, hemlock, and other conifers as well as hardwood trees. The area north and east in this country includes approximately 132 million acres of commercial forests, with more than 62 billion board feet of softwoods and over 108 billion board feet of hardwoods.

The *Central Hardwood Forest,* extending roughly through the central-eastern section of the United States, has mostly hardwoods comprising over 47 million acres with over 46 billion board feet of hardwoods and nearly 3 billion board feet of softwoods.

The *Southern Forest* stretches from Virginia through eastern Texas and from Oklahoma to the Gulf. The yellow pines —longleaf, shortleaf, loblolly, and slash —are predominate. Cypress is found in the southern lowlands, and considerable hardwood grows among the pines. This area exceeds 183 million acres with nearly 194 billion board feet of softwoods and over 144 billion board feet of hardwoods.

The *Western Forest* is included in the twelve western states, which cover about 35 per cent of the area of continental United States. About 100 million acres are considered commercial forest land and contain over 500 billion board feet of softwood timber, chiefly ponderosa, Idaho-white, and sugar pines, and some hardwoods.

The *Pacific Coast Forest* extends along the moist, western slopes of Washington, Oregon, and northern California. The timber in Washington and Oregon is mostly Douglas fir, with some hemlock, western red cedar, Sitka spruce and others. In northern California the characteristic tree is redwood, one of the world's largest. The Pacific Coast Forest exceeds 28 million acres, having more than 550 billion board feet of timber. Less than 4 billion board feet are in hardwoods, including alder, maple, oak, and some others.

American forests rate very high as creators of national wealth. The value of the many products from them exceeds 1 billion dollars each year. Transportation of logs and forest products pays the third largest annual freight bill in America.

With all this potential wealth in woodlands, however, there is a tremendous waste in the destruction from fires. It is estimated that one forest fire starts every 3 minutes or an average of 170,000 forest fires each year, which burn an area as large as the state of Indiana. If it were not for the reforestation plans which many agencies promote, our supply of timber could become exhausted. Figure 35-6 shows graphically how the various regions in the United States are furnishing lumber and how each is being replenished. The

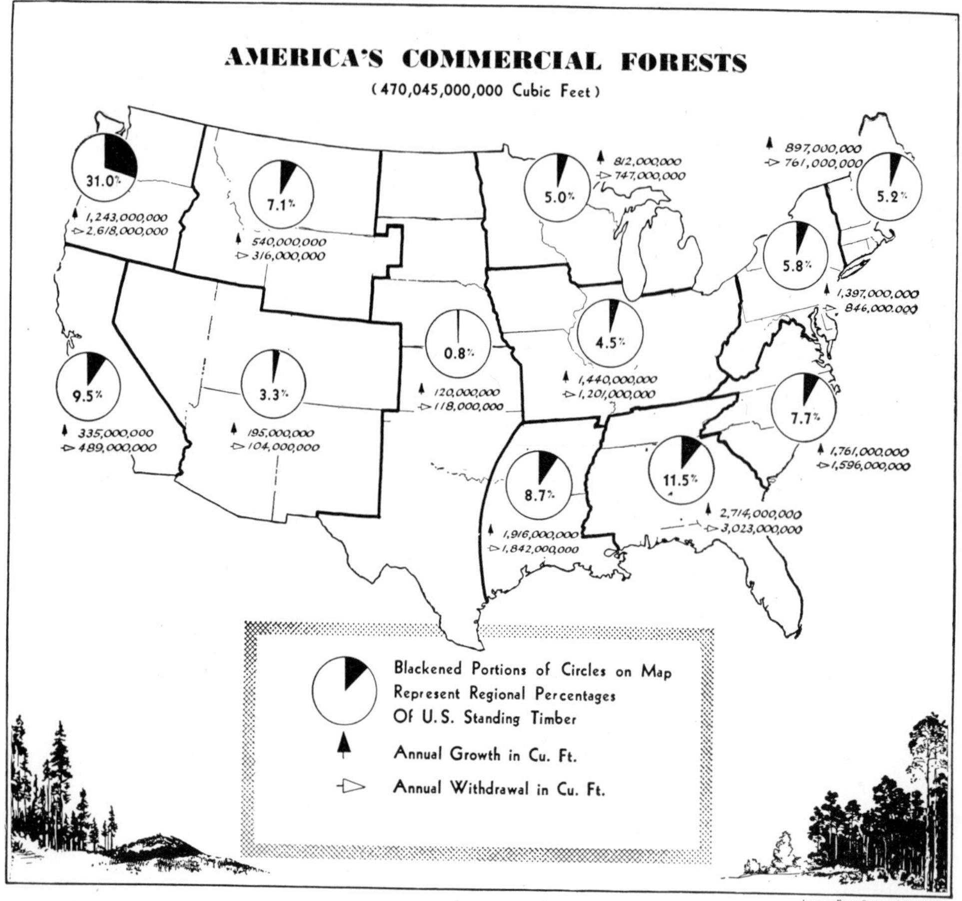

FIG. 35-6. Regional growth and output of timber in the United States. (*American Forest Products Industries.*)

many acres of forest land burned each year would produce enough timber to build 86,000 modern homes. Another way of viewing this disastrous situation is that this same amount of timber could make the paper which prints all United States newspapers for the year. Because of our failure to adopt adequate conservation measures, our forests are not being grown as fast as they are being depleted.

Only about two-thirds of forest acreage is commercial; the remaining one-third includes forest land valuable for watershed protection, grazing, wild life, and other purposes. The consumption of timber in the United States has grown so great that we can no longer depend upon our forests to provide all our needs but send away, to Canada primarily, for more than 80 per cent of our newsprint.

Four hundred and twenty-eight million acres of the nation's 642 million acres in forest land are in private ownership. This means that public ownership by state and Federal governments comprises only approximately one-third of the total acreage. Most of the public-owned forest land is in national forests. It is evident, therefore, that the nation is primarily dependent upon private lands for its timber.

Discussion Topics

1. Name the three main parts of a tree.
2. What are the growing parts of a tree?
3. What do the annular rings of a tree denote?
4. How will thinning a forest affect those trees remaining?
5. Diagram two methods of sawing a log to get a particular cut of lumber.
6. Why do trees differ from other natural resources, such as oil or coal?
7. Name the five commercial forests in the United States, and give one characteristic type of tree found in each.
8. What is the world's largest type of tree? Where does it grow?
9. What is the greatest menace and destructive agent to our forests? Discuss in detail.
10. Give the approximate percentage of forest owned by the public. What is this acreage primarily used for?

Unit 36. Common Woods

Trees constitute one of the most valuable resources of America. One-third of the land is well suited for growing them. Although there are more than 1,000 species found in American forests, only approximately 100 kinds are used for lumber or for making other manufactured products.

There are two main types of trees in our forests: *hardwoods* and *softwoods.*

Hardwoods

Hardwoods have broad leaves that usually fall off in wintertime. Oak, maple, elm, poplar, hickory, gum, magnolia, and walnut are well-known types. Besides these native hardwoods there is mahogany, a type imported from tropical America and Africa and one which is used extensively in furniture manufacture. Figure 36-1 gives a fine view of a large mahogany tree growing in the Central American jungle.

Softwoods

The leaves of most softwood trees are needle-like. Because these trees remain green the year round, they are called *evergreens.* Some of the more common types of softwoods are pine, fir, hemlock, spruce, cedar, and redwood. Figure 36-2 shows three softwood species growing in a western pine region.

Characteristics, Uses, and Habitat

Wood is used in more than four thousand ways in our daily living. Wood-using industries, public forestry agencies,

FIG. 36-1. A mahogany tree growing in the Central American jungle. (*Mahogany Association, Inc.*)

FIG. 36-2. Softwoods in a western pine region. The tree on the left in the foreground is ponderosa pine, the two trees in the center are sugar pine, and the tree on the right is a white fir. (*American Forest Products Industries.*)

and scientists work together to improve the care and use of our forests.

The increasing importance of research is being stressed in the usefulness of forest products. The government-owned Forest Products Laboratory in Wisconsin has accomplished some striking results in laminated wood, improved plywoods, wood- and paper-base plastics, and other industrial products such as Impreg, Compreg, Staypak, and the Uralloys. Some of these will be discussed in Unit 38, "Uses of Forest Products," page 164.

People employed in the woods industries must know the characteristics and uses of woods. The few species described here are the more common ones known to the woodworker. The descriptive material gives the common and Latin botanical name of the wood; illustration of the leaf or needle; the general shape of the tree with one side in summer foliage, the other in winter outline; the fruit or nut; the characteristics and uses of the wood; and the habitat.

Ash, white (*Fraxinus americana*). (Fig. 36-3.) The bark is dark gray or gray-brown, deeply furrowed. The wood is heavy, hard, elastic, tough, and brown. It is used in the manufacture of

FIG. 36-3. White ash. (*S. C. Johnson & Son, Inc.*)

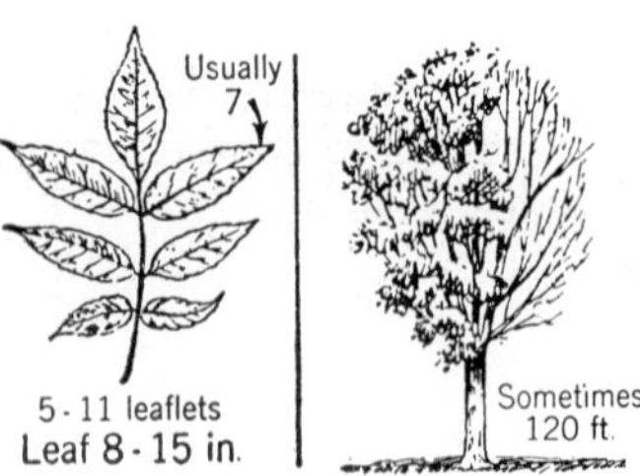

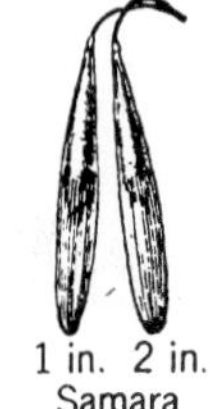

agricultural instruments, furniture, and oars. The tree is common in rich, moist, cool woods, in fields or on riverbanks and is found from Nova Scotia to Minnesota and from Florida to Texas.

Basswood or linden (*Tilia americana*). (Fig. 36-4.) The bark is deep brownish-gray. The wood is soft, straight-grained, light brown, and easily worked. It is used for general woodenware, furniture, or wood pulp, and the inner bark is used for mat fiber. The tree is common in rich woods or fertile soil, and its range is from Maine to Georgia, westward to Texas, and northward to Lake Superior.

Beech (*Fagus grandifolia*). (Fig. 36-5.) The bark is a light, warm gray and very smooth. The wood is close-grained, hard, and pale brown or buff. It is used for fuel, woodenware, chairs, and shoe lasts. The nuts are edible. The tree is common in rich uplands and on moist, rocky ground. It grows throughout the eastern United States from Maine west to Lake Superior and south to Florida and Texas. It is most abundant in New England, New York, and Pennsylvania.

Birch, yellow (*Betula lutea*). (Fig. 36-6.) The bark on young trees is silvery or yellow with thin, papery scales.

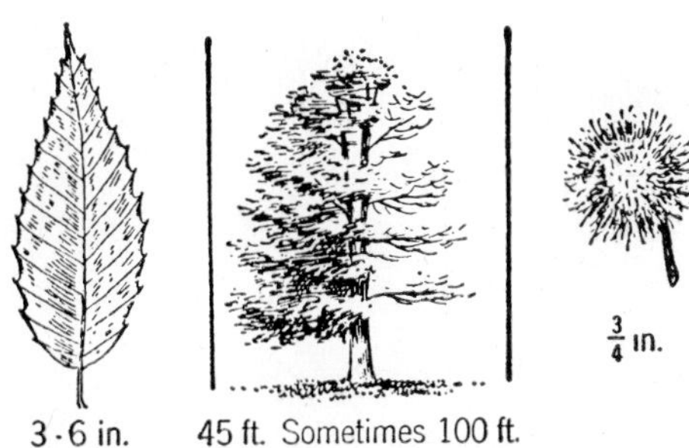

FIG. 36-5. Beech. (*S. C. Johnson & Son, Inc.*)

On old ones it is made up of large, thin, dull plates, grayish in color. The wood is heavy, strong, hard, and close-grained. It is used for distinctive and pleasing grain figures in woodworking, curly birch being the most distinctive. It is widely used for furniture, flooring, and interior finishes. The tree grows in rich uplands, in swamps, and on the border of streams and is distributed from Minnesota to Newfoundland, south to Pennsylvania, and along the mountains of North Carolina and Tennessee.

Cedar, red (*Juniperus virginiana*). (Fig. 36-7.) The bark is a light, ruddy brown. The wood is light, soft, brittle, close-grained, fragrant, and durable. It is called the cedar-chest wood. It is used in chests, closets, fence posts, and lead pencils. The tree grows in all kinds of

FIG. 36-4. Basswood, or linden. (*S. C. Johnson & Son, Inc.*)

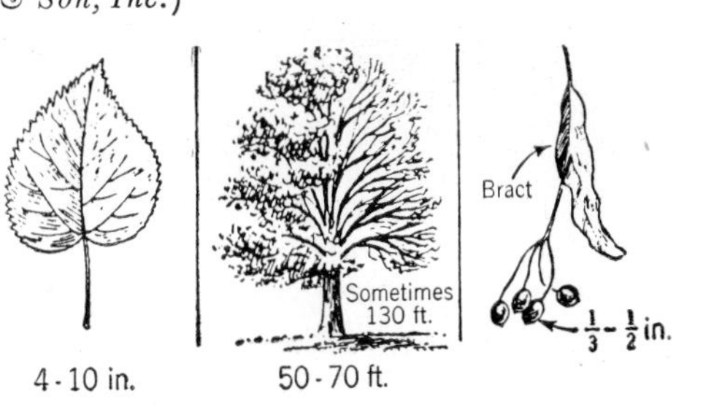

FIG. 36-6. Yellow birch. (*S. C. Johnson & Son, Inc.*)

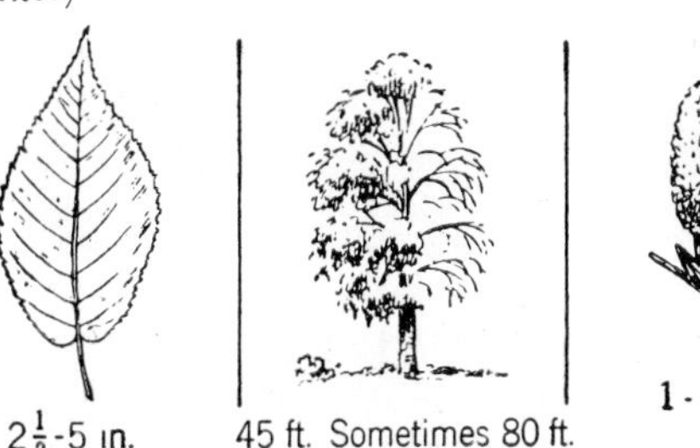

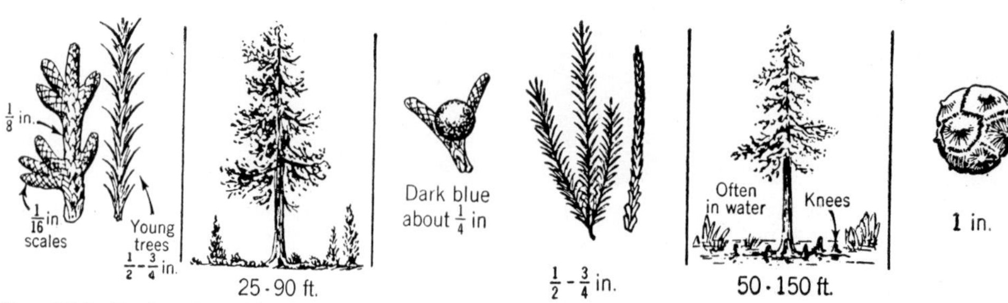

FIG. 36-7. Red cedar. (*S. C. Johnson & Son, Inc.*)

FIG. 36-9. Bald cypress. (*S. C. Johnson & Son, Inc.*)

soils, from swamps to rocky ridges, and is found from Nova Scotia to South Dakota, south to Florida, and over into Texas.

Chestnut (*Castanea dentata*). (Fig. 36-8.) The bark is a warm gray-brown growing in ridges. The wood is light, soft, coarse-grained, pale brown, durable, but not very strong. It is used for furniture, picture frames, railroad ties, posts, and piling. The tree grows in light, good soil, in pastures and in rocky woods. It is found from Maine to Michigan and south to the Carolinas, Georgia, and Arkansas.

Cypress, bald (*Taxodium distichum*). (Fig. 36-9.) The bark is thick, with a pale ruddy-brown color, and grows in long, thin scales. The wood is straight-grained, easily worked, and a light brown. It is used for general construction and is effective in paneling. The tree grows most in southern swamps and is found from Virginia to Florida and in a broad belt along the Gulf of Mexico to Texas.

Elm, American or white (*Ulmus americana*). (Fig. 36-10.) The bark is a brown-gray, divided by short furrows. The wood is heavy, tough, hard, coarse-grained, and pale brown. It is used for wheel hubs, saddletrees, barrels, and in shipbuilding. The tree is common in most rich soil, and its range extends from Newfoundland west to the Rocky Mountains and south to Florida and Texas.

Fir, Douglas (*Pseudotsuga taxifolia*). (Fig. 36-11.) The bark is dark, gray-brown, and rough. The wood is light, ruddy, or tan-yellow. It is used for construction purposes, railroad ties, and

FIG. 36-8. Chestnut. (*S. C. Johnson & Son, Inc.*)

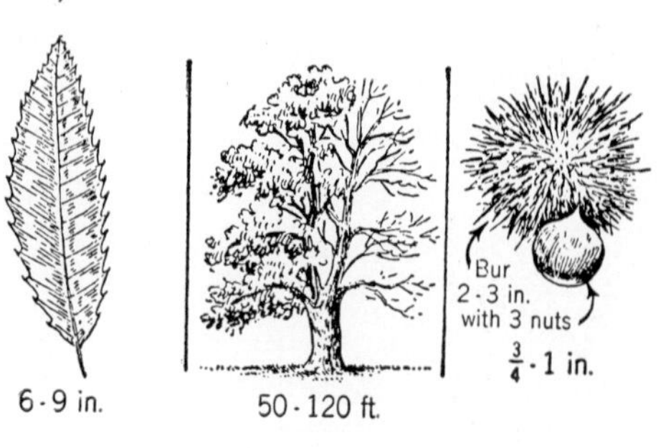

FIG. 36-10. American, or white, elm. (*S. C. Johnson & Son, Inc.*)

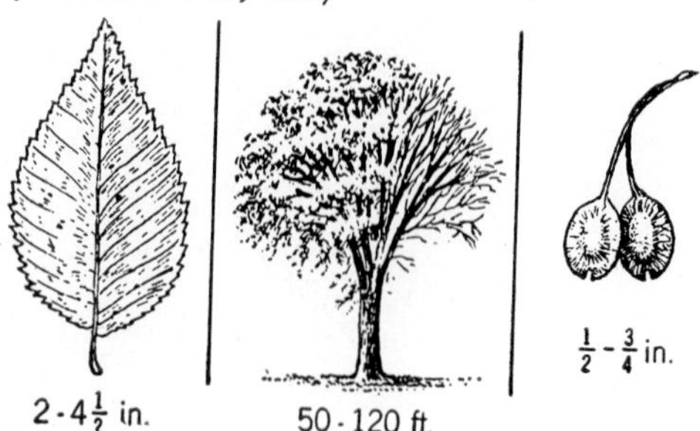

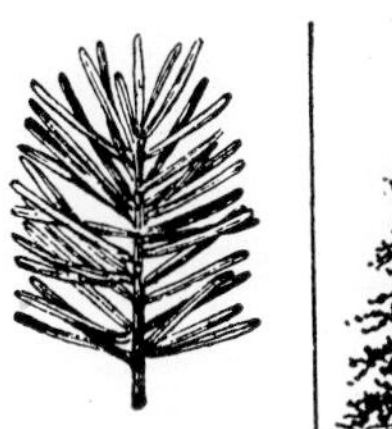

FIG. 36-11. Douglas fir. (*S. C. Johnson & Son, Inc.*)

FIG. 36-13. Sweet, or red, gum. (*S. C. Johnson & Son, Inc.*)

piles. The tree grows in the Rocky Mountains, especially in the north. Its natural range is from the Rocky Mountains to the Pacific Coast and from central British Columbia to northern Mexico.

Gum, tupelo, sour, or black (*Nyssa sylvatica*). (Fig. 36-12.) The bark is brown-gray, smooth or rough. The wood is pale buff, heavy, rather soft, tough, and fine-grained. It is used for wheel hubs, ox yokes, and boxes. The tree is common along watercourses, on rich alluvial land, and in swamps and is found from Maine to Florida and west to Michigan and Texas.

Gum, sweet or red (*Liquidambar styraciflua*). (Fig. 36-13). The bark is gray-brown and deeply furrowed. The wood is hard, heavy, close-grained, and reddish-brown. It is used for building and for furniture, and can readily be stained to resemble mahogany. The sap is used for chewing gum and medicine. The tree grows in rich, wet lowlands and is found from Connecticut to Florida and west to Kansas.

Hemlock, eastern (*Tsuga canadensis*). (Fig. 36-14.) The bark is a coarse, dull, gray-brown. The wood is light, tough, and coarse-grained and splinters easily. It is used for timber and joists and the bark is used for tanning. The tree grows in cold swamps, on mountain slopes, in ravines, and in rocky woods. It is found principally in the Great Lakes states and in the mountains of the eastern part of the United States.

Hemlock, western (*Tsuga heterophylla*). (Fig. 36-15.) The bark is red-

FIG. 36-12. Tupelo, or sour gum. (*S. C. Johnson & Son, Inc.*)

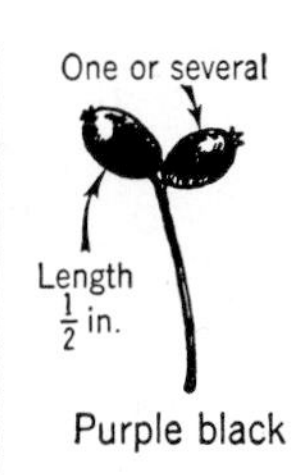

FIG. 36-14. Eastern hemlock. (*S. C. Johnson & Son, Inc.*)

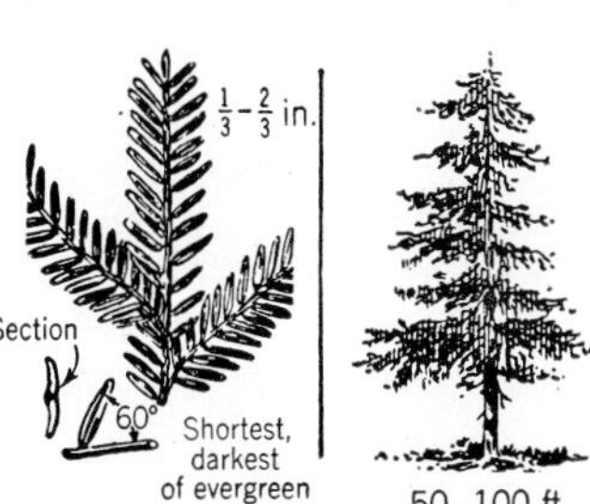

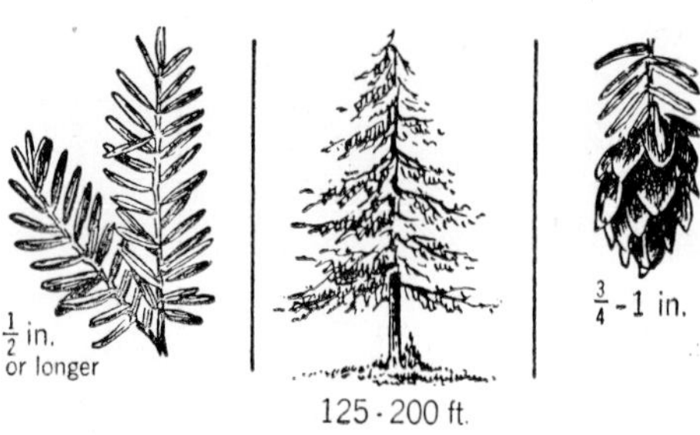

Fig. 36-15. Western hemlock. (*S. C. Johnson & Son, Inc.*)

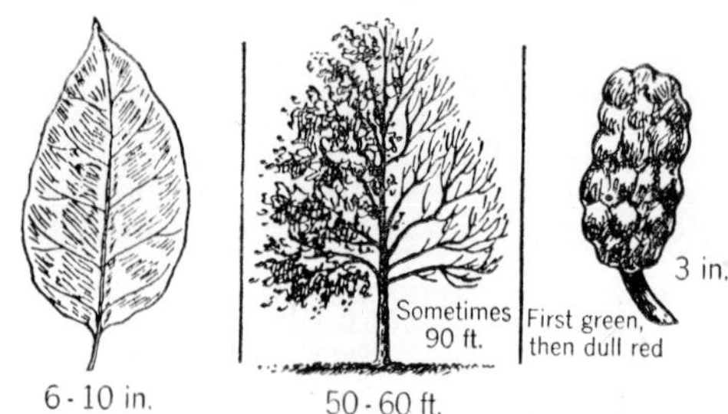

Fig. 36-17. Magnolia. (*S. C. Johnson & Son, Inc.*)

dish-brown, broad, with scaly, interrupted fissures. The wood is tough, durable, light, strong, and brown. It is used in building and the bark is used for tanning. The tree grows in moist valleys and uplands from tidewater to an elevation of 6,000 feet. It is found in abundance in the coastal region from southern Alaska down to Oregon.

Hickory, shagbark (*Carya cvata*). (Fig. 36-16.) The bark is a pale brown-gray and shaggy. The wood is "tough as hickory," very hard, close-grained, flexible, and a pale brown. It is used for agricultural implements, wagons, tool handles, baskets, and fuel. The nut is good to eat. The tree is common in rich uplands and is found from Quebec to Minnesota and south to Florida and Texas.

Fig. 36-16. Shagbark hickory. (*S. C. Johnson & Son, Inc.*)

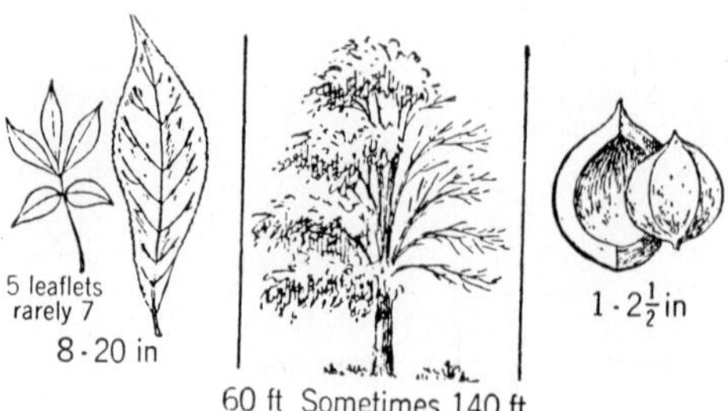

Magnolia (*Magnolia grandiflora*). (Fig. 36-17.) The bark is brownish-gray and rough with short, thin scales. The wood is moderately heavy and hard and is of a creamy color with a satiny luster. It is easily worked. The wood is used for planing-mill products, furniture, fixtures, venetian blinds, finish, siding, boxes, and crates. The tree flourishes in rich, moist soil. It is found along the coast from North Carolina to Florida and westward to Texas. It also grows up the Mississippi to Arkansas.

Mahogany (*Swietenia mahagoni, Swietenia macrophylla, or Khaya ivorensis*). (Fig. 36-18.) The bark is ridged and not unlike the bark of an elm tree. The wood is tough, strong, and highly stable in fashioned form. It is easy to work, polishes very well, and has a rich, golden-brown color that deepens with age. Mahogany has acquired the reputation of possessing all the characteristics of an ideal cabinet wood and is used extensively in the manufacture of furniture, boats, cabinets, and interior trim. Mahogany veneers are available in a wide range of figures and patterns. The tree grows in tropical American and African forests. Principal sources now

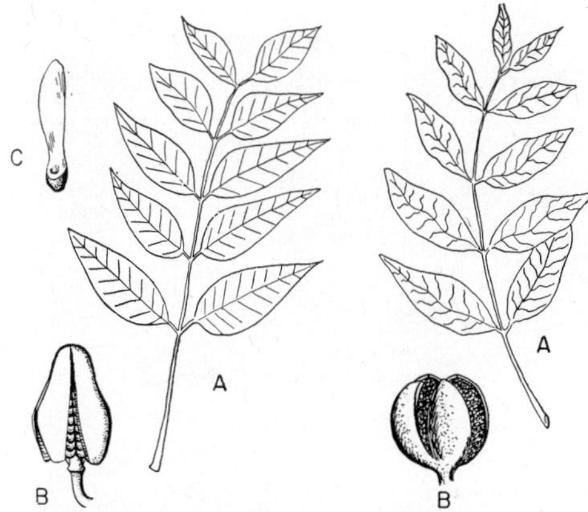

FIG. 36-18. Mahogany. *Left,* a tropical American mahogany, *Swietenia macrophylla:* (*A*) compound leaf with leaflets like those of an ash; (*B*) fruit pod larger than an egg; when it splits open, it liberates many seeds; (*C*) flattened seed with wing mostly at one end. *Right,* African mahogany, *Khaya ivorensis:* (*A*) compound leaf with leaflets like those of an ash; (*B*) fruit similar in structure to that of *Swietenia* but shorter and more rounded. (*Mahogany Association, Inc.*)

are southern Mexico and Central America, the upper Amazon River region, and the west coast of Africa.

Maple, sugar (*Acer saccharum*). (Fig. 36-19.) The bark is light, brown-gray, and deeply furrowed. The wood is heavy, very hard, strong, close-grained, and takes a fine polish. It is used for interior finish, floors, turnery, shipbuilding, shoe lasts, and fuel. The sap is the source of maple sugar. The tree is common in rich woods and rocky hillsides and grows in every state east of the Mississippi, although it is relatively rare in the South.

FIG. 36-19. Sugar maple. (*S. C. Johnson & Son, Inc.*)

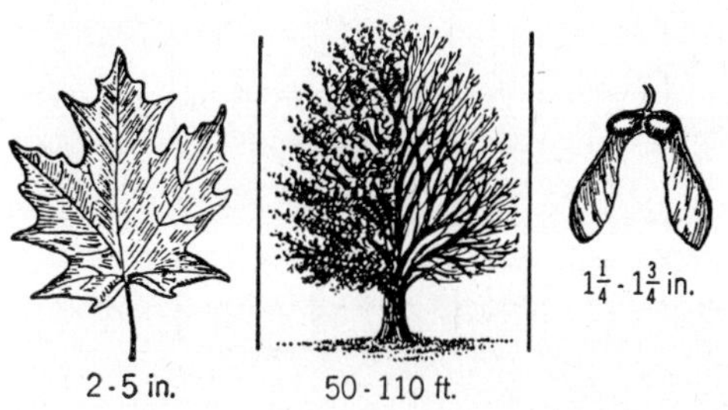

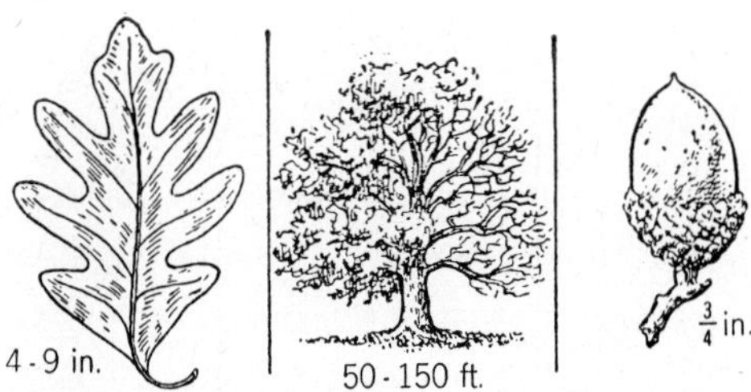

FIG. 36-20. White oak. (*S. C. Johnson & Son, Inc.*)

Oak, White (*Quercus alba*). (Fig. 36-20.) The bark is whitish-gray, firm, and deeply furrowed. The wood is strong, heavy, hard, tough, and pale brown. The important uses of the wood are for building and for furniture wood. It is also used for floors, beams, and shipbuilding in particular, because of its strength. The tree grows in dry uplands, on sandy plains, and on gravelly ridges. It is found in practically the entire eastern half of the United States.

Pine, western white (*Pinus monticola*). (Fig. 36-21.) The bark is lavender-gray and broken into rough

FIG. 36-21. Western white pine. (*S. C. Johnson & Son, Inc.*)

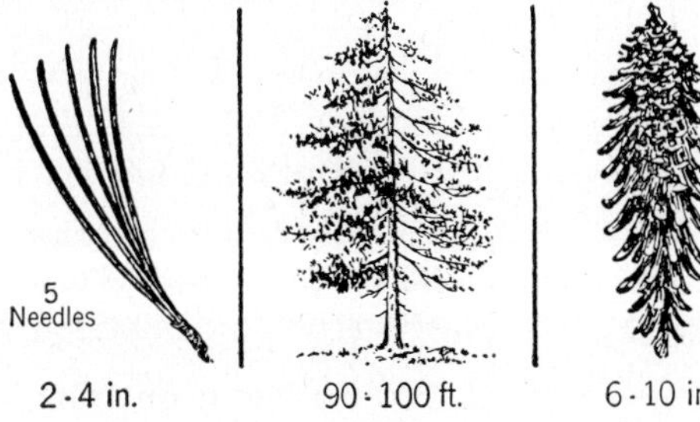

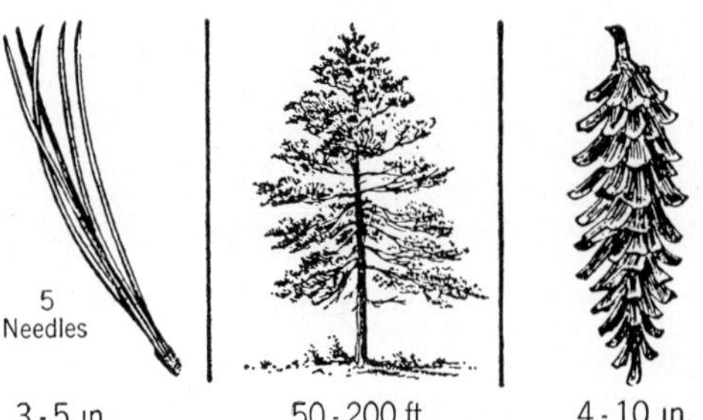

FIG. 36-22. White pine. (*S. C. Johnson & Son, Inc.*)

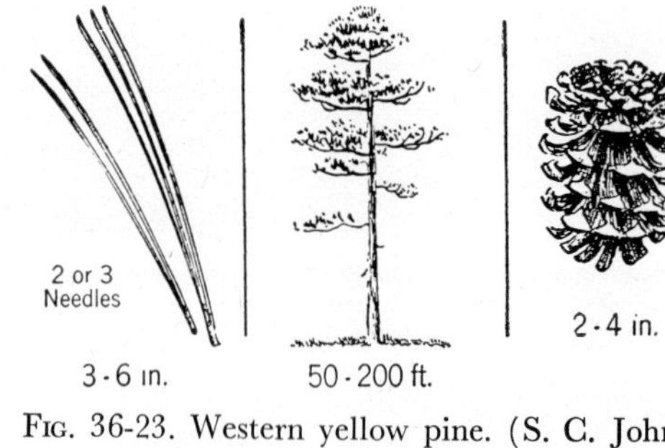

FIG. 36-23. Western yellow pine. (S. C. Johnson & Son, Inc.)

squares. The wood is light, soft, pale brown, and commercially of very great value. It is used for cabinetwork, knotty paneling, millwork, exterior and interior finishes, and siding and is the principal wood used in the manufacture of wooden matches in the United States. The tree grows west of the Rocky Mountains, being most abundant in Idaho and adjacent parts of Montana and Washington. It grows best on exposed mineral soil.

Pine, white (*Pinus strobus*). (Fig. 36-22.) The bark is rough, gray-brown, and formed in small segments. The wood is pale, buff-yellow, soft, durable, and easily worked. It is used for building purposes. The tree grows in light, sandy soil and is found throughout the northwestern United States, from Iowa and Minnesota eastward, in southeastern Canada, and southward along the Appalachian Mountains to Northern Georgia.

Pine, western yellow (*Pinus ponderosa*). (Fig. 36-23.) The bark is a light russet-red with a scaly surface. The wood is hard, strong, and light in color, ranging from pale yellow to terra-cotta red. It is one of the most valuable lumber trees of the West and sometimes lives 500 years. The wood is used for sash, doors, frames, siding, knotty paneling, and exterior and interior finish. Large quantities are also consumed in the manufacture of crates and boxes, and in the making of wood novelties, toys, and caskets. The tree grows in open, parklike forests, in dry or moist soils, and from southern British Columbia south through the region west of the Rocky Mountains to northern Mexico.

Poplar, yellow or tulip tree (*Liriodendron tulipifera*). (Fig. 36-24.) The bark is brownish-gray and rounded in confluent ridges. The wood is pale buff, close, straight-grained, light, soft, easily worked and does not readily split, warp, or shrink. It is prized for interior and cabinetwork and also makes an excellent core for veneers. The tree grows

FIG. 36-24. Yellow poplar, or tulip tree. (*S. C. Johnson & Son, Inc.*)

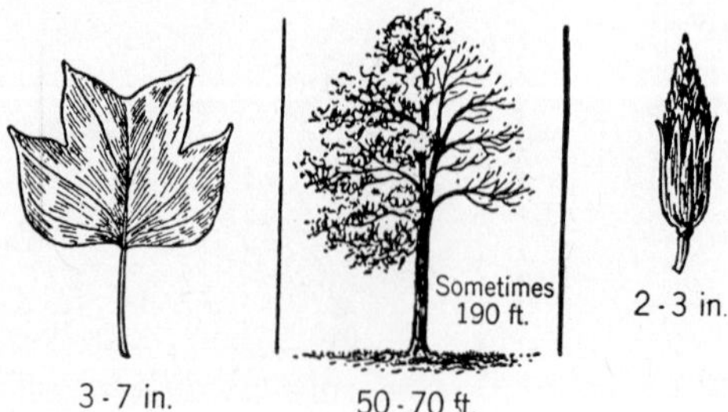

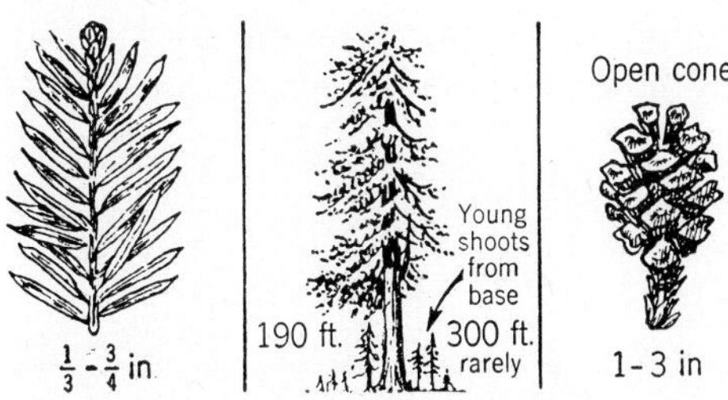

FIG. 36-25. Redwood (*S. C. Johnson & Son, Inc.*)

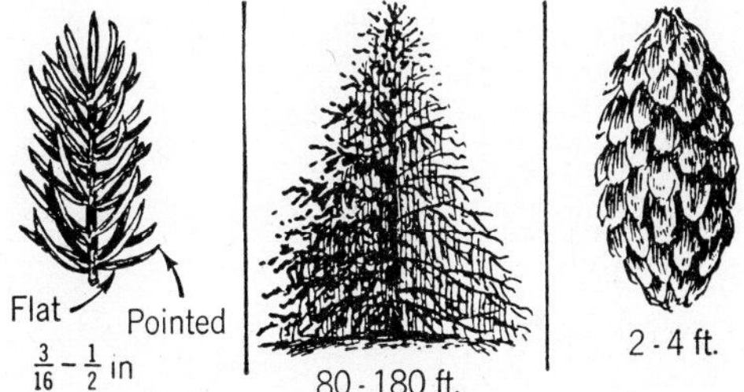

FIG. 36-27. Sitka spruce. (*S. C. Johnson & Son, Inc.*)

commonly in rich, moist soil and ranges from Rhode Island to Michigan and south to Georgia and Arkansas.

Redwood (*Sequoia sempervirens*). (Fig. 36-25.) The bark is deep cinnamon-brown, gray-tinged. The wood is crimson-brown, soft, brittle, straight-grained, and easily worked. It is of great commercial importance, is manufactured into interior finish and woodwork, and is very useful in outdoor structures, such as silos, barns, tanks, bridges, pipelines, flumes, mill roofs, and cooling towers. The tree grows in the West within the fog belt and sometimes lives to be 1,200 to 1,400 years old. The range of growth is confined to a narrow belt about 20 miles wide along the Pacific coast from southern Oregon to Monterey County in California. It is the tallest tree in the world, attaining a height of 200 to 350 feet.

FIG. 36-26. Black (bog, red) spruce. (*S. C. Johnson & Son, Inc.*)

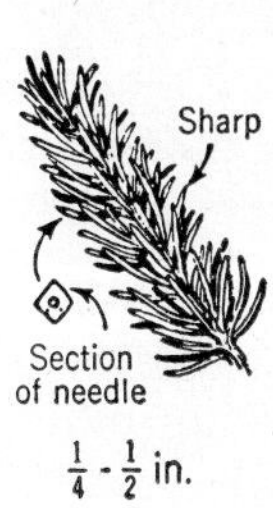

Spruce, black, bog, or red (*Picea mariana*). (Fig. 36-26.) The bark is thin, close-fitting, reddish-brown, and formed in small scales. The wood is light, buff-yellow, soft, elastic, resonant, and straight-grained. It is used in the manufacture of paper pulp, light furniture, joists, sills, and musical instruments and also furnishes spruce gum. The tree grows in bogs and swamps as well as on uplands and mountain slopes from Newfoundland west to Minnesota, south to New Jersey and Pennsylvania, and along the Allegheny Mountains to Georgia.

Spruce, Sitka (*Picea sitchensis*). (Fig. 36-27.) The bark is reddish-brown, thin, and scaly. The wood is light, soft, straight-grained, satiny, and light reddish-brown in color. It is used for boats, buildings, fencing, wooden utensils, boxes, and barrels. The tree is common in moist, sandy soil and in swamps. It is remarkable for its rapid growth, great size, beauty as an evergreen, and great age. It is found in a restricted area along the Pacific coast from the Kodiak Islands in Alaska to Mendocino County, California.

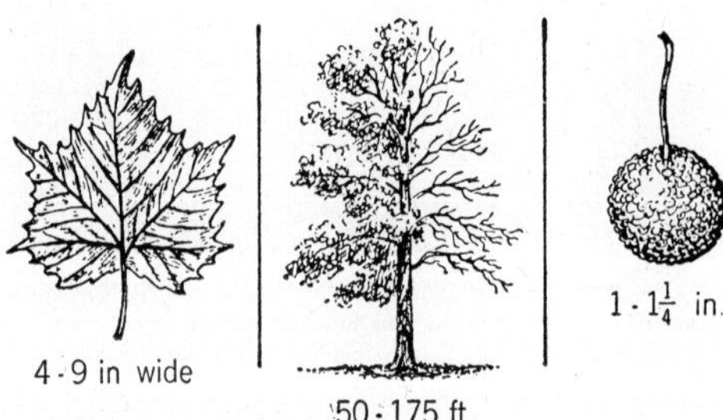

FIG. 36-28. Sycamore. (*S. C. Johnson & Son, Inc.*)

Sycamore (*Platanus occidentalis*). (Fig. 36-28.) The bark is greenish-gray and flakes off yearly in broad scales exposing a white, greenish inner bark. The wood is heavy, coarse-grained, hard, strong, and of a light ruddy-brown color. It is used for cigar boxes, ox yokes, furniture, and butcher's blocks. The tree grows in rich bottom lands or in moist woodlands and is native from Maine to Minnesota and south to Florida and Texas.

Walnut, black (*Juglans nigra*). (Fig. 36-29.) The bark is thick, dark brown, and deeply divided into broad, rounded ridges. The wood is deep brown, hard, heavy, rather brittle, nonwarping, evenly textured, and it takes a beautiful polish. It is used for fine furniture, woodwork, boatbuilding, gunstocks, and veneers. The nut is well-known for its tastiness and nutritive qualities. The tree is found in rich woodlands, is easily propagated, and grows readily. Its commercial source is the area of Missouri, Kansas, Iowa, Illinois, Indiana, Ohio, Kentucky, and Tennessee.

FIG. 36-29. Black walnut. (*S. C. Johnson & Son, Inc.*)

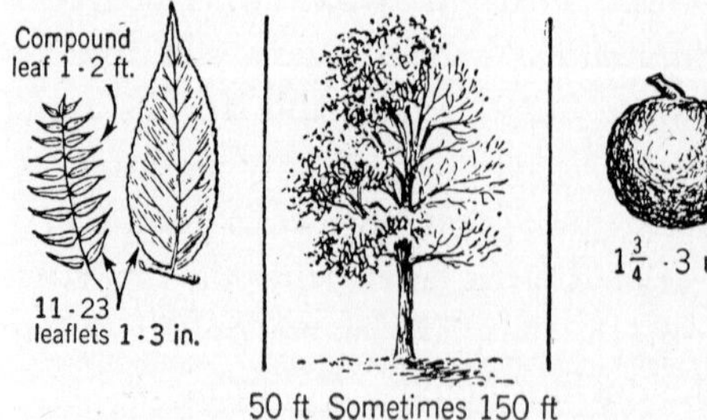

Discussion Topics

1. Distinguish between hardwoods and softwoods.
2. From what places is mahogany imported?
3. Where is the government Forests Products Laboratory located?
4. Name four products of research developed at the Forest Products Laboratory.
5. Describe the bark of both the young yellow birch and the sycamore.
6. Name a fragrant wood and tell its outstanding use.
7. Where does bald cypress grow?
8. What wood stains readily to resemble mahogany?
9. Name a wood having a cream color and a satiny luster.
10. What type of pine is one of the most valuable lumber trees of the West?
11. Give the source of the wood most used for the following articles: (*a*) cigar boxes, (*b*) musical instruments, (*c*) wooden matches, (*d*) core for veneers, (*e*) barrels, (*f*) oars, (*g*) ox yokes, (*h*) mat fiber, (*i*) agricultural implements, and (*j*) picture frames.
12. What two woods are used especially in the construction of fine furniture and in the making of veneer?

13. Name three woods particularly useful in shipbuilding.
14. Name two trees that grow to great size and age.
15. What types of trees can be found most frequently along the Pacific coast from Alaska to California?
16. What trees yield the bases for maple sugar, chewing gum, and leather-tanning solution?

Unit 37. Production of Lumber

One who works with wood will naturally be interested in learning something of its sources and of the processes employed in bringing it from the forest (Fig. 37-1) to the lumberyards or shops. Many scientific studies must be made to determine the volume and suitability of the timber in a particular area as well as to figure out the most practical method of logging. The amount or volume of timber is estimated by men called *cruisers* (Fig. 37-2), who make a sampling of the number of trees by species and sizes. On the basis of this information, commercial companies secure the maximum timber from their cutting. The cruisers also plan transportation routes.

If the timber stands in remote areas, it is sometimes necessary to build a log-

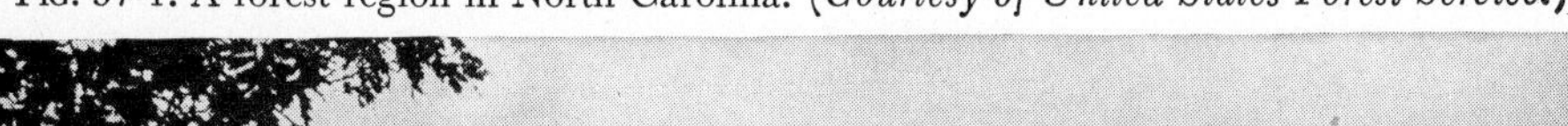

Fig. 37-1. A forest region in North Carolina. (*Courtesy of United States Forest Service.*)

FIG. 37-2. A timber cruiser measuring representative samples of woods. (*Courtesy of West Coast Lumbermen's Association.*)

ging camp to house the workers and to construct roads in order to make the region accessible (Fig. 37-3).

LOGGING

The first actual operations in logging are those of felling and bucking. In these processes the trees are cut down (Fig. 37-4) and the trunks are cut into suitable lengths (Fig. 37-5) for transportation to mills.

After they have been cut, the logs must be skidded or hauled from their original place (Fig. 37-6) to loading sites. The most modern method of skidding is by use of tractors. Specially designed logging trucks are used extensively in hauling logs to the mills (Fig. 37-7). However, in some parts of the country logs are still loaded on railroad

FIG. 37-3. Tractors and bulldozers being used to build a logging road. (*Caterpillar Tractor Company.*)

FIG. 37-4. Felling a tree. (*Caterpillar Tractor Company.*)

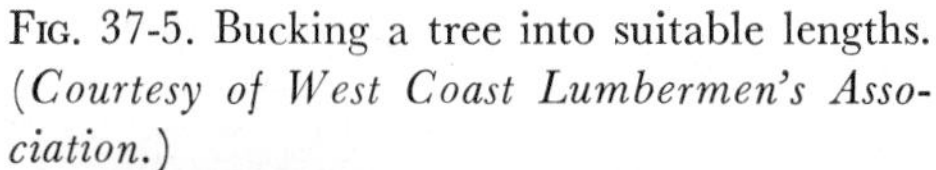

FIG. 37-5. Bucking a tree into suitable lengths. (*Courtesy of West Coast Lumbermen's Association.*)

FIG. 37-6. Skidding fir logs to loading site by tractor with a winch. (*Caterpillar Tractor Company.*)

cars for shipment (Fig. 37-8) or floated down rivers and streams to mills (Fig. 37-9). Where this latter method is feasible, it is the least expensive transportation. The chief disadvantages are that considerable damage is done to logs in transit and that there must be adequate water supply to keep the mill supplied with logs for a year.

PRODUCTION OF LUMBER

Most of the lumber produced in the United States is processed at power-driven sawmills, which range in production from 3,000 to 1,000,000 board feet of lumber per day. The larger mills (Fig. 37-10) are usually steam-powered, while the smaller ones often use gasoline or diesel engines. When logs are received at the sawmill, they are usually dumped into a log pond where they are sorted according to

FIG. 37-7. Huge logs being loaded on a truck. (*Weyerhaeuser Sales Company.*)

species and grades. From the pond they are carried up an incline to the deck of the mill, where they are washed in readiness for sawing (Fig. 37-11).

FIG. 37-8. Pine logs decked for loading onto trains. (*Caterpillar Tractor Company.*)

The log to be sawed is clamped securely on a movable carriage which operates on a straight track and carries it past a stationary band saw or circular saw (Fig. 37-12). The larger mills generally use the band saw; the *smaller* ones, the circular saw.

After the board has been cut from the log, it falls on a set of rollers which carry it for further processing. Small mills often possess no other equipment but the saw; hence, each piece is cut to length and width individually. In large sawmills a machine called an *edger,* (Fig. 37-13) rips rough edges off boards and cuts them to standard widths. They are then cut into standard lengths with *trimmer* saws (Fig. 37-14). The manufacturing processes of cutting the log into boards, ripping the boards into widths, and cutting them into

Fig. 37-9. Logs being floated to a mill. (*Courtesy of West Coast Lumbermen's Association.*)

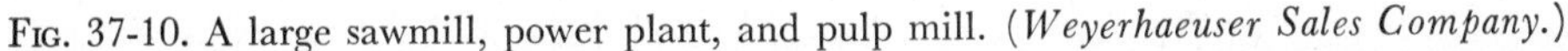

Fig. 37-10. A large sawmill, power plant, and pulp mill. (*Weyerhaeuser Sales Company.*)

FIG. 37-11. Washing a yellow-pine log before it enters the sawmill. (*Caterpillar Tractor Company.*)

FIG. 37-13. Edger ripping a board to standard width. (*Weyerhaeuser Sales Company.*)

lengths are the three basic steps in the manufacture of lumber.

At larger mills lumber is graded, sorted, and seasoned. The grading and sorting is according to standardized grading rules, and the seasoning is either by air drying (Fig. 37-15) or by drying in kilns (Fig. 37-16). The length of time required for air drying varies according to the kind of weather, the wood, the dimensions of the board, the arrangement of the yard, and the method of piling. Kiln drying takes less time and eliminates some danger of deterioration.

After the boards have dried, the lumber may be sent to a planing mill (Fig. 37-17), where the boards can be planed and the edges jointed or prepared for

FIG. 37-12. Sawing a Douglas-fir with a band saw. (*Courtesy of West Coast Lumbermen's Association.*)

FIG. 37-14. Trimmer saw cutting a board to standard length. (*Courtesy of West Coast Lumbermen's Association.*)

FIG. 37-15. Seasoning lumber by air drying. (*Caterpillar Tractor Company.*)

a tongue-and-groove joint. They may also be fabricated into any number of manufactured products, such as window frames, sash, and doors.

The final marketing of lumber is highly organized and competitive, as is marketing of all commercial products. Lumber may be sent directly from the sawmill to local retail dealers or to wholesale yards; these, in turn, provide needed materials to builders and individual customers.

Discussion Topics

1. Name two duties of a timber cruiser.
2. Name the two initial operations in logging.
3. Name a modern method of skidding logs.
4. Name three methods of getting logs to a sawmill.

FIG. 37-16. Stacks of lumber emerging from kilns. (*Weyerhaeuser Sales Company.*)

Fig. 37-17. Modern lumber carrier truck. (*Courtesy of The Timberman.*)

5. How is power furnished in sawmills?
6. What purpose does the log pond at a mill serve?
7. What kinds of saws are used to saw a log in a mill?
8. What is an "edger"? A "trimmer" saw?
9. Explain two methods of drying lumber.
10. Name the three basic steps in the manufacture of lumber.
11. What is the function of a planing mill?

Unit 38. Uses of Forest Products

There are, as a result of modern science and research, endless applications of forest products to everyday life. Forests provide the raw materials for the countless products essential to our modern living, such as shelter, fuel, clothing, and for many scientific wonders as well. Most homes are built of wood, or at least have some wood in their construction. Furniture, books, magazines, radio cabinets, baseball bats, rolling pins, turpentine for paint, resin for soap, and even sugar are some of the products of our forests. Plastics, rayons, and photographic film are just a few of the many newer products made from wood.

More than 10,000 products of wood are being used today, and wood enters in some degree into the manufacture, processing, or delivery of practically all other products. During the Second World War wood was required for some 1,200 items of military equipment, and the armed forces used a greater tonnage of forest products than of steel. Modern technology is constantly developing new uses for wood, and the prospects are that our needs for timber will increase in the future.

Veneers and Plywoods

The ancient Egyptians conserved their rare and beautiful woods by slicing them into thin veneers, which they glued to more common woods of lesser beauty, just as furniture makers do today. These veneers were the ancestors of our modern all-purpose plywoods.

Veneer is a very thin sheet of wood which has been sliced from a log with a straight knife blade or with a rotary cutter. The straight-knife-blade method shears thin material the width of the log (Fig. 38-1). The rotary method pushes the log against a long, sharp steel blade, which cuts it into one long

Fig. 38-1. Slicing veneer with a straight knife blade. (*Mahogany Association, Inc.*)

Fig. 38-3. Plywood showing direction of grain and method of lamination. (*Mahogany Association, Inc.*)

continuous sheet the width of the log Fig. 38-2). This latter process resembles the unwinding of a large roll of wrapping paper. Veneer is matched into very beautiful patterns to form table tops, cabinets, panels, and other pieces of handsome furniture or the embellishments for them.

Plywood is an example of making thick pieces of wood from thin ones. It is built by gluing three or more veneer strips into panels which have the grain of the wood running crosswise on alternate layers (Fig. 38-3). This construction gives greater strength and resistance with a minimum of weight. Panels are available in various plys, sizes, and thicknesses. Plywood, when properly worked, can be formed into many shapes and designs (Fig. 38-4). Plywood manufactured for exterior construction is bonded together with synthetic resin glues which are unaffected

Fig. 38-2. A continuous sheet of veneer sliced by the rotary method. (*Courtesy of The Timberman.*)

Fig. 38-4. Plywood formed in various shapes and designs. (*American Forest Products Industries.*)

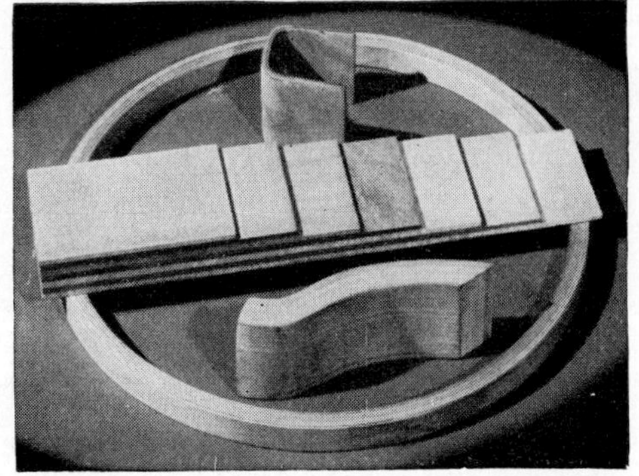

Fig. 38-5. Glued laminated arch segments for a building. (*American Forest Products Industries.*)

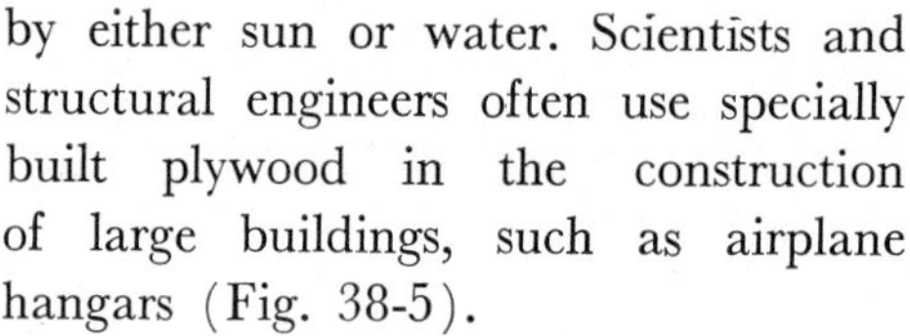

by either sun or water. Scientists and structural engineers often use specially built plywood in the construction of large buildings, such as airplane hangars (Fig. 38-5).

Compreg is a product similar to plywood, which is made by soaking or impregnating sheets of wood with raw resin, piling one upon another, and then placing the combination under great pressure until the resin has set (Fig. 38-6). The resulting product looks like wood, because it has a grain like that of wood, but it has been changed by the pressure and by the resin which fills its cells to a harder, firmer, heavier substance capable of many new uses.

Fig. 38-6. Compreg (*right*), compressed wood which forms a new, hard product. (*American Forest Products Industries.*)

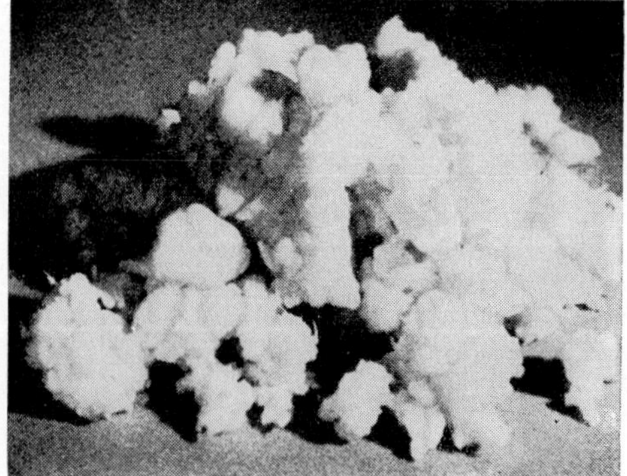

Fig. 38-7. Cotton-like cellulose made from wood fibers. (*American Forest Products Industries.*)

Paper Products

This book would not be available if it were not for our forest crop. Six per cent of the timber harvest is used for making pulp from which paper is manufactured. Wood is converted into pulp by separating cellulose fibers, through the process of chopping the wood into fine chips, then soaking the fibers in a chemical solution (Fig. 38-7), and finally mixing them with water to the desired consistency. This pulp flows onto a continuous metal belt pierced with many holes, often 4,500 to the square inch. As the belt moves, the water drops through the holes, leaving a thin, damp film of fiber. The paper is being formed, but after further processing, it must pass on to an endless belt of felt, for it is not strong enough to travel alone while being pressed. After the paper has dried and is strong enough to maintain its own weight, it leaves the felt belt and runs on to driers, large steam-heated cylinders which completely evaporate all moisture. From here it is rolled, ready for shipment (Fig. 38-8).

FIG. 38-8. Finished newsprint being rolled for shipment. (*American Forest Products Industries.*)

A laminated paper product called *Papreg* (Fig. 38-9) has been produced by impregnating sheets of paper with resin and subjecting them to heat and pressure. This material is lighter than, but as strong as, metal and can be compressed into simple shapes or molded into curved patterns. It has numerous industrial uses, including a place in aircraft construction.

FIG. 38-9. Papreg, layers of compressed impregnated paper having a metal-like strength. (*American Forest Products Industries.*)

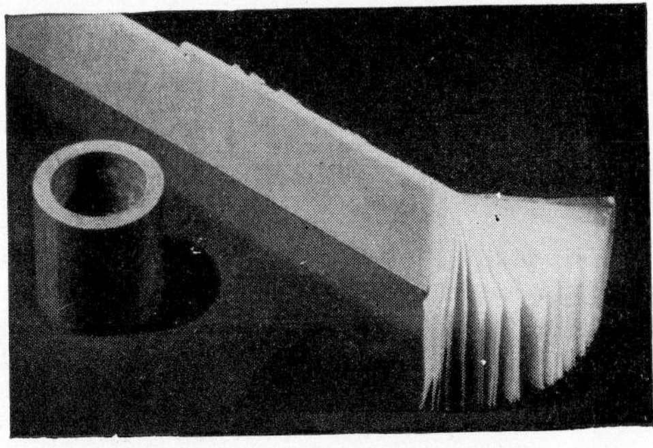

Figure 38-10 shows a few of the many thousands of paper products.

INSULATION AND FUEL

Practically every bit of the tree serves some useful purpose. In many of the modern mills waste, such as slabs, shavings, sawdust, and scrap wood, is proc-

FIG. 38-10. A few paper products. (*American Forest Products Industries.*)

FIG. 38-11. Attractive rayon evening gown made from wood. (*American Forest Products Industries.*)

essed into various types of insulating material, wallboard, and pressed-wood products. When waste can serve no other purpose, it is burned as fuel to hopper-fed furnaces.

RAYON AND WOOD WOOL FABRICS

Wood pulp is the source material for more than 75 per cent of all rayons manufactured in the United States. Research has found that cellulose fiber can be treated to form one of the ingredients of rayon. Wood chips are reduced to a pulp and mixed with chemicals to form a gelatinous substance. This thick mass is forced through tiny holes in platinum sieves to form hair-like strands which are twisted together to form yarn of the desired size and texture.

Rayon is especially suited for the manufacture of the cords which form the body of pneumatic tires. The fibers can also be woven into practically any serviceable cloth or fabric (Fig. 38-11). Other items made from wood cellulose include soft, fluffy blankets and warm, woolly coats.

TREATMENT OF WOOD

The scientist has discovered that wood consists primarily of two classes of substances, which he calls *cellulose* and *lignin.* About two-thirds of all wood is cellulose, and the other third is lignin. They are sometimes called the *magic twins of the forest* for from them new products are made.

Paper and rayon are only two of the many articles made from cellulose. By various chemical and mechanical means it also gives us gunpowder, imitation leather, felt, plastics, lacquers, glycerine, sugar, alcohol, molasses, yeast, and food proteins.

Lignin is a tough, durable substance which acts as a kind of binder in a tree, cementing cells together. It is the cause of the woodiness of wood. Scientists still find its exact composition a mystery, but they have found many uses for it, such as a tanning agent for leather, a binder in mixing concrete, a water softener and purifier, a base for fertilizers, and a flavor, vanillin.

Lignin is also used to make plastics. During the Second World War it served in bomb fuses, shell cases, instrument panels for airplanes, ships, tanks, and the cases of storage batteries. Other useful, everyday items made of plastic are fountain pens, telephones, radio cabinets, electrical equipment, combs, handles on kitchen utensils, and even jewelry (Fig. 38-12).

Additional scientific yields from wood include Buna rubber, which is made by chemical methods from alcohol. Since alcohol can be made from wood, synthetic rubber can be derived from wood. (Natural rubber, of course, comes from trees which grow in the tropics.) Even the fuel burned in cars can be mixed with alcohol made from wood, and, in countries where supplies of petroleum are inadequate, alcohol is used to a large extent for this purpose. Many of these newer uses of wood require no greater harvest from our forests. The branches, bark, sawdust, and slabs of wood from sawmills, formerly leftovers, are now the vital ingredients of scientific products.

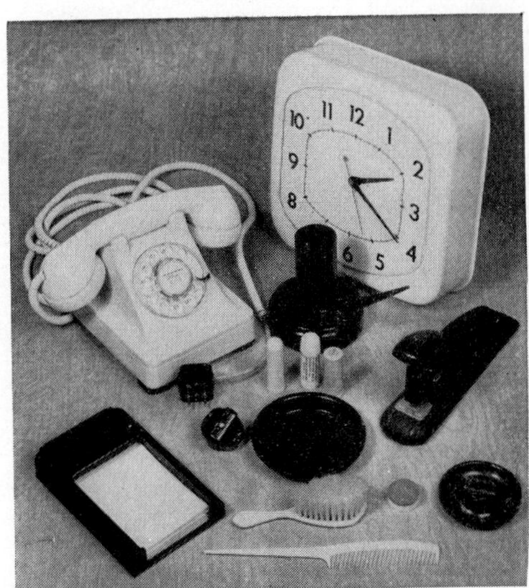

FIG. 38-12. Plastic articles using cellulose and lignin. (*American Forest Products Industries.*)

PRODUCTS EXTRACTED FROM TREES

Solvents, sugar, dyes, drying agents, and spirits necessary in many manufacturing processes are extracted from trees. Southern pine trees yield oleoresin for the paint industry. Turpentines and resins extracted from oleoresin are employed as driers and solvents for paint, varnish products, and printing inks. They are also important in making soap, paper, and many other items. Turpentine and resins are also obtained from an extract which is the product of a molasses-like substance (gum resin) which drips from the tree after the bark has been chipped.

Distillates, such as wood alcohol and acetone, and other important chemicals are also by-products of trees. Dyes extracted from hemlock bark are used in leather tanning. Other forest products include such table delicacies as maple sugar, maple syrup, and a wide variety of fruits and nuts.

Discussion Topics

1. Differentiate between "veneer" and "plywood."
2. Name six articles made from plywood.
3. Describe the two methods of producing veneer.
4. What is the advantage of plywood over solid wood?
5. Describe briefly how paper is made.
6. What are the differences between

cellulose and lignin? Name some uses of each.
7. What are some scientific products made for everyday use from wood?
8. Name and give the uses of eight products made from trees.
9. Mention four products extracted from trees.

Unit 39. Occupations in Woods

Occupational opportunities in the general field of woodworking are many. They are dependent largely upon the education, interests, and initiative of the individual. These opportunities range from the unskilled type of work demanding manual dexterity through semiskilled and skilled, which requires ability in the woodcrafts, to professional positions in industrial teaching, industrial research, and forestry. This summary does not include the many occupations related to, and depending upon, wood and wood fabrication and the products resulting from it.

The unskilled type of work requires very little education but entails a tremendous amount of manual labor; the highly skilled tasks and professions, however, require an expensive education, usually at least college graduation, mental alertness, and constant application to the assignment at hand.

It is essential for the student who desires to go into the wood or wood-products industries to receive excellent training in shopwork, English, science, mathematics, and the social sciences. A combination of these subjects enables one to understand problems of economics, sociology, mathematics, chemistry, and physics as they pertain to our technology.

As a general rule, wages and salaries are dependent upon the educational qualifications of the individual.

Forests and wood products are important forces in our economy. More than 1 million workers and their families obtain their living directly from the forests—in lumber and paper mills and in wood-using industries. The forests contribute indirectly to the support of many more millions: for example, in the railroad and other transportation industries, in the construction industries, in water and power utilities, in retailing, in sports-goods manufacture, and in business serving tourists and recreation. Nine states have more forest workers than workers in any other industrial classification (Fig. 39-2), and for every one of these workers there are others whose jobs are closely dependent upon timber harvest. Payrolls from these people help to support many other industries and services.

The farmer has a very important interest in our timber lands. He derives substantial income from the sale of woodland products directly as lumber. It is said that woodlands occupy more acreage than any other crop on American farms (Fig. 39-1) and help support more than 2,500,000 farm families.

Over 300,000 wage earners are employed directly in the manufacture of

Fig. 39-1. Forester estimating a lumber crop. (*Courtesy of The Timberman.*)

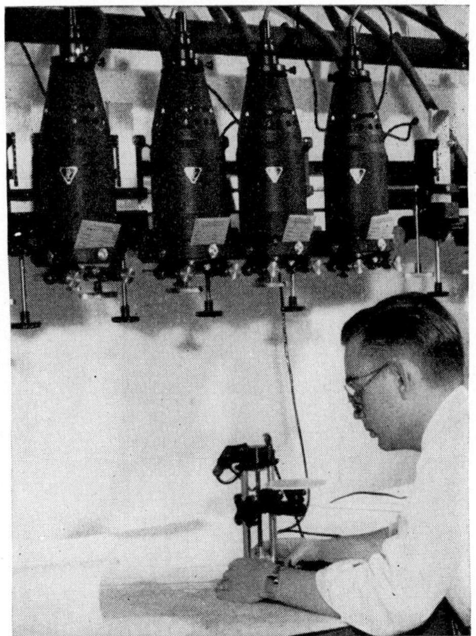

Fig. 39-3. Forestry research technician in a laboratory. (*Courtesy of The Timberman.*)

furniture. It is estimated that an additional 1,000,000 are hired as carpenters or fabricators of wood products or buildings. One-third of a million persons make paper from wood, and hundreds

Fig. 39-2. Forestry involves many types of training. (*Courtesy of The Timberman.*)

of thousands of printers use it to produce our magazines and newspapers. Many more tens of thousands are employed in the professional and technical occupations as teachers, research technicians, and scientists. At the present time there are listed more than 10,000 wood products. New uses, which are being found daily, are the result of research and experimentation in the laboratories (Fig. 39-3).

The natural resource of timber is providing employment for approximately 12 million people either directly or indirectly.*

* Detailed data of woodworking occupations is available in a bulletin entitled "Job Descriptions for the Lumber and Lumber Products Industries," which can be obtained from The United States Government Printing Office, Washington 25, D.C.

Discussion Topics

1. List the occupations in your community which are directly dependent on wood.
2. Visit a local industry which uses wood for its basic material and list the many types of jobs in it.
3. How many states have more forest workers than workers in any other industrial classification?
4. What basic school subjects should one study if he is interested in employment in the wood or wood-products industries?
5. Approximately how many people are employed directly and indirectly as a result of the natural resource of timber in the United States?
6. Name some specific occupations in the field of timber and woods which are associated with teaching and research.

Unit 40. Period Designs in Furniture

Much has been written and said about designs in furniture. To have an understanding of these designs, which have contributed so much to our daily living, it is important to study the styles of the different periods of furniture. There are many variations in furniture design, but this chapter is confined to the consideration of a few outstanding periods in furniture design which have proved their worth through the years.

FIG. 40-1. Original period furniture distinguished by expert craftsmanship. (*Mahogany Association, Inc.*)

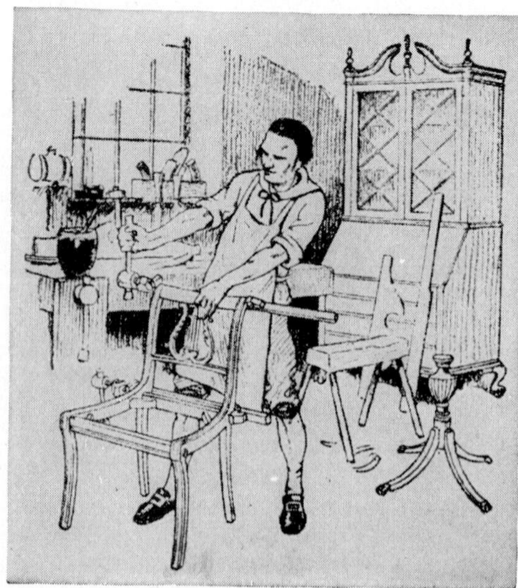

The early styles of furniture overlapped as one cabinetmaker borrowed ideas from another. Clear-cut delineation of each period is impossible, but outstanding characteristics of each predominate and are recognizable when seen. Several styles were designated by the names of the ruling monarchs, while others took on the names of the individual craftsmen or designers. Figure 40-1 presents a pictorial conception of an early craftsman at work on a period piece.

QUEEN ANNE

One of the early Georgian styles in furniture, which flourished from about 1700 to 1750, was named after Queen Anne. This style is characterized by the simple Queen Anne lines of the cabriole

Fig. 40-2. Queen Anne chair. (*Mahogany Association, Inc.*)

leg (shaped like a bent knee), the club foot, the animal claw-and-ball foot, and the solid fiddle-shaped splats in the backs of chairs.

Chippendale

Thomas Chippendale, the second of three generations of this same name, was, beyond doubt, the leading fashionable cabinetmaker of London from 1750 to 1775. He perpetuated his ideas on furniture design through his book, *The Gentleman and Cabinet Maker's Director*. His early work was an improvement upon the decorated Queen Anne style. In chairs the fiddle-shaped splat became the delicate, ribbon back, and the cabriole leg and Dutch foot became the ball and claw and was later re-

Fig. 40-3. Chippendale chair. (*Mahogany Association, Inc.*)

Fig. 40-4. Adam chair. (*Mahogany Association, Inc.*)

Fig. 40-5. Hepplewhite chair. (*Mahogany Association, Inc.*)

Fig. 40-6. Sheraton chair. (*Mahogany Association, Inc.*)

placed by the straight leg, as shown in Fig. 40-3.

Adam

Robert Adam distinguished himself not only as a builder but as a designer of furniture and as a decorator. He usually employed vertical lines for his chair and table supports (Fig. 40-4). Ornamentation was derived from classical sources, chiefly architectural. The Adam style was in vogue in England during the American Revolution, and so was not very popular in America, but since that time this design has been accepted here.

Hepplewhite

George Hepplewhite was a practical cabinetmaker and designer who first created strictly in the Adam mode. Later he developed in his own way the treatment of the shield-back chair (Fig. 40-5). The use of light-toned woods was developed during the middle of the eighteenth century, and Hepplewhite employed them to create a more subtle contrast for inlays. He always avoided massiveness in design and is particularly famous for his chairs and sideboards.

Sheraton

Although few examples of his own handiwork are known of today, Thomas Sheraton is regarded as one of the foremost furniture designers. His style became influential through his manuals of design, especially the *Cabinet-Maker and Upholsterer's Drawing Book*. His style of furniture is essentially feminine

Fig. 40-7. Louis XV chair. (*Mahogany Association, Inc.*)

Fig. 40-8. Louis XVI chair. (*Mahogany Association, Inc.*)

in appearance but is structurally strong and sound (Fig. 40-6). He favored the oval, the lyre, latticework, and slender urns in the backs of chairs. His designs employed both square and turned legs, finely tapered, often with the spade foot or thimble toe. He was a preacher, pamphleteer, and a business failure, who lived and died in poverty during the last half of the eighteenth century.

Louis XV

The furniture design developed and referred to as Louis XV is somewhat similar to the style created during the reign of his predecessor, Louis XIV. While Louis XIV furniture featured elaborate carving and symmetrical lines, Louis XV furniture avoided symmetry. Both types were ornate, Louis XV pieces being smaller and better adapted to smaller rooms (Fig. 40-7).

Louis XVI

This style, arising in the latter part of the eighteenth century, is characterized by pieces delicately scaled, smaller in structure than those of the preceding period, simple, and graceful in appearance. They are evidence of a refined taste in ornamentation (Fig. 40-8).

French Empire

During the years from 1800 to 1814 the designers of furniture, influenced by Napoleonic conquests, turned to Greek, Roman, and Egyptian schools for inspiration. The lines of their furniture were stiff and ungainly (Fig. 40-9), and ornament was chiefly metal or gilding. Although this style did not fit the times, it

Fig. 40-9. French Empire chair. (*Mahogany Association, Inc.*)

Fig. 40-10. Colonial American chair. (*Mahogany Association, Inc.*)

was carried to England and then to the United States where it was modified by American influence. Regency is the name under which English furniture of the French Empire influence is best known.

Colonial American

The era in design prior to 1700 in America is often referred to as Pre-Revolutionary. There were two types of design which depicted the tastes of the colonial settlers: one was known as the primitive type, consisting of furniture crudely made by carpenters, wheelwrights, or joiners. The lines were not beautiful, but the furniture was substantial and functional. The second type was the result of importations of fine furniture from England by the wealthy settlers and planters of Virginia. The Colonial American design of the better type was greatly influenced by Chippendale (Fig. 40-10). After 1750 furniture produced and designed in America, even though patterned after English design, was fully equal to it in artistic lines and quality.

Federal American

The American Revolution produced a new design in furniture referred to as Federal American or Post-Revolutionary. During this time the influence of Chippendale declined in American cabinetmaking. The emphasis shifted to the pleasing designs of Hepplewhite and Sheraton. In 1800 Federal American furniture design was a mixture of Hepplewhite and Sheraton, with some semblance of French Empire, owing

FIG. 40-11. Federal American chair. (*Mahogany Association, Inc.*)

FIG. 40-12. Duncan Phyfe chair. (*Mahogany Association, Inc.*)

to the influence of Duncan Phyfe. Many authorities contend that Federal American styles are among the most attractive ever produced (Fig. 40-11).

DUNCAN PHYFE

Duncan Phyfe was the first outstanding furniture designer in America. He was born in Scotland but came to America with his parents at the age of sixteen years. During the early part of the nineteenth century he received patronage from the John Jacob Astor family. In his early work the Adam-Sheraton influence predominated, but this was followed by furniture that grew out of the forms of the French Directoire and Early Consulate. Furniture designed by Duncan Phyfe has balance, structural integrity, and economy of construction. He is best characterized by his use of the lyre, brass ferrules, Pompeiian designs, and graceful outcurved legs for chairs and tables (Fig. 40-12).

OTHER DESIGNERS

During the last half of the eighteenth century, America had many first-class cabinetmakers and designers. Some of these men were Elijah and Jacob Sanderson, most outstanding cabinetmakers of Salem, Massachusetts, who shipped furniture to southern cities and to South America; Samuel McIntire, a Salem, Massachusetts, architect, designer, and wood carver who was noted for carved modifications of several styles; William Savery, of Philadelphia, a cabinetmaker famous for design applications to highboys and lowboys (Fig. 40-13); John Gillingham, also from Philadelphia,

FIG. 40-13. Reproduction of a highboy with Chippendale effect, representing the climax in design and craftsmanship of Philadelphia cabinetmakers (1770). (*Mahogany Association, Inc.*)

noted for Gillingham chairs with trefoil backs; Thomas Afleck, a leader of the Philadelphia Chippendale school; and John Folwell, a Philadelphia cabinetmaker and designer and a follower of Chippendale design, who is credited with making the famous Speaker's Chair in Independence Hall.

NINETEENTH CENTURY

The major contribution to furniture making during the nineteenth century was the development of woodworking machinery and the introduction of

FIG. 40-14. Nineteenth-century rocker. Replica of that used by Abraham Lincoln. (*Mahogany Association, Inc.*)

machine-made furniture. This accounts for the enormous quantity which is manufactured today at a cost relatively low in comparison with the cost of custom-made furniture. Americans in the nineteenth century were generally so concerned with the building of a great nation that an element of art and beauty was lost. Lincoln's chair (Fig. 40-14) is a typical example of the overdecoration of the nineteenth century.

Some of our great furniture styles deteriorated because of the overenthusiasm with which knickknacks and gingerbread were applied to solid, basic styles. Victorian was the most popular style of this period, and even today the antique market offers Victorian articles, especially chairs and sofas.

MODERN

One of the most spectacular furniture styles to emerge during the present cen-

FIG. 40-15. Twentieth-century modern group of furniture. (*Mahogany Association, Inc.*)

tury has been the so-called *modern*. The early modern of the 1920s was characterized by being unsymmetrical and with boxlike lines. Later it acquired the waterfall front, then went gingerbread with an overdose of veneer treatment, and more recently, uses the popular blond-type finishes. Present-day modern is characterized by the simplicity of the Swedish Modern curvilinear lines. Modern design is now built upon four centuries of furniture tradition, combining a little from several of the eighteenth century styles with twentieth-century functionalism (Fig. 40-15). The ever-popular Chippendale influence is evinced in present-day functional treatment of furniture (Fig. 40-16).

FIG. 40-16. Chippendale influence on modern functional furniture. (*Mahogany Association, Inc.*)

Discussion Topics

1. What is meant by "period furniture"?
2. From where did the styles of period furniture derive their names?
3. Name two distinctive characteristics of Queen Anne furniture.

4. Who was the leading fashionable cabinetmaker in London from 1750 to 1775?
5. How did Chippendale alter the fiddle-shaped splat of the Queen Anne style? How did he alter the cabriole leg and Dutch foot?
6. From what sources did Robert Adam obtain his ornamentation?
7. Why was Adam's style unpopular in America at first?
8. What cabinetmaker was one of the first to use light-toned wood for inlays? When?
9. What characterizes the back of a Hepplewhite chair?
10. Give three outstanding characteristics of a Sheraton chair.
11. Give two outstanding characteristics of both a Louis XV and Louis XVI chair.
12. How did Napoleon influence French Empire style furniture?
13. What is the origin of our Regency style?
14. Discuss two types of furniture designed in American during the Colonial era.
15. What period of American furniture has the best design according to some experts?
16. What English cabinetmaker influenced Colonial American design most?
17. Who was the first oustanding furniture designer in America? Give four important characteristics of his design.
18. Name four American furniture designers who flourished about 1770, and give one reason for each of them being famous.
19. What is meant by a "trefoil back" in a chair?
20. Why was furniture more easily obtained in the nineteenth century than before that time?
21. Why did taste in design deteriorate in America in the nineteenth century?
22. Give two characteristics of modern design in the 1920s and two of present-day modern.

Unit 41. The Home Workshop

Many pleasant and profitable hours can be spent in the home workshop by all members of the family. Woodworking has become a hobby which ranks as one of the most popular in the United States. A hobby is a diversion, occupation, or avocation in which a person has more than a casual interest. It is something which is real and vital in his life; it has been referred to as "That thing that you can't wait to get to doing!" In some cases an avocation is an escape from the cares and worries of a troubled business world; for young people it is a means of exploration and learning. Practically all great men have hobbies of one description or another, many of them in woodworking and carpentry.

Some people have a hobby for pleasure, while others follow it for profit.

In either case the projects which are made with the hands in a home workshop bring you, and others who help you, an indescribable feeling of happiness and satisfaction. Woodworking is a creative hobby, and its popularity is partly due to the fact that one can construct useful and ornamental articles for the home, yard, and garden by the use of tools which cost a relatively small amount of money.

Space required for a home workshop can be the very minimum, or it can be an entire room or a garage. Its size will depend upon the purpose of the home workshop and the type of tools and equipment which one wishes to use. Generally, however, one can make provision for this hobby in one of six places: the cellar or basement, the attic, the garage or barn, a spare room, an enclosed rear porch, or a specially built or converted hobby house.

Location of Workshop

If the *basement* or *cellar* affords the logical space, select a dry corner away from the laundry tubs or water to prevent the lumber from warping and the tools from rusting. Since natural lighting will probably not be available, have plenty of artificial lights. If possible, the walls should be lightened in color, possibly with whitewash. It will be better for the worker and for the lumber if the workshop is located where there is not too much heat.

The *attic* often provides ample space

Fig. 41-1. Garage workshop.

for a hobby room. If it is not enclosed under the rafters, it is advisable to cover them with an insulating board to keep the room warm in the winter as well as cool in the summer. Besides, the board makes a much neater appearance. Here again ample lighting facilities must be provided as well as heat in the winter. If a stairway is not already built to the attic, it is possible to install a disappearing-ladder arrangement. One of the chief obstacles in an attic workshop is that lumber will probably have to be cut in shorter lengths for transportation through the house and up into the attic.

In the *garage or barn* one will want to observe the basic suggestions given for the previous two locations and also to use personal ingenuity in arranging for ventilation, good lighting, and convenient electrical outlets. Heating may be a problem, but this will depend upon the utilities available for it. Since many garages are attached to the house, it may not be too great a problem. Figure 41-1 illustrates an excellent garage workshop which occupies one-half of a double garage.

A *spare room,* especially if it is a downstairs one, makes an ideal area for any hobby or workshop activities. Lighting and utilities are already present; so there will probably be no unusual problems to solve.

The *enclosed rear porch* often becomes the center for storing tools. However, they can be fastened to the walls on panels to provide easy access for all members of the household, even though

FIG. 41-2. Rear-porch work area.

this is a somewhat congested area. The photograph in Fig. 41-2 depicts such an area with a built-in work table.

A separate *hobby house* is unquestionably the best arrangement. Noise from working with tools and equipment will not interfere with the activities of the home, and projects can be put down and left for future attention without being in the way. The hobby-house interior in Fig. 41-3 shows the result of converting a garden tool shed into such an ideal setup. The expense involved in converting this particular building was not too great since the hobby of the worker was carpentry, cabinetmaking, and crafts and the materials used were odd-sizes and salvaged plywood. The windows, screens, and doors were surplus from a remodeled house.

It is difficult to establish any particular criteria or to draw up plans for a home workshop or benches because these will depend upon available materials, facilities, and the imagination and ingenuity of the home craftsman.

Tools and Equipment

Tools and equipment will depend upon how extensively one wishes to go into the woodworking hobby and the investment one can afford to make. If a reasonable variety of woodworking is planned, there will be need for all the hand tools listed:

Fig. 41-3. Hobby-house interior.

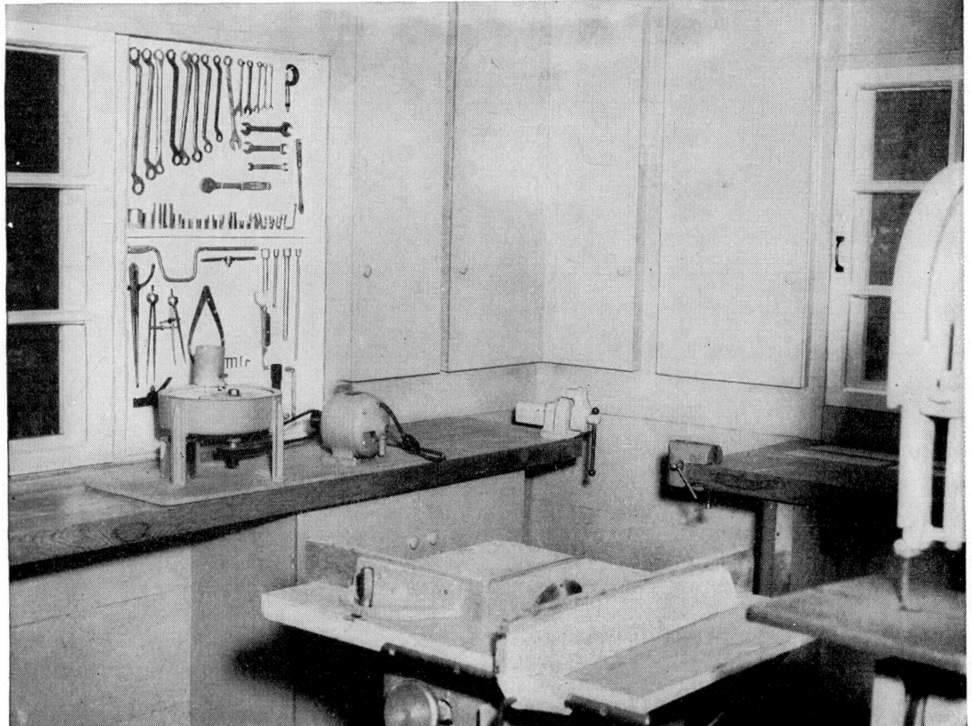

- Awl
- Braces and bits
  - Auger bits, ranging from $\frac{1}{4}$ to $\frac{3}{4}$ inch
  - Countersink bit
  - Hand drill
  - Ratchet brace, 8-inch
  - Screw-driver bit
  - Twist drills,   to $\frac{3}{8}$ inch
- Chisels, wood, ranging from $\frac{1}{4}$ to 1 inch
- Clamps
  - Bar clamps, 4-foot (four)
  - C clamps (three)
  - Hand-screw clamps (four)
- Hammer, claw, 14-ounce
- Handsaws
  - Backsaw, 12-inch
  - Coping-saw frame and blades
  - Crosscut, 8-point, 24-inch
- Hack saw, 10- or 12-inch
  - Ripsaw, 5-point, 26-inch
- Nail set
- Oilstone, combination
- Planes
  - Block plane, 5- or 6-inch
  - Jack plane, 14-inch
- Pliers (one pair)
- Rule, 2-foot
- Scraper, cabinet

Fig. 41-4. Wooden workbench. (*Stanley Tools.*)

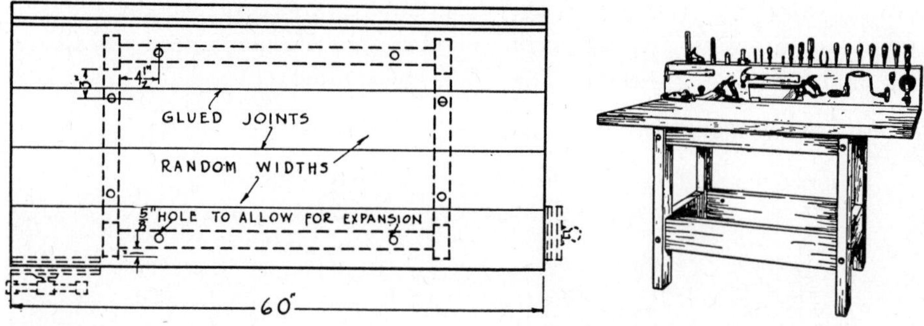

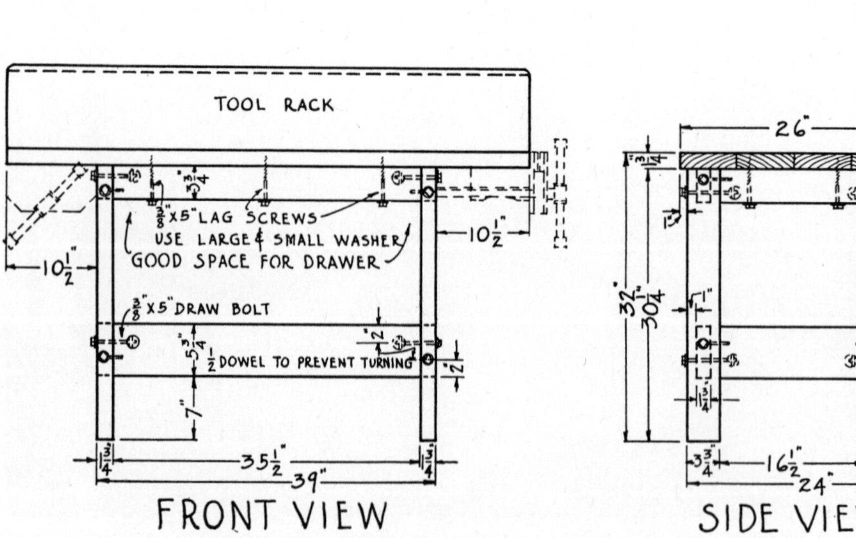

Screw drivers, 6- and 8-inch (two)
Spokeshave
Squares
  Carpenter's steel square
  Try square
Vise, woodworker's, 7-inch jaw
Wood file, half-round, 10-inch
Wood mallet

The foregoing list of hand tools and equipment may seem quite comprehensive, but many of these tools may already be in your household.

One of the interesting projects which the homecraftsman will want to build first is a *workbench.* Figure 41-4 presents a sketch and working drawing of a typical wooden bench.

Figure 41-5 is a working drawing of a very satisfactory *tool cabinet.* In planning your tool cabinet or panel, lay out the tools on heavy wrapping paper, grouping them according to their use. Bear in mind how these tools must be reached when in a vertical position.

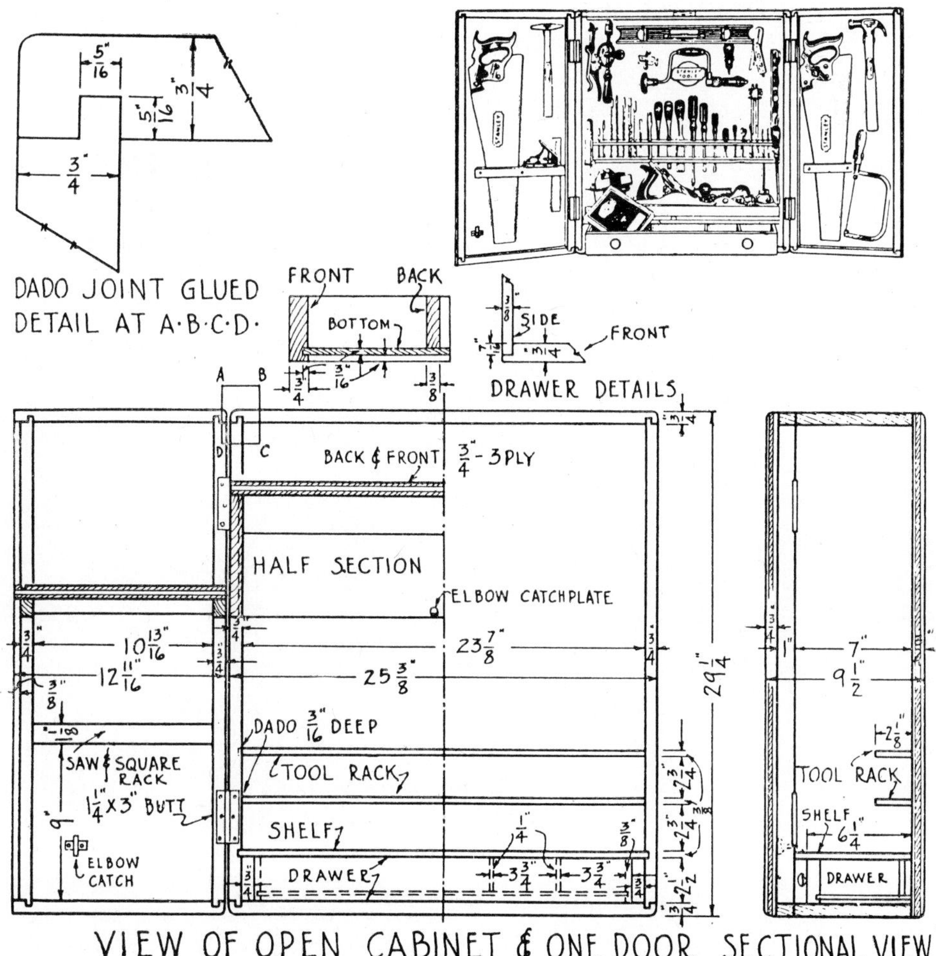

Fig. 41-5. Tool cabinet. (*Stanley Tools.*)

Some home craftsmen prefer to keep tools in a *portable tool chest*. A chest of suitable size is shown in Fig. 41-6.

After the novice has gained some experience and confidence, he will probably want to add a few *power-machinery tools*. It is difficult to determine which pieces should be purchased, because this again depends upon whether the craftsman wants the hobby shop to maintain the home or merely desires to gain satisfaction from building small items out of wood.

A *power table or power circular saw* is helpful. One using 6- or 8-inch diameter blades is adequate. The most prac-

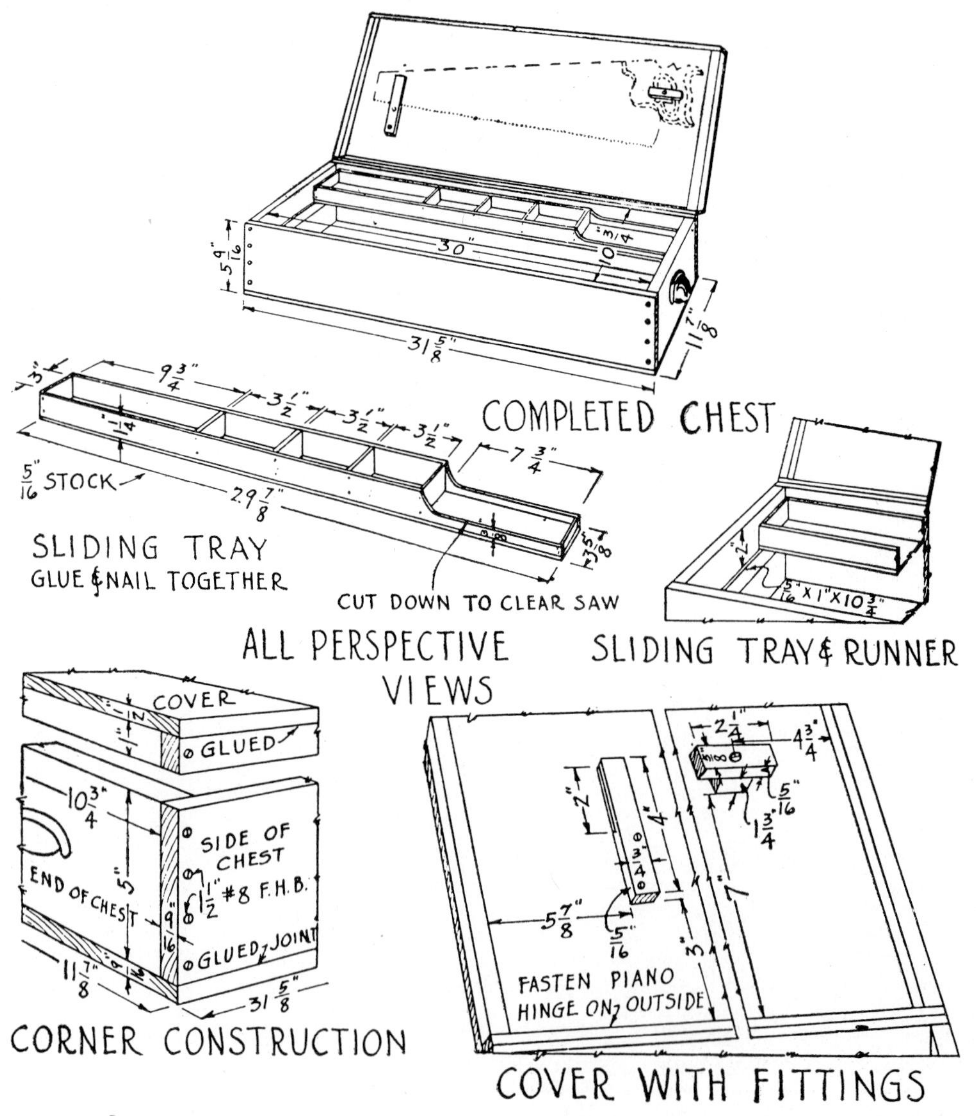

FIG. 41-6. Large tool chest. The "1½" #8F.H.B." specification shown on the "Corner Construction" refers to a 1½-inch No. 8 flat-head brass screw. (*Stanley Tools.*)

tical type of blade for this purpose is the combination type which can be used for either crosscutting or ripping without being changed.

Other pieces of home-workshop machinery which have proved practical are:

Band saw, 12- to 14-inch
Drill press, table or floor model
Jig saw, 12- to 24-inch throat
Grinder
Jointer plane, 4- or 6-inch
Lathe, wood-turning, with 8- to 12-inch swing and 30 to 36 inches between centers
Shaper, small

Several of these machines are to be seen in the home-workshop photographs presented in this chapter.

The novice should not undertake to buy and work with power tools without advice and instruction from an experienced home craftsman or shop teacher. Understanding and observation of safety rules are absolutely essential for a safe, happy, and profitable experience.

Section V. SUGGESTED PROJECTS

PROJECT 1. WALL KNIFE HOLDER

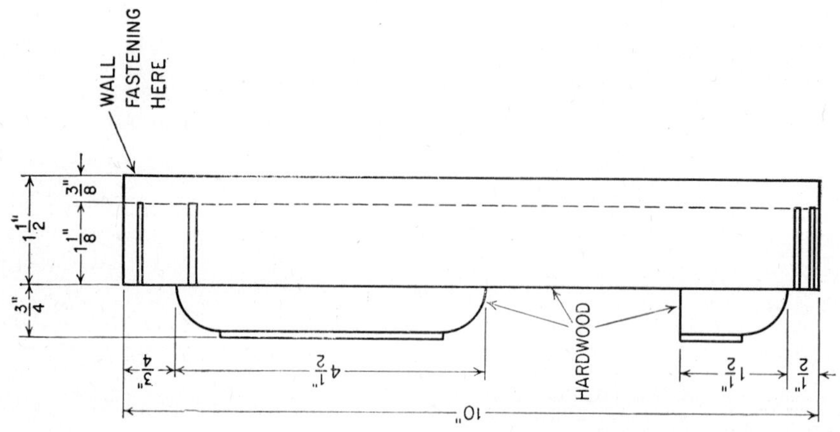

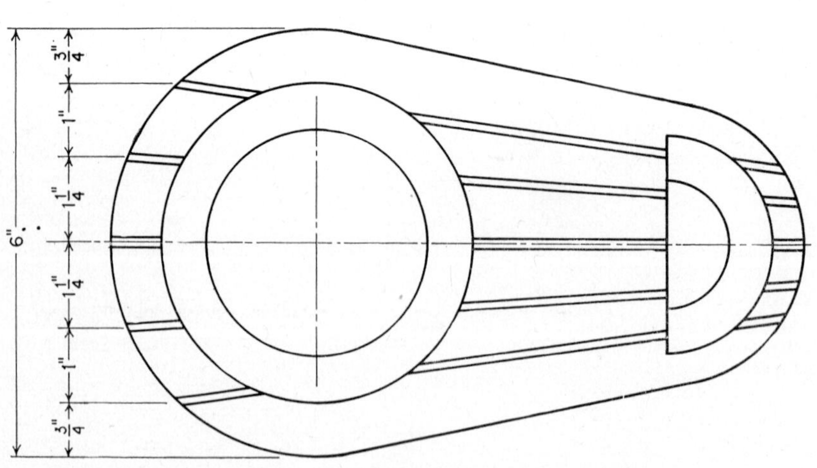

PROJECT 2. HANGING COLONIAL WALL SHELF

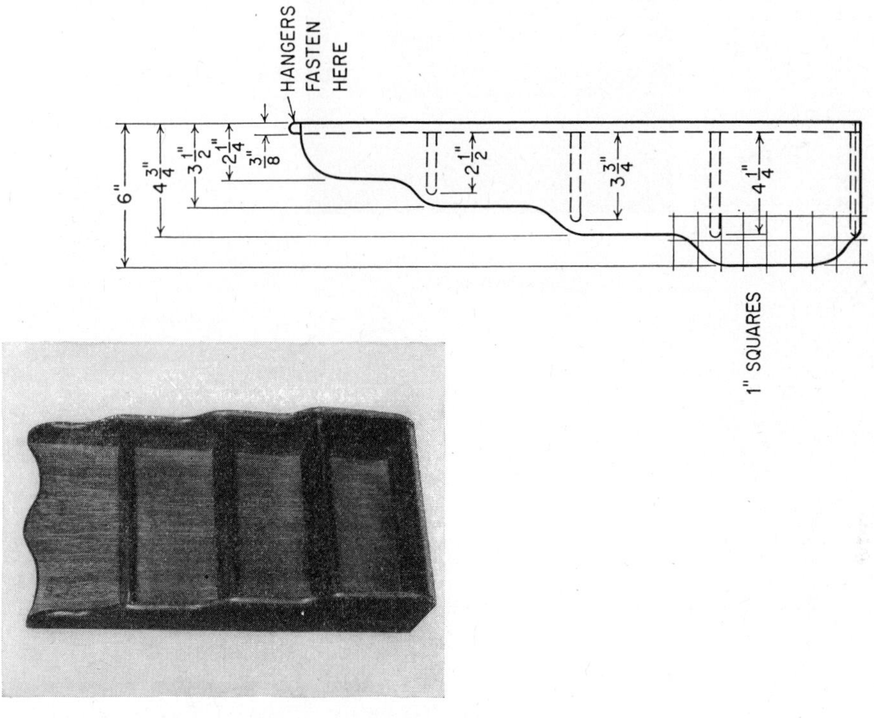

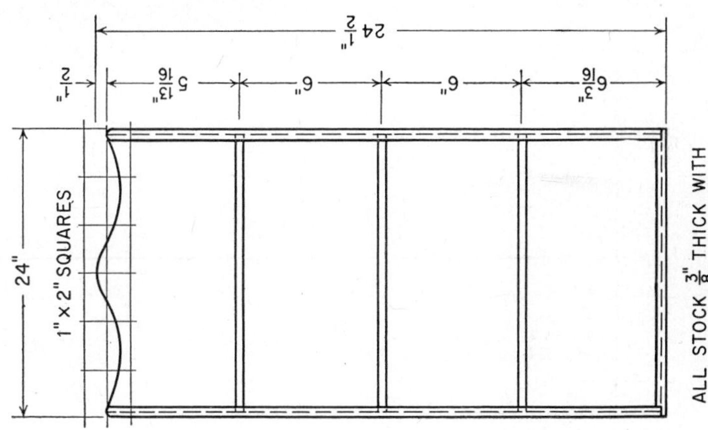

PROJECT 3. TURNED BOWL

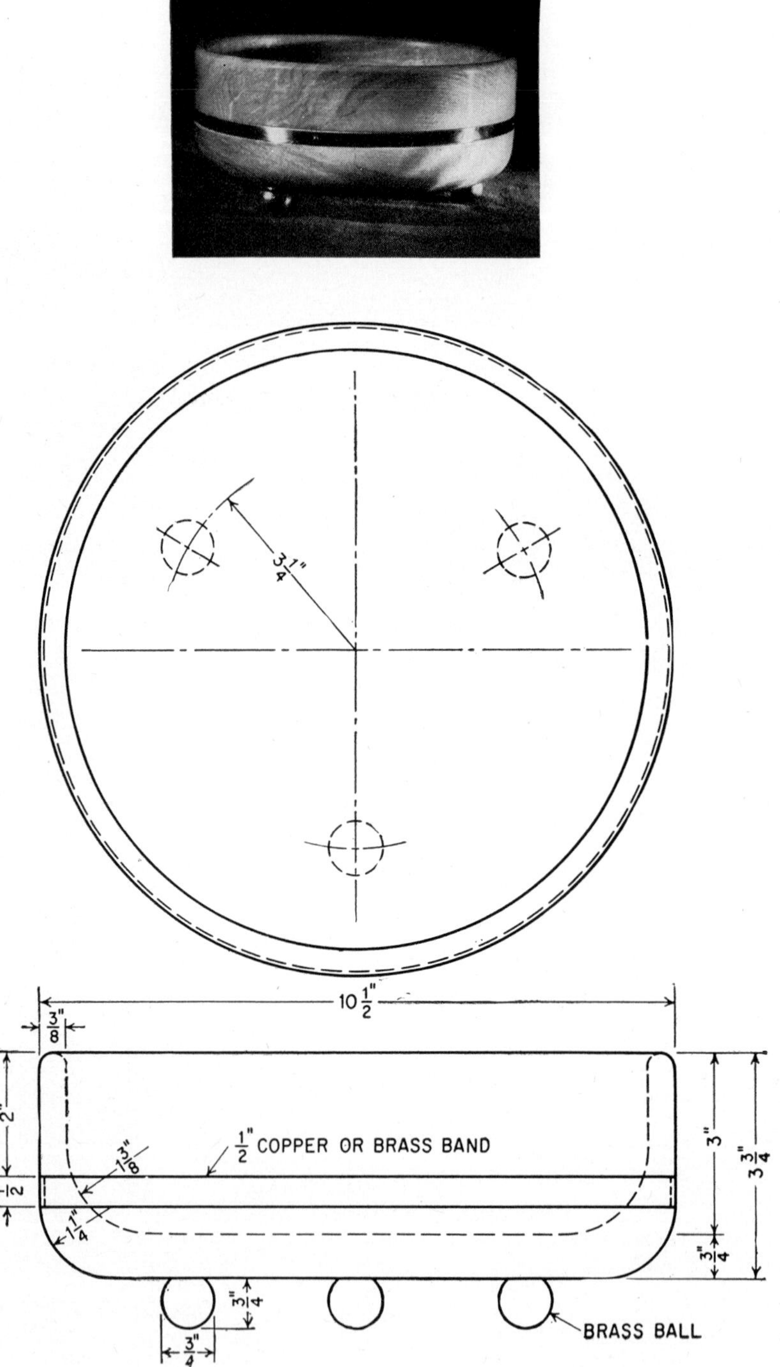

PROJECT 4. TURNED MODERN LAMP

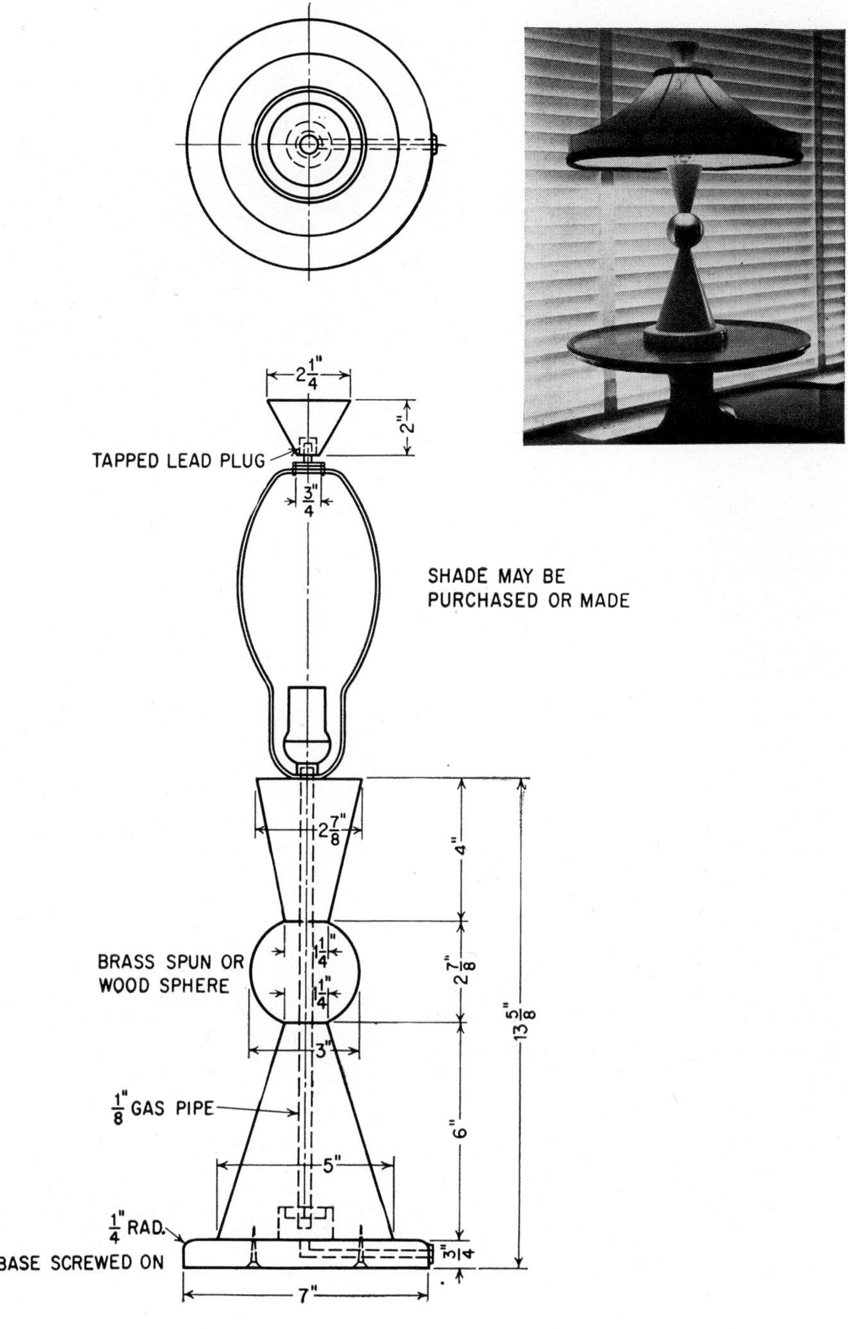

PROJECT 5. MAGAZINE RACK

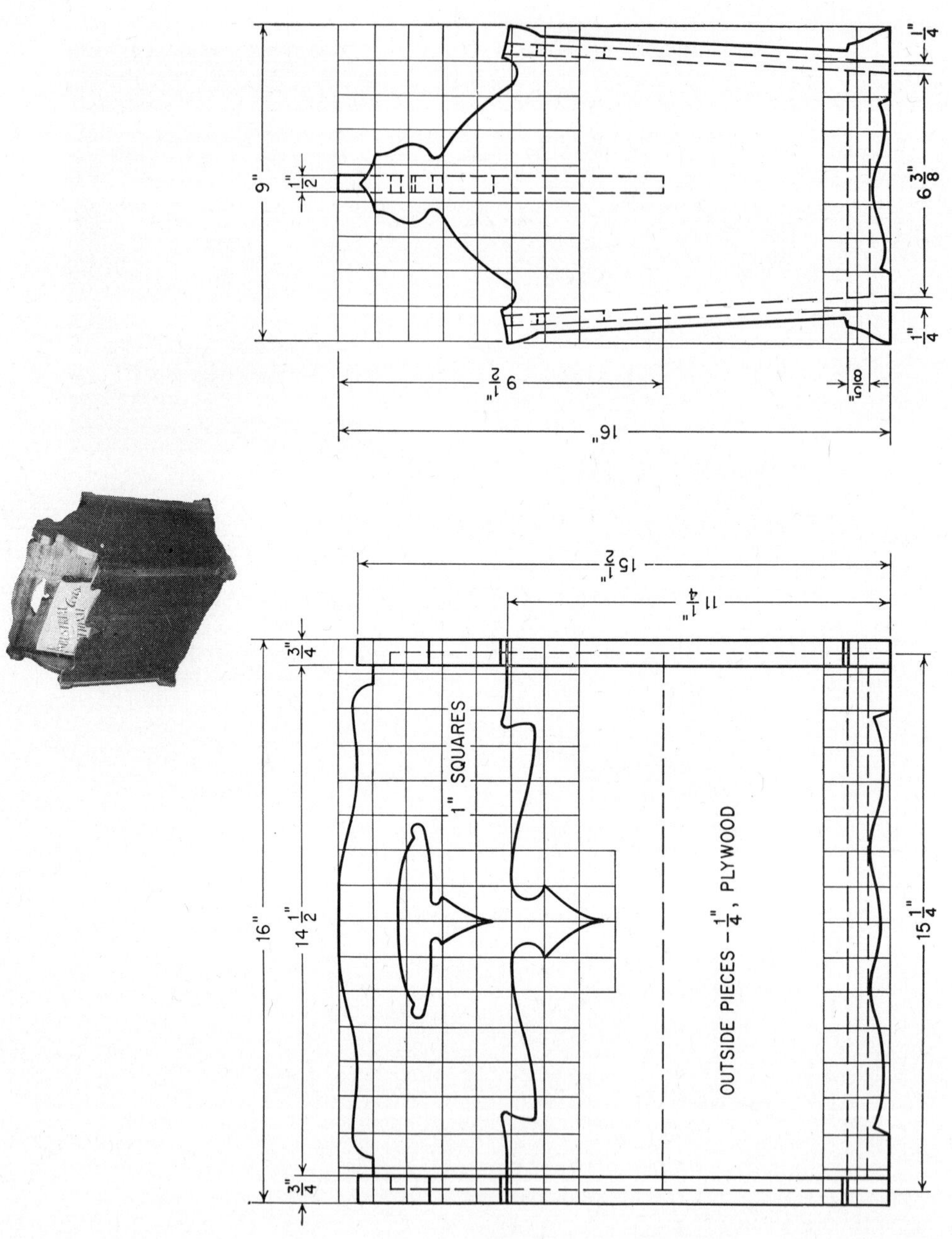

PROJECT 6. GUN RACK

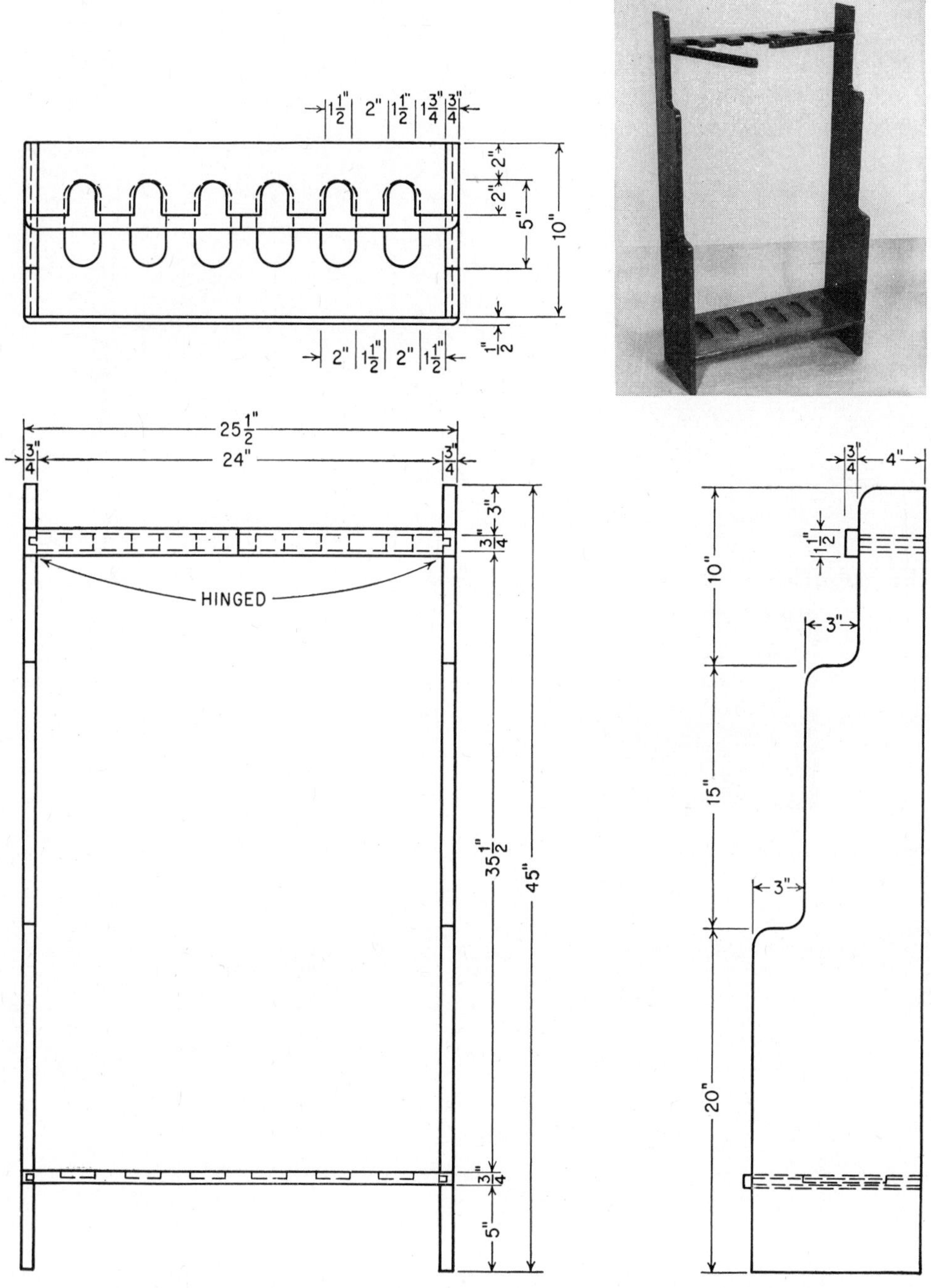

PROJECT 7. COFFEE TABLE

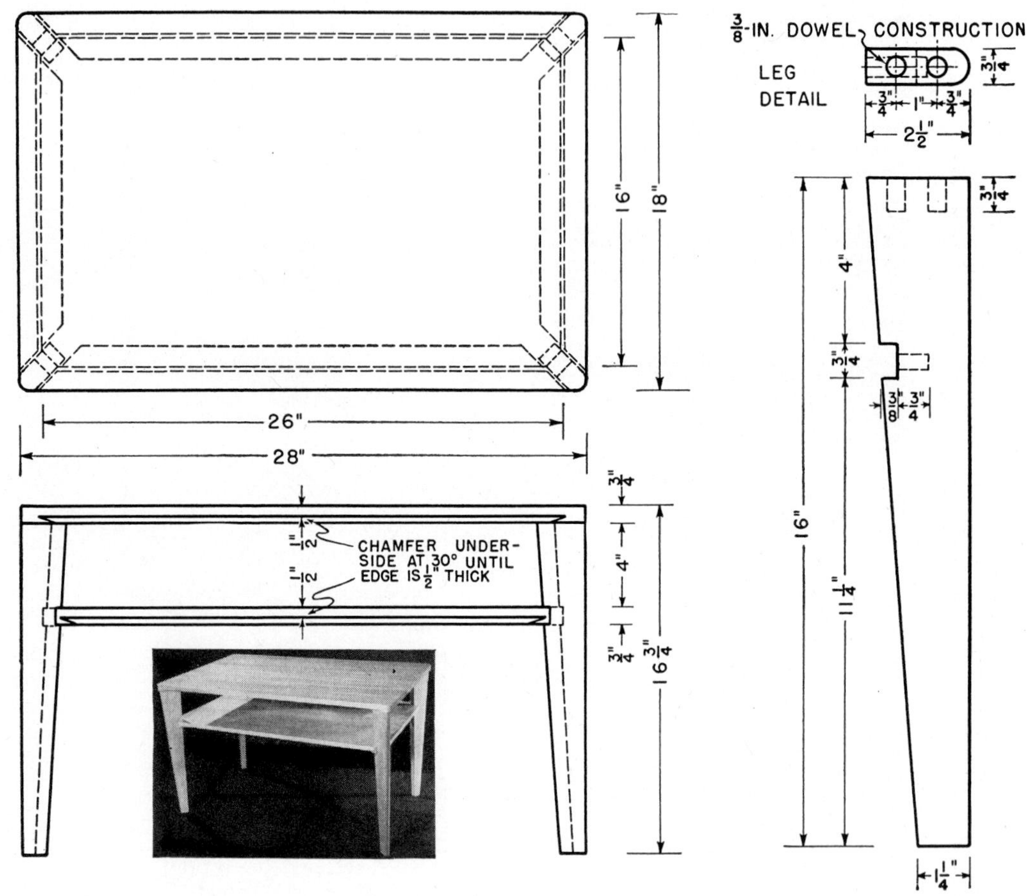

PROJECT 8. MODERN COFFEE TABLE

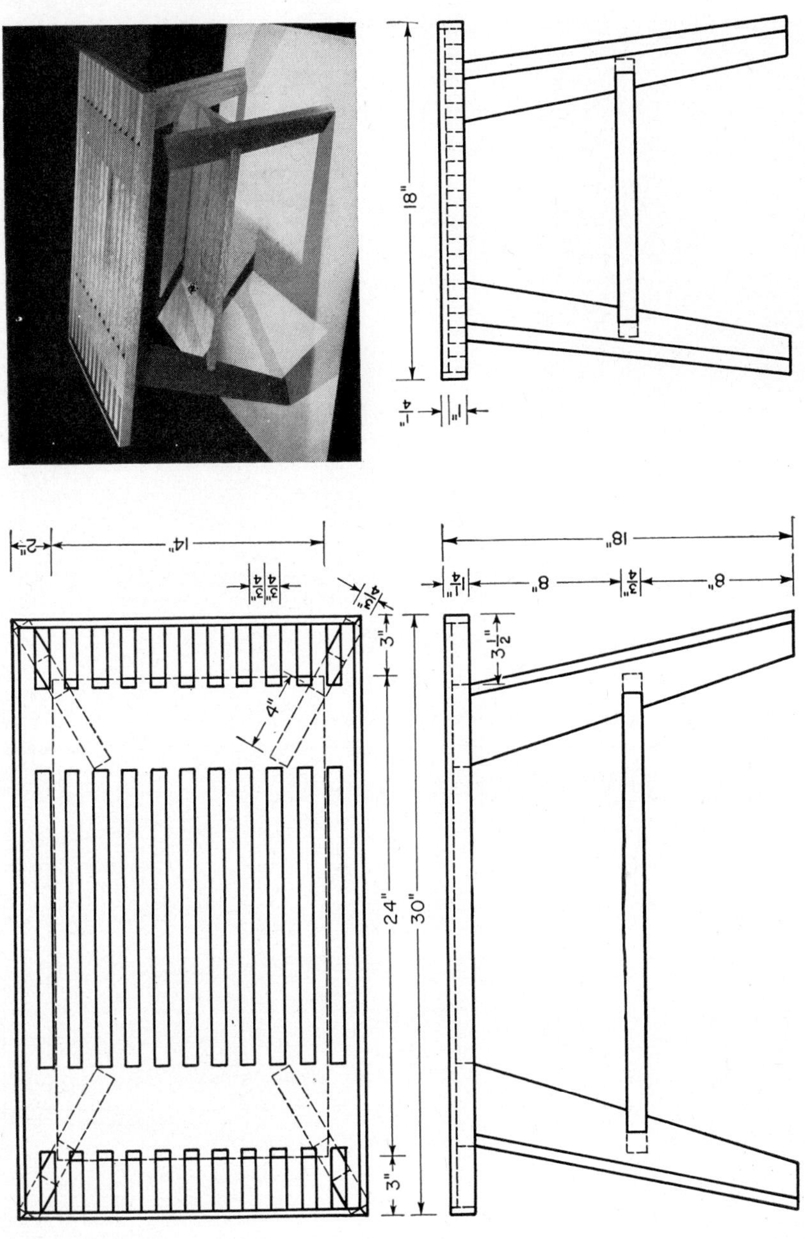

PROJECT 9. MODERN END TABLE

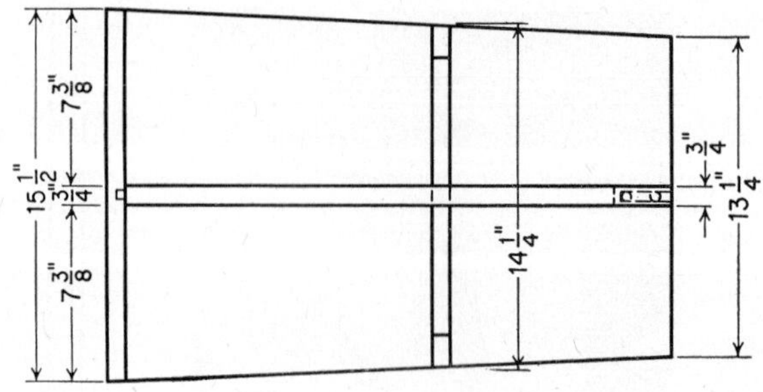

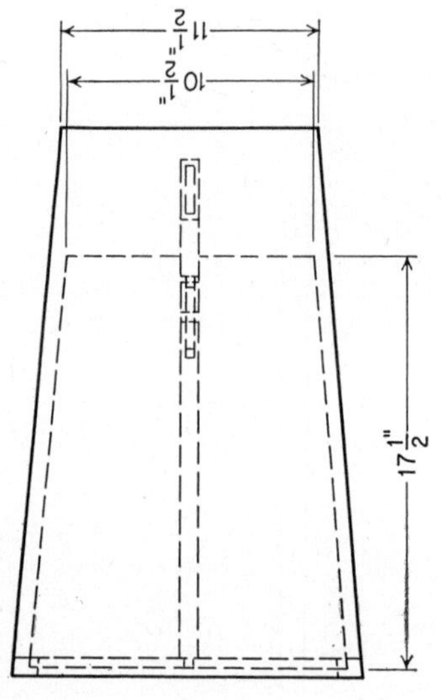

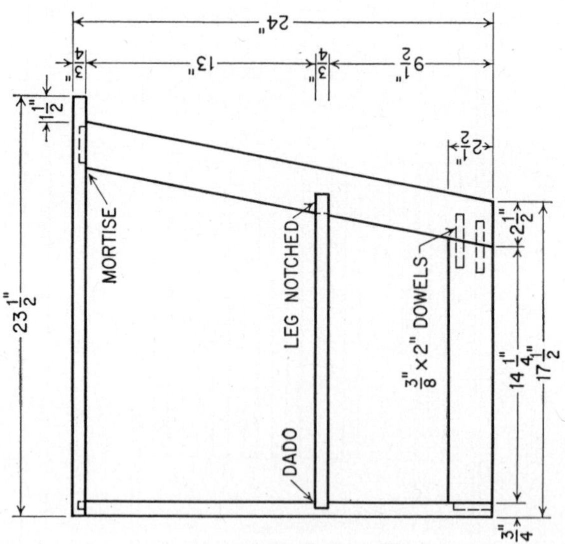

PROJECT 10. MODERN LAMP

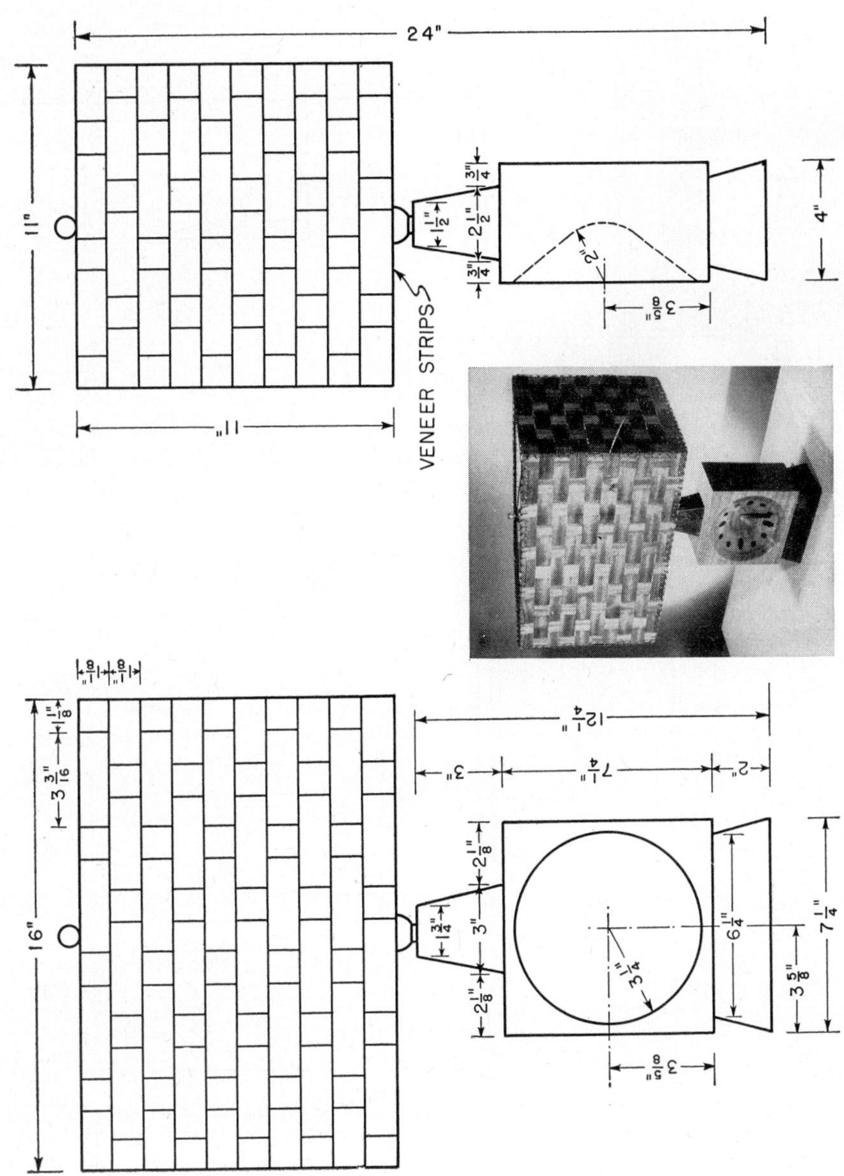

PROJECT 11. BOOK SHELF

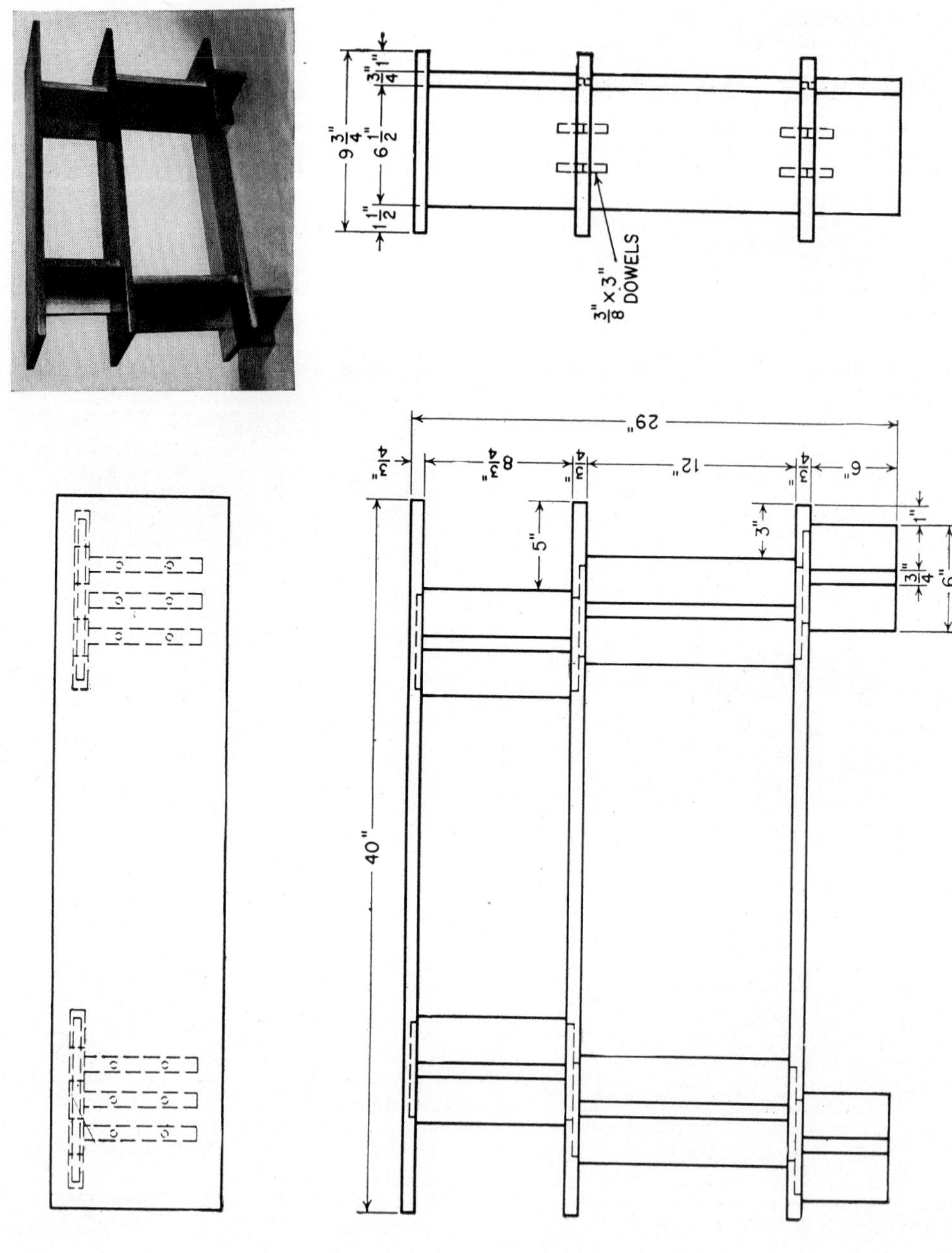

PROJECT 12. BOOK CASE

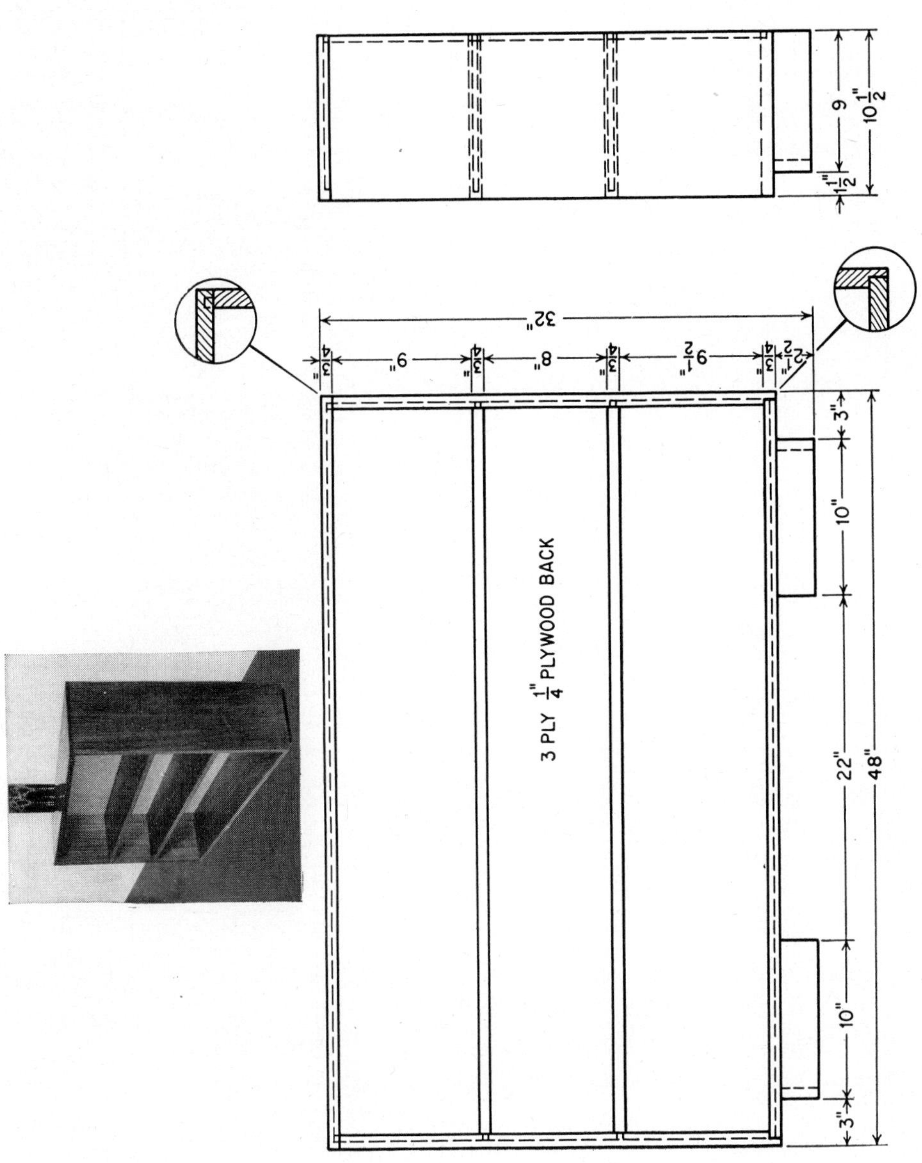

PROJECT 13. JEWEL CHEST—MINIATURE

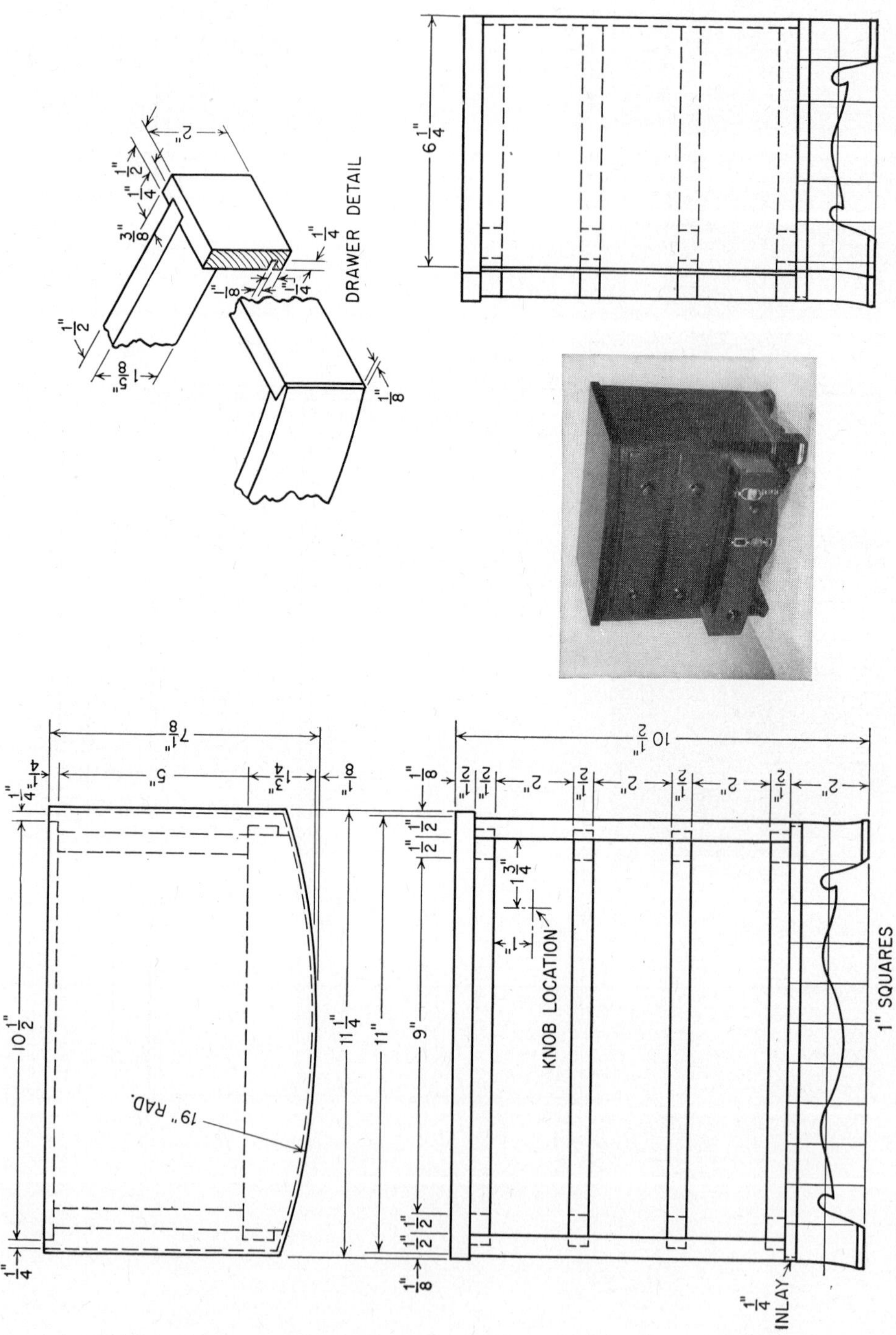

PROJECT 14. FOLDING CARD TABLE

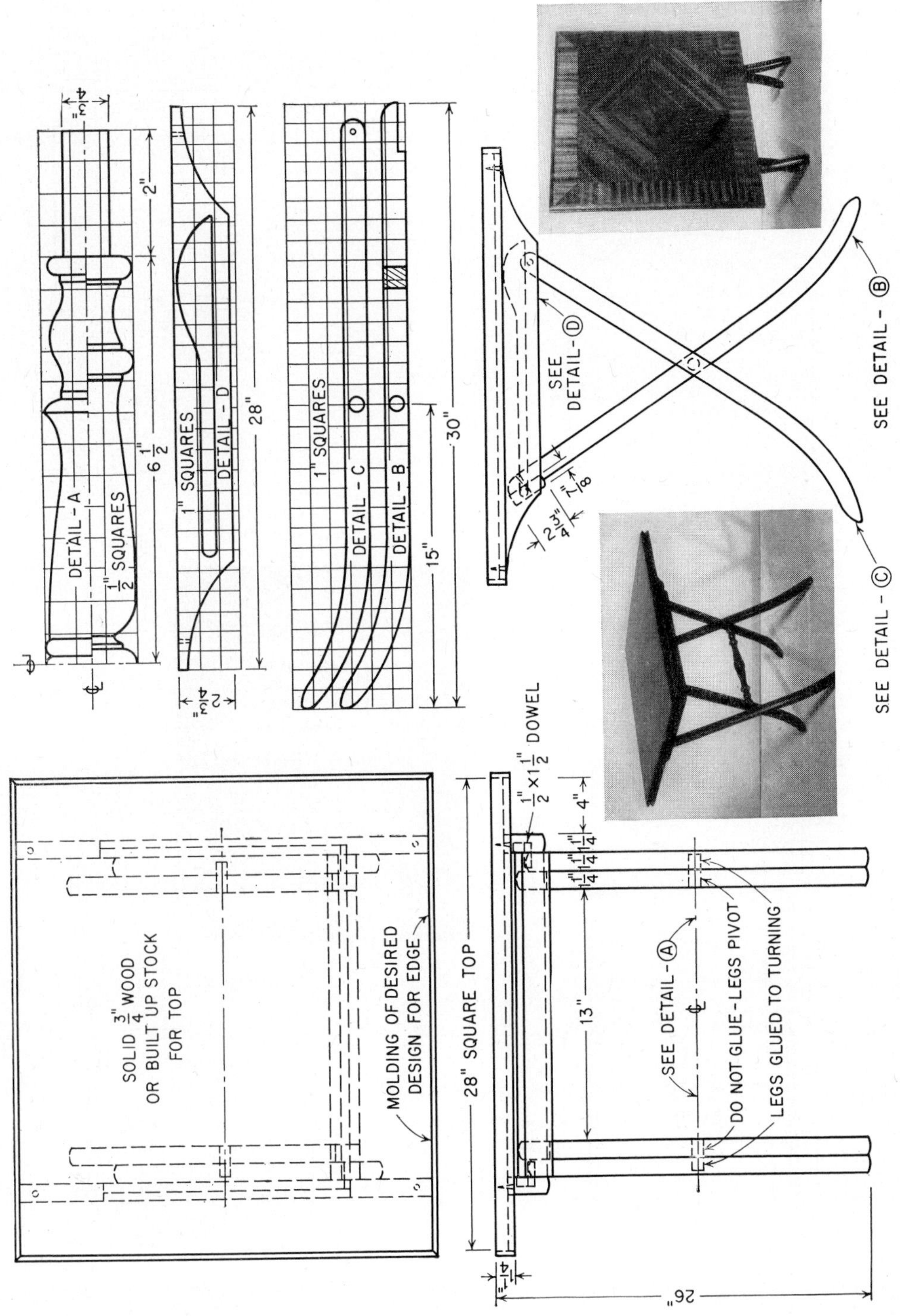

PROJECT 15. FORMED PLYWOOD TELEPHONE CHAIR

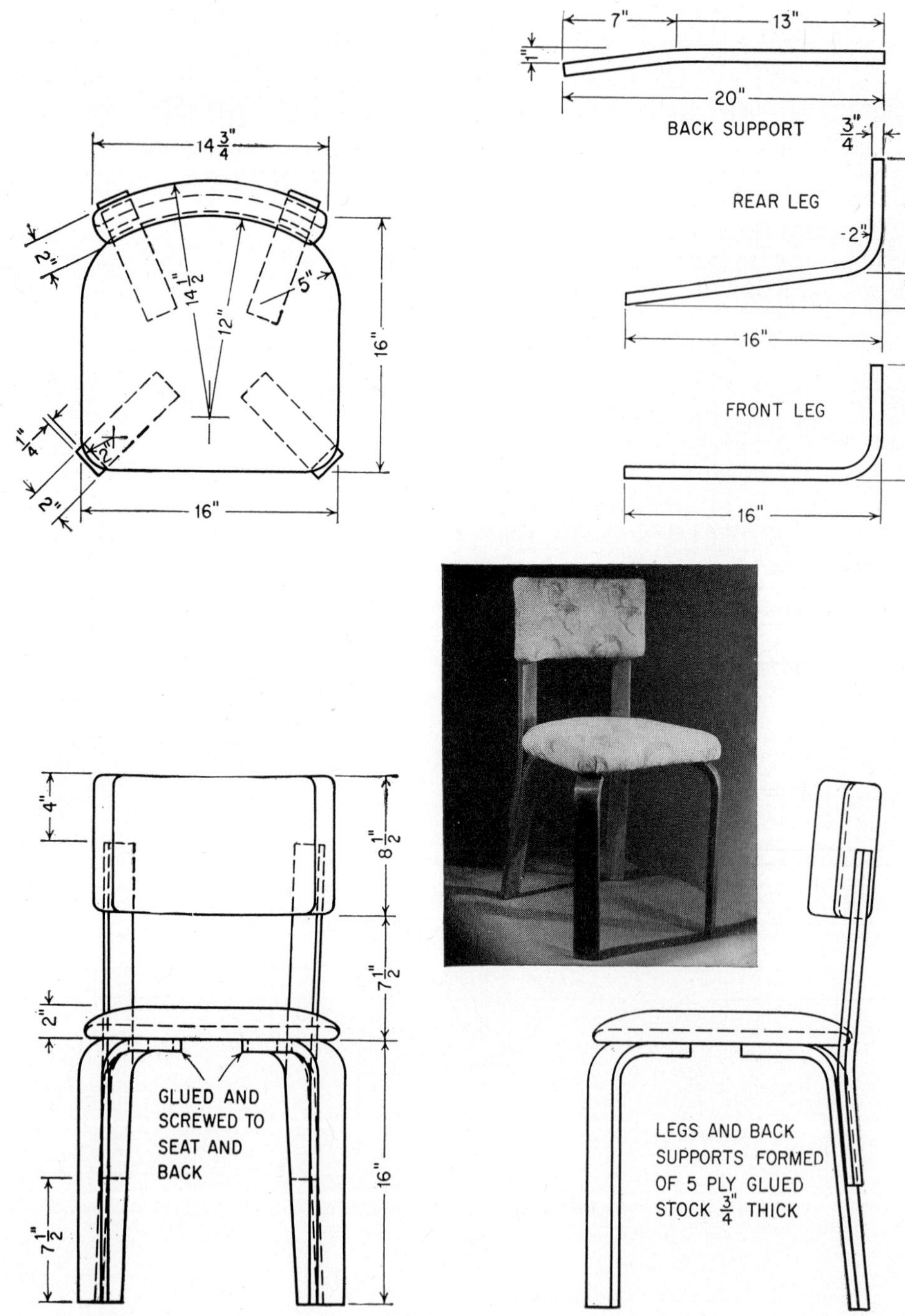

PROJECT 16. FORMED PLYWOOD MAGAZINE RACK

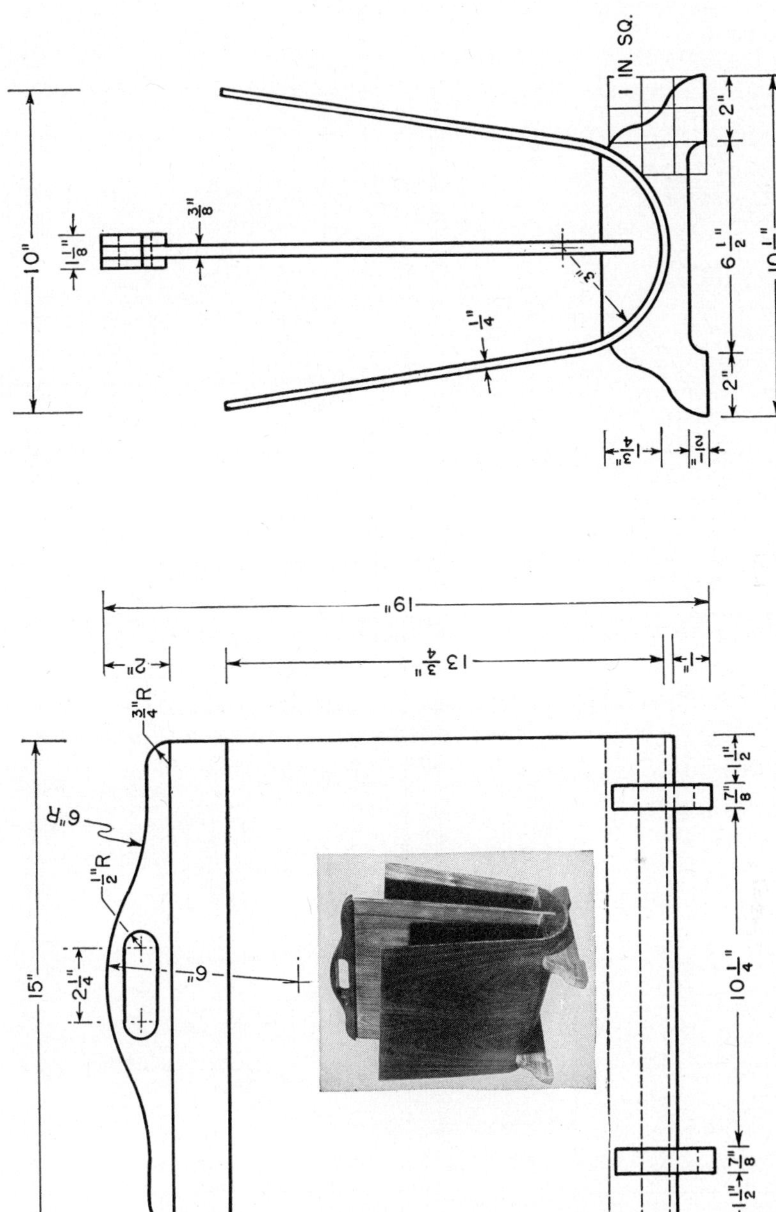

PROJECT 17. DRESSING TABLE

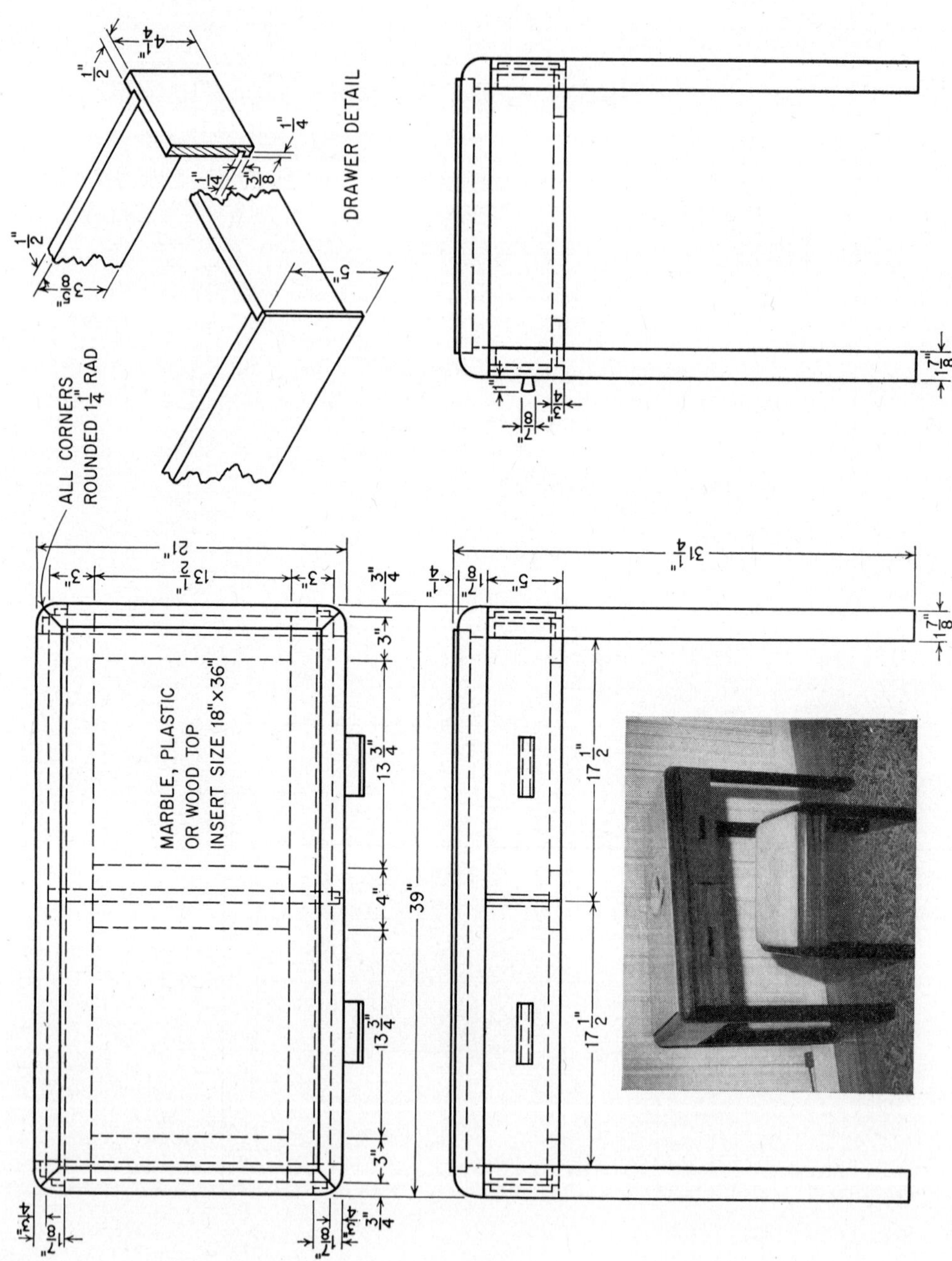

PROJECT 18. MODERN VANITY STOOL

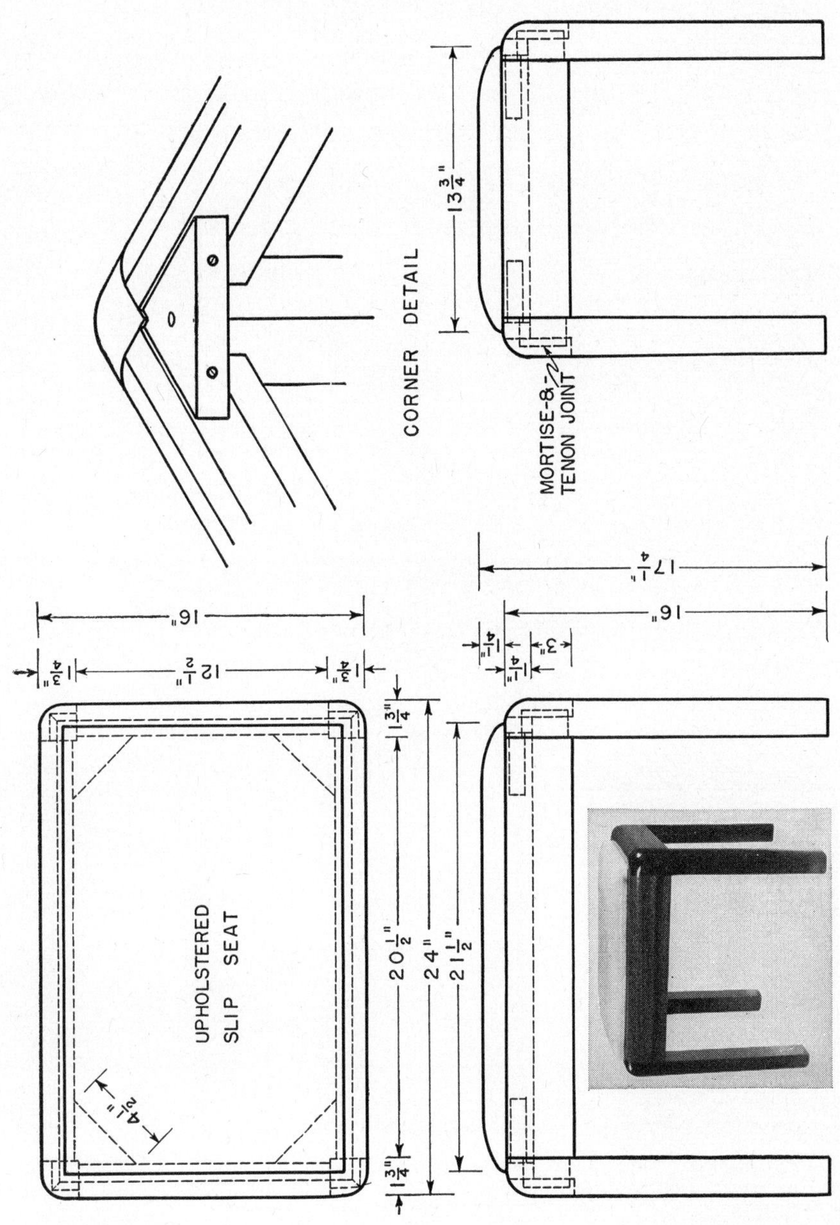

PROJECT 19. SPRING-SEAT OTTOMAN

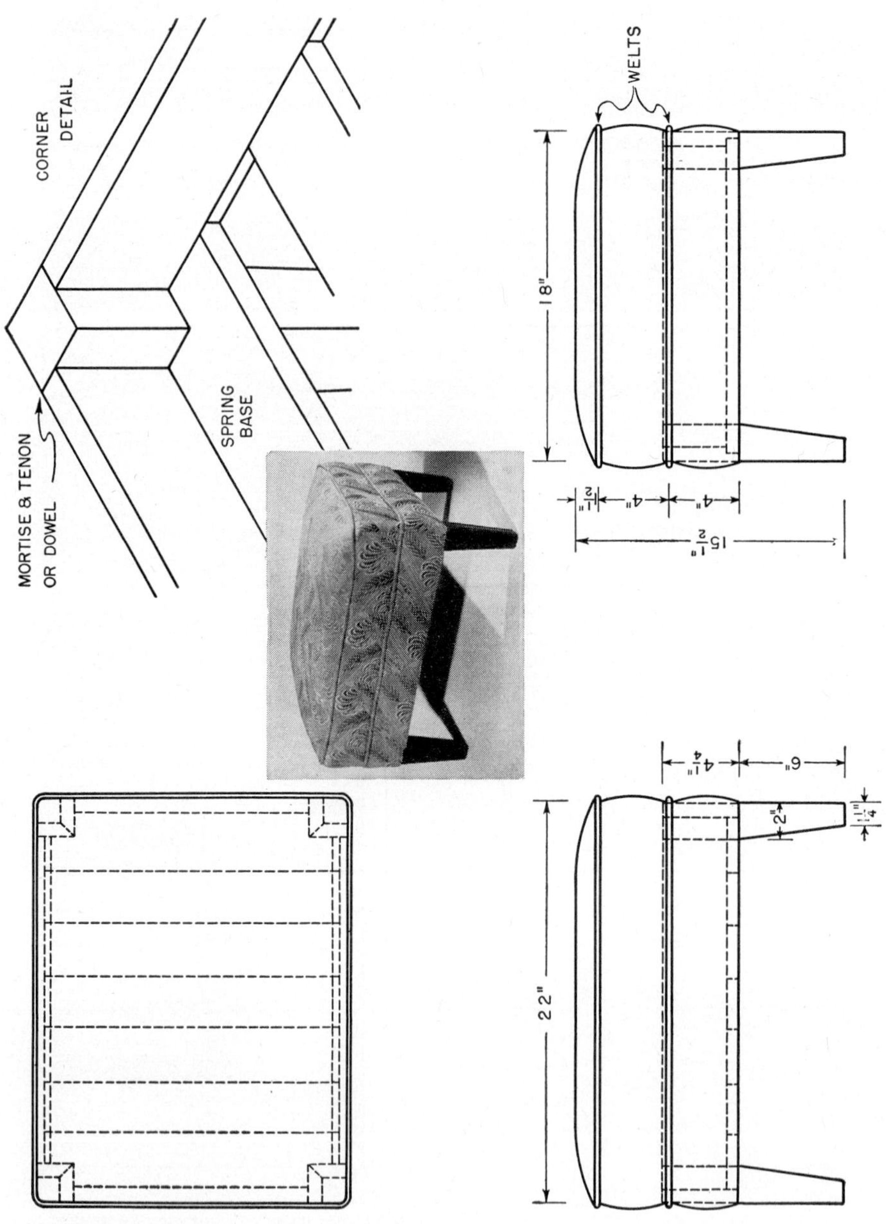

Correlated List of Visual Aids

The visual materials listed below and on the following pages can be used to supplement the subject matter of this book. We recommend, however, that each film be reviewed before using in order to determine its suitability for a particular class or group.

Both motion pictures and filmstrips are included in this list of visual materials, and the character of each one is indicated by the self-explanatory abbreviations "MP" or "FS." Immediately following this identification is the name of the producer; and if the distributor is different from the producer, the name of the distributor follows the name of the producer. Abbreviations are used for the names of producers and distributors, and these abbreviations are identified in the list of producers and distributors (with their addresses) at the end of the bibliography. In most instances, the films listed in this bibliography can be borrowed or rented from local or state 16mm film libraries. A list of such libraries, compiled by the U.S. Office of Education and entitled *A Directory of 2,002 16mm Film Libraries,* can be purchased for a nominal price from the Superintendent of Documents, U.S. Government Printing Office, Washington 25, D.C.

Unless otherwise indicated, the motion pictures listed in this bibliography are 16mm sound films, and the filmstrips are 35mm silent.

How-to-do-it Films

Beveling, Mitering, Rabbeting, and Dadoing (MP USOE/UWF 19min). How to cut a bevel with tilted fence; set a miter gauge; use a stopblock in mitering; set the fence and blade for cutting rabbets; install and use a dado head. Supplementary filmstrip (35 frames), same title, also available. (Variety saw series.)

Beveling, Stop Chamfering, and Tapering Square Stock (MP USOE/UWF 20min). How to set fence for bevel cutting; adjust the proper amount of cut; cut chamfer; set the infeed and outfeed tables and stopblocks; cut tapers. Supplementary filmstrip (62 frames), same title, also available. (Jointer series.)

Cutting Cove Molding and a Corebox (MP USOE/UWF 19min). How to select stock for cove molding; cut and rip cove molding; select the proper blade for oblique cutting; cut a deep hollow. Supplementary filmstrip (41 frames), same title, also available. (Variety saw series.)

Cutting Grooves with Circular Saw

Blades (MP USOE/UWF 22min). How to set up the machine to cut grooves in stiles and rails; cut grooves for splines; cut stop channels in mirror-frame members. Supplementary filmstrip (56 frames), same title, also available. (Spindle shaper series.)

Cutting Tenons and Segments (MP USOE/UWF 15min). How to lay out and cut a tenon; prepare a jig to trim and miter segments; guide the jig, using a sliding miter gauge. Supplementary filmstrip (32 frames), same title, also available. (Variety saw series.)

Drilling in Metal, Wood, and Plastics (MP USN/UWF 21min). Six basic drilling steps; how to lay out wood and plastics with drill press, electric and hand drills.

Face Planing Uneven Surfaces (MP USOE/UWF 13min). How to surface wide stock on one side; use a pusher; make and use a feather board; use a backing block for facing thin stock. Supplementary filmstrip (40 frames), same title also available. (Jointer series.)

Face Turning a Collar (MP USOE/UWF 16min). How to prepare a faceplate chuck; attach work to it; turn a fillet; taper-turn a recess. Supplementary filmstrip (39 frames), same title, also available. (Wood lathe series.)

Furniture Joinery (FS SVE 62 frames). Basic principles of making good furniture joints. (Woodworking series.)

Hand Sawing (MP Handy 20min). Fundamentals of handling hand saws and choosing the right saw for the job.

How to Finish Plywood (MP Douglas 22min). How plywood is painted, stained, enameled, wallpapered, etc., for various exterior and interior finishes.

Jointing an Edge for Gluing: Installing Knives (MP USOE/UWF 21min). How to determine when knives are dull; remove dull knives; install sharp knives on the cutter head and adjust them for proper cutting; straighten crooked stock; join edges for gluing. Supplementary filmstrip (54 frames), same title, also available. (Jointer series.)

Jointing Edges and End Grain 90 Degrees to a Face (MP USOE/UWF 17min). How to set the fence and infeed table to proper height; feed with the grain; joint end grain so as to prevent tearing. Supplementary filmstrip (62 frames), same title, also available. (Jointer series.)

Language of Drawing (MP McGraw 10min). Explains the necessity for a knowledge of mechanical drawing, the common language of the building world. (Mechanical-drawing series.)

Laying Out and Forming Plywood (MP USOE/UWF 21min). How to lay out plywood using blueprints and templates; form plywood in a press; reinforce plywood; and apply glue and varnish. Supplementary filmstrip (39 frames), same title, also available. (Wood fabrication series.)

Making a Project with Hand Tools (FS SVE 61 frames). How to convert rough stock into a useful but easy-to-make project; how to square a board and use saws, planes, and other tools. (Woodworking series.)

Planing Rough Surfaces to Dimensions (MP USOE/UWF 17min). How to adjust the table for desired thickness; set feed rolls for proper speed; feed with the grain; surface short pieces and glued stock. Supplementary filmstrip (46 frames), same title, also available. (Surfacer series.)

Rabbeting and Shaping an Edge on Straight Stock (MP USOE/UWF 18min). Principle of the shaper operation; how to set up the machine for cutting rabbets; cut rabbets; shape a molding. Supplementary filmstrip (50 frames), same title, also available. (Spindle shaper series.)

Ripping and Crosscutting (MP USOE/UWF 19min). How each working part of the variety saw functions; how to check saw blades; set the fence; change saw blades; use a cutoff gauge; use a hinged block in crosscutting. Supplementary filmstrip (43 frames), same title, also available. (Variety saw series.)

Safety Know How in the Workshop (FS SVE 55 frames). Safe way to cut stock on the circular saw, band saw, jointer, and other equipment. (Woodworking series.)

Sanding Flat and Irregular Surfaces (MP USOE/UWF 19min). How the belt sander operates; how to prepare a sanding belt; sand flat stock on a belt sander; and sand curved molding. Supplementary filmstrip (47 frames), same title, also available. (Sander series.)

Sawing a Reverse Curve and a Bevel Reverse Curve (MP USOE/UWF 18min). How to select and lay out stock to avoid waste; reverse curves to contour lines; use the table-tilting gauge; saw a beveled, reverse curve; saw a newel post having reverse curves. Supplementary filmstrip (38 frames), same title, also available. (Band saw series.)

Sawing with Jig and Changing Band (MP USOE/UWF 20min). How to select the proper band-saw blades for the job; adjust saw guides; mark stock and cut to the mark; prepare a jig; cut disks, using a jig. Supplementary filmstrip (44 frames), same title, also available. (Band saw series.)

Shaping after Template and Shaping Curved Edges (MP USOE/UWF 17min). How to make a template for the job; install knives in the spindle; use the template when smoothing squared edeges; set up equipment for shaping a curved edge; shape a curved edge. Supplementary filmstrip (39 frames), same title, also available. Spindle shaper series.)

Shop Procedures (MP McGraw 17min). Shows how finished drawings are used as detailed instructions in all steps of manufacturing. Supplementary filmstrip, same title, also available. (Mechanical-drawing series.)

Turning a Cylinder between Centers (MP USOE/UWF 17min). How to choose and center stock for a job; mount stock in the wood lathe for turning between centers; use the parting tool and the skew chisel; sand turning work. Supplementary filmstrip (46 frames), same title, also available. (Wood lathe series.)

Turning Taper Work (MP USOE/UWF 12min). How to center cylindrical wood stock for spindle turning; make clearance cuts; establish the diameters of a taper; turn a single taper; establish diameters for turning two tapers from a single piece of material; turn the tapers. Supplementary filmstrip (49 frames), same title, also available. (Wood lathe series.)

Turning Work in a Chuck (MP USOE/UWF 15min). How to mount work on a faceplate; turn one face of the work; make a chuck for the opposite face; fit the finished face to the chuck; turn the second face. Supplementary filmstrip (38 frames), same title, also available. (Wood lathe series.)

Turning Work on a Faceplate (MP USOE/UWF 15min). Types of faceplates; how to attach the stock to the faceplate; true up the work; scribe the work for inside turning; use the roundnose and diamond-point chisels; smooth the bottom of the recess. Supplementary filmstrip (48 frames), same title, also available. (Wood lathe series.)

Use and Care of Woodworking Tools (FS Photo 58 frames). How to use simple woodworking tools. (Produced by Science Service.)

Woodworking Machines (FS SVE 42 frames). How to use the lathe, drill press, sander, shaper, circular saw, band saw, and jointer. (Woodworking series.)

Woodworking Tools and Machines (FS Handy 60–70 frames each). Series of 14 filmstrips with the following self-explanatory titles:

1. *Hand Tools; Hammers; Saws*
2. *Planes; Bits; Knives; Chisels; Screw Drivers; Files*
3. *Tool Grinder*
4. *Drill Press*
5. *Jig Saw*
6. *Band Saw*
7. *Disk Sander*
8. *Belt Sander*
9. *Lathe; Parts; Spindle Turning*
10. *Lathe; Faceplate Turning; Other Operations*
11. *Planer*
12. *Jointer*
13. *Circular Saw; Parts; Installing a Blade*
14. *Circular Saw; Setting-up; Operating*

Related Informational Films

Everyman's Empire (MP USDA 20min). The national forests and their value to the people of the United States as a supply of lumber, storehouse of water, cattle and sheep ranges, and recreation areas.

Forest Conservation (MP EBF 11min). Exploitation and depletion of forests and forest resources; the need for conservation. Produced by the Conservation Foundation in cooperation with the New York Zoological Society. (Living forest series.)

Forest Grows (MP EBF 11min). How forests grow and the elements that contribute to a mature forest. Produced by the Conservation Foundation in cooperation with the New York Zoological Society. (Living forest series.)

Forest Produces (MP EBF 11min). Forests and their products utilized by man. Produced by the Conservation Foundation in cooperation with the New York Zoological Society. (Living forest series.)

Forestry and Forest Industries (MP VGF 11min). Work of people engaged in harvesting, processing, and distributing forest products. (Your life work series.)

Furniture Craftsmen (MP EBF

11min). Roles of designer and skilled craftsmen in making custom-built furniture. (Art series.)

Magic of Lumber (MP WSLA 22min). Characteristics of different trees, grading rules, work of the lumber grader, and classification of lumber grades on the basis of use.

Masterpieces in Mahogany (MP Mahogany 30min silent). Reproduction of an eighteenth-century mahogany table, from design and shop drawings, through construction to final sanding, waxing, and polishing.

Pine Ways to Profit (MP USDA 20min). New industrial uses of pine; improving yield and quality of trees for forest products; dangers of old custom of woods burning; making paper from pine pulp; and distilling turpentine.

Redwood Saga (MP Simmel 11min). Cutting, loading, transportation, mill sawing, and finishing operations of the redwood lumber industry of northern California.

Science and Wood Utilization (MP Coronet 6min). Work of the Forest Products Laboratory in Madison, Wis. in discovering ways to utilize the products of wood.

There's More Than Timber in Trees (MP USDA 33min). History of lumber industry in New England, Lake States, South, and Northwest; effect of cutting practices; need for nationwide program to conserve forests.

Woodworker (MP VGF 11min). Skills and techniques of woodworkers; training and experience required; vocational opportunities. (Your life work series.)

Sources of Films Listed

Coronet—Coronet Films, Coronet Bldg., Chicago 1, Ill.

Douglas—Douglas Fir Plywood Association, 301 Tacoma Bldg., Tacoma 2, Wash.

EBF—Encyclopaedia Britannica Films, Inc., 1150 Wilmette Ave., Wilmette, Ill.

Handy—The Jam Handy Organization, 2821 East Grand Blvd., Detroit 11, Mich.

Mahogany—Mahogany Association, Inc., 75 East Wacker Drive, Chicago 1, Ill.

McGraw—McGraw-Hill Book Co., Inc., Text-Film Department, 330 West 42nd Street, New York 36, N.Y.

Photo—Photo Lab, Inc., 3825 Georgia Ave., Washington 11, D.C.

Simmel—Simmel-Meservey, 321 South Beverly Drive, Beverly Hills, Calif.

SVE—Society for Visual Education Inc., 1345 West Diversey Parkway, Chicago 14, Ill.

USDA—U.S. Department of Agriculture, Washington 25, D.C.
Films may be borrowed from USDA depositories or purchased from United World Films.

USN—U.S. Department of the Navy, Washington 25, D.C.
Films released for civilian educational use through U.S. Office of Education and sold, under government contract, by United World Films; may be borrowed or rented from 16mm film libraries which have purchased prints.

USOE—U.S. Office of Education, Washington 25, D.C.

Films sold, under government contract, by United World Films; may be borrowed or rented from 16mm film libraries which have purchased prints.

UWF—United World Films, Inc., 1445 Park Ave., New York 29, N.Y.

Sales distributor for many U.S. Government films.

VGF—Vocational Guidance Films, Inc., 215 East 3rd St., Des Moines 9, Iowa.

WSLA—West Coast Lumbermen's Association, 1410 S.W. Morrison Street, Portland 5, Oregon.

For Further Reading

General Woodworking contains basic information on carpentry, furniture and cabinetmaking, finishing, and upholstering. If you wish to know more about any one of these, you will find among the following list of books one that will be helpful to you.

Basic Woodworking Processes, Herman Hjorth, The Bruce Publishing Company, Milwaukee, 1945.

General Shop Woodworking, V. C. Fryklund and A. J. LaBerge, McKnight & McKnight Publishing Company, Bloomington, Ill., 1946.

General Woodworking, W. H. Johnson and L. V. Newkirk, The Macmillan Company, New York, 1946.

Finishing Materials and Methods, George A. Soderberg, McKnight & McKnight Publishing Company, Bloomington, Ill., 1952.

General Woodwork (Related Information), University of New York State Education Department, Delmar Publishers, Inc., Albany, N.Y., 1950.

Industrial Arts Woodworking, John L. Feirer, Chas. A. Bennett Company, Inc., Peoria, Ill., 1950.

Machine Woodworking, Robert E. Smith, McKnight & McKnight Publishing Company, Bloomington, Ill., 1948.

Modern Woodwork, Ralph J. Vernon, The Steck Company, Austin, Tex., 1954.

New Essentials of Upholstery, Herbert Bast, The Bruce Publishing Company, Milwaukee, 1946.

Units in Hand Woodworking, J. H. Douglas and R. H. Roberts, The McCormick-Mathers Publishing Company, Wichita, Kan., 1946.

Woodwork Visualized, Ross C. Cramlet, The Bruce Publishing Company, Milwaukee, 1950.

Index

N

O

P

Q

R